The Doppler Effect

The Doppler Effect

An Introduction to the Theory of the Effect

T. P. GILL

LOGOS PRESS
ACADEMIC PRESS

© *T. P. Gill 1965*

Published by
LOGOS PRESS LIMITED
in association with
ELEK BOOKS LIMITED
2 All Saints Street, London, N.1

Distributed by
ACADEMIC PRESS INC.
111 Fifth Avenue, New York, N.Y. 10003
and
ACADEMIC PRESS INC. *(London)* LIMITED
Berkeley Square House, Berkeley Square, London, W.1

Library of Congress Catalog Card Number 65–19285

Printed in Great Britain by Bell and Bain Ltd., Glasgow.

Contents

Introduction

THE importance of the Doppler effect lies in its applications to astronomy and to navigation in the broadest sense. The theory of the effect is so simple that it might well seem unnecessary to devote as much space to it as has been done here. There are however, unexpected subtleties, which, I feel, justify the inclusion of material which has at present little practical application. By the Doppler effect is meant the change in the apparent time interval between two events which arises from the motion of an observer together with the finite velocity of transmission of information about the events. This is slightly different from and more general than, the usual definition in terms of the change in frequency of a periodic process. For example, one might think of a Doppler effect arising when letters are posted from successive railway stations on a long train journey. The intervals between the times of arrival will differ from the intervals between the times of posting and the theory of this effect will bear a close resemblance to the theory of the Doppler effect. Having made this point about the method of defining the Doppler effect, it must at once be admitted that all practical applications of any importance are concerned with periodic processes.

The first application of the Doppler effect was to astronomy, and, strangely enough, took place long before Doppler and Fizeau published their work on the subject. When Romer in 1676 used the apparent variation in the periods of Jupiter's satellites to deduce the velocity of light, he was, in effect, using a Doppler method, inverting the more common procedure of determining an unknown velocity in terms of the known velocity of light. Naturally he worked from first principles, and presumably because of the direction from which he approached the problem did not go on to generalise it.

The Doppler principle is applicable to any periodic process whether it be the period of rotation of a heavenly body or the much shorter period associated with γ-radiation. Since no information can be transmitted instantaneously over a distance, the time scales of all phenomena must show some effect when motion relative to an observer is involved. It would seem logical that the term Doppler shift, or Doppler effect should be confined to effects arising directly from the finite velocity of transmission of information. Thus, it is in a sense misleading to speak of the relativistic " time dilatation " as a Doppler shift, as is sometimes done, since this will not be affected by the means used to transmit the signals defining a time interval. This point of view may not be acceptable to all, and it may be argued that the only correct method of deriving the relativistic Doppler formula is by applying the Lorentz transformations to the light wave, in which case both that which one might call the " Doppler shift proper ", and the " time dilatation ", are obtained in the one expression and are in no way separable. This is true, but of course only so when signals are being transmitted with velocity c. If waves of some other velocity are used to transmit information it becomes clear that two factors are involved, the time dilatation, or transformation of time intervals from one frame of reference to another, and the effect of a finite velocity of transmission. This point is relevant both to the discussion of the relativistic Doppler effect in Chapter I and the consideration of the dispersive media in Chapter II.

Doppler himself propounded his principle in 1842, first in relation to sound, and then to light. He used the principle to explain the differences among the colours of the stars, ranging from red to blue, as due to their line of sight velocities. It so happened, as Fizeau pointed out, that this was not the correct explanation, and Fizeau was first to suggest the use of sharp spectral lines to observe the Doppler shift in the radiation from stars. Nevertheless, this conjecture of Doppler's suggests the interesting question—" What is the effect of relative motion on the spectral distribution of black body radiation ? " This is perhaps rather an academic problem but it is discussed in Chapter VIII in some detail, since it provides an interesting example of the application of the Doppler effect to a source emitting a continuous spectrum. The effect of the angular aperture on the line width of a molecular beam source has been included in this chapter rather than in Chapter III because it involves somewhat similar ideas.

Possibly only since the second world war has the Doppler effect had any wide application in fields other than astronomy, but its use in navigation, missile and satellite tracking, radar, etc., is steadily growing. I have included some brief remarks on the experimental confirmation of the effect. These may indeed seem rather pointless in view of the very fundamental nature of the effect, the simplicity of its derivation, and its wide practical application. The success of the application of a theory over a wide field provides valuable evidence for its correctness. It is however somewhat in the nature of circumstantial evidence, and it is satisfying to be able to add to this, direct evidence, where as far as possible the effect considered is studied in isolation. The actual amount of evidence supporting the relativistic Doppler effect formulae is not very great at all. It is accepted because the remainder of the theory has to be accepted on the basis of a wide variety of experimental evidence. It is outside the scope of this work to study the problem of how well or how little a particular theory is supported by its relevant body of experimental evidence. To do this would involve an enquiry into how much of each particular theory consists of genuine hypotheses about the nature of things, and how much is definition, convention and a specialised language.

The discussion in Chapter IV on the subject of the spectroscopic binaries may seem to the non-specialist to loom too large, or to the astronomer to be treated in too elementary a fashion. The intention here, however, is not to enable the reader to reduce observations on spectroscopic binaries but to illustrate in greater detail what I feel is perhaps the most interesting feature of the theory of the effect. This concerns the art of combining a knowledge of the laws of motion of a system with otherwise insufficient observational data in order to determine the motion of the system. The art of doing this is of importance in rocket and satellite work since instrumental failures often reduce the amount of tracking data to something less than the theoretical minimum required for an arbitrary trajectory. Thus, a rocket whose motor has cut out, may be assumed to be acted on, under some conditions, by vertical forces alone, the trajectory will be plane, and so on. One is reminded here of Plato's cave dwellers who are able only to see the shadows of the real world (i.e. its projection on a plane). This is reminiscent of the position of astronomers who see the universe projected on the plane of the sky, and who are able to derive the motions of the double stars because of their confidence in the universal applicability of Newton's laws of motion. If all our knowledge of dynamics had been derived from the observations only of the projections or shadows of real systems, would the problems of Newtonian dynamics have been solved, or would the laws of motion now be couched in statistical language ? The Doppler effect deals with motion in a direct and simple manner, and its study provides a very useful introduction or accompaniment to the study of Special Relativity, a theory which is especially concerned with motion. It

A*

should not be necessary to remind the reader that the nature of motion is only little better understood now than in the days of Zeno. Its laws are now well understood, but the question of its nature has long been dismissed by many as meaningless.

I

Introductory Theory

Consider two bodies, one, T, called the transmitter, the other, R, the receiver, and suppose that they are in motion with velocities whose magnitudes are u and v respectively. Let us also suppose that these velocities u and v are measured relative to a medium which is capable of transmitting signals with a fixed velocity c. The directions of u and v need not lie in the same plane (see fig. 1). At time t a signal is emitted from T, at which instant the distance between T and R is r. This signal will intercept the path of R at time t' such that R has travelled a distance $v(t' - t)$ and the signal has travelled a distance $c(t' - t)$. We use the symbol c for the velocity

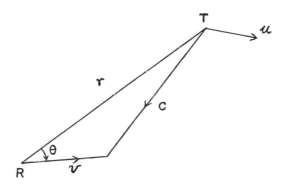

Fig. 1.

of the signal relative to the medium, since in most, if not all, practical applications of the Doppler effect, we are concerned with electromagnetic radiation of one form or another. We then have, from elementary trigonometry,

$$c^2(t' - t)^2 = v^2(t' - t)^2 + r^2 - 2rv(t' - t) \cos \theta$$

θ being measured in the sense shown in fig. 1. This leads, on solving for $t' - t$ to

$$t' - t = \frac{r}{c^2 - v^2}\left(- v \cos \theta \pm \sqrt{c^2 - v^2 \sin^2 \theta} \right) \tag{1}$$

1

The ambiguity of the sign corresponds to the fact that a wavefront from a single point is spherical and so the path of R may intercept it twice. This ambiguity may be removed by means of a few practical considerations. Firstly $t' - t > 0$, the signal cannot be received before it is emitted, and of course for interception to occur c^2 must be greater than $v^2 \sin^2 \theta$. It will also be assumed that $c^2 > v^2$ since in most cases this is so. Consider now the two cases, $\cos \theta > 0$ and $\cos \theta < 0$ ($\cos \theta = 0$ presents no problem). For $\cos \theta > 0$, in order to have $t' - t > 0$ the positive sign is necessary, for $\cos \theta < 0$, the expression in the brackets becomes

$$+ \mid v \cos \theta \mid \pm \sqrt{c^2 - v^2 + v^2 \cos^2 \theta}$$

Now if $c > v$, the second term is greater than the first which would make the whole expression negative. The positive sign must therefore be used, giving

$$t' = t + \frac{r}{c^2 - v^2} \left(\sqrt{c^2 - v^2 \sin^2 \theta} - v \cos \theta \right) \qquad (2)$$

This gives the time taken for the signal to reach R. Our purpose however is to determine the time interval between the reception of two signals whose transmission times are separated by a short interval Δt.

To do this, assuming Δt sufficiently small, differentiate (2) with respect to t. Then $\Delta t'$, the interval between received signals is given by

$$\Delta t' = \Delta t \left\{ 1 + \frac{d}{dt} \left[\frac{r^2}{c^2 - v^2} \left(\sqrt{c^2 - v^2 \sin^2 \theta} - v \cos \theta \right) \right] \right\}$$

which is readily reduced to

$$\Delta t' = \Delta t \left\{ 1 + \frac{dr}{dt} \cdot \frac{1}{(c^2 - v^2)} \left[\sqrt{c^2 - v^2 \sin^2 \theta} - v \cos \theta \right] \right.$$
$$\left. + \frac{d\theta}{dt} \cdot \frac{r \sin \theta}{(c^2 - v^2)} \left[v - \frac{v^2 \cos \theta}{\sqrt{c^2 - v^2 \sin^2 \theta}} \right] \right\} \qquad (3)$$

Further investigation of this general formula is not justified at this stage, but instead, consider the case where T and R are moving along the same straight line, i.e., $\theta = 0$ or π

$$\theta = 0 \text{ leads to } \Delta t' = \Delta t \left[1 + \frac{1}{c + v} \frac{dr}{dt} \right]$$

and $\theta = \pi$ leads to $\Delta t' = \Delta t \left[1 + \dfrac{1}{c - v} \dfrac{dr}{dt} \right]$

We have hitherto taken v as the magnitude of the velocity. If, however, we regard motion which tends to increase r as positive and give v its appropriate sign, the two formulae are seen to be both included in

$$\Delta t' = \Delta t \left[1 + \frac{1}{c - v} \cdot \frac{dr}{dt} \right] \qquad (4)$$

which is often approximated further to

$$\Delta t' \approx \Delta t \left[1 + \frac{1}{c} \frac{dr}{dt} \right]$$

FIG. 2.

Before proceeding further, one other special case is worth considering. Suppose T moves with uniform speed U in a circle at the centre of which R is situated, and the whole system moves with uniform velocity V through the medium (fig. 2). Then u becomes the vector sum of U and V while v is replaced by V and dr/dt is zero. θ is Ut/r and $d\theta/dt = U/r$. Substituting these values in (3)

$$\Delta t' = \Delta t \left[1 + \frac{U \sin \theta}{c^2 - v^2} \left(V - \frac{V^2 \cos \theta}{\sqrt{c^2 - V^2 \sin^2 \theta}} \right) \right] \qquad (5)$$

and when $\theta = 0$ there is no Doppler shift but when $\theta = \pi/2$ we have

$$\Delta t' = \Delta t \left[1 + \frac{UV}{c^2 - V^2} \right]$$

$$\approx \Delta t \left[1 + \frac{UV}{c^2} \right] \tag{6}$$

a result which will be needed later.

If, however, we have the transmitter at the centre and allow the receiver to rotate we now have both

$$\frac{dr}{dt} = 0 \text{ and } \frac{d\theta}{dt} = 0$$

and there is no Doppler shift. The marked difference between the two cases should be noted.

In all cases where it makes sense to talk of our transmitters and receivers moving relative to the medium which carries the signal, then which of these moves is of great significance. A supersonic aircraft can readily escape a sound wave sent after it but no matter how rapidly it moves its sound will be received by a stationary observer. The time intervals Δt and $\Delta t'$ may be defined in any way and Δt can be regarded as the period of a wave transmitted by T. Then the received period will be $\Delta t'$. Since the frequency of the wave is $1/\Delta t$, equations (4) to (6) can be rewritten in terms of frequency. That is,

$$f' = f \left[1 + \frac{1}{c - v} \frac{dr}{dt} \right]^{-1} \tag{7}$$

and so on, for equations (2), (3) and (5).

The method of deriving the effect given above is not the only one, nor necessarily the best. In some elementary texts, methods of counting extra waves added to or taken from the intervening space between T and R are used, and these often cause unnecessary confusion. If only motion in a straight line is required, the above method becomes extremely simple. A somewhat more sophisticated approach, however, and one which may have some advantage, perhaps, if non-uniform motion is to be considered, is to take the equation of the surface representing a spherical disturbance spreading out from a point T, (x_T, y_T, z_T).

$$(x - x_T)^2 + (y - y_T)^2 + (z - z_T)^2 = c^2 t^2 \tag{a}$$

and the parametric equation of the receiver's motion

$$x = \alpha_1 t + \beta_1, \; y = \alpha_2 t + \beta_2, \; z = \alpha_3 t + \beta_3$$

or $\qquad x = X(t), \; y = Y(t), \; z = Z(t)$ (b)

and after substituting for x, y, and z from (b) in (a) proceed to differentiate as previously to find $\Delta t'$ as a function of Δt. However it must be remembered that x_T, y_T and z_T will in general be functions of t. Cases involving non-uniform motion, such as arise when considering double stars, can always be treated by our previous formulae, a sufficient condition for this being that the velocity, and therefore the received frequency, may be regarded as constant over the period required for each single observation of it. If, for example, the velocity changes appreciably during a few cycles of the emitted wave, then our simple treatment is no longer valid and each case must be treated individually from first principles. A minor point should perhaps be mentioned in this connection. In Formula (4) the value of dr/dt is that corresponding to the instant at which the signal is emitted and it is assumed that Δt is sufficiently small for this to be reasonably constant over the period Δt, but $t' - t$ need not of course be small.

As an example consider the following method of deriving the Doppler effect for the case where R is fixed and T moves along a straight line passing through R. Wave motion in this case is governed by the one dimensional wave equation

$$\frac{\partial^2 \psi}{\partial x^2} = \frac{1}{c^2} \frac{\partial^2 \psi}{\partial t^2}$$

The moving source imposes the condition that, at a point moving with velocity u, the disturbance is a periodic function of t, say $g(t)$ of period P. Now a solution of the wave equation is $\psi_1(x - ct)$, ψ_1, being a fairly general type of function. The boundary condition above implies that at a moving point defined by $x = x_0 + ut$ the disturbance is a prescribed periodic function $g(t)$, i.e.,

$$\psi_1[x_0 - (c - u)t] = g(t)$$

and has a period P. If $\psi_1[x - (c - u)t]$ has a period P then $\psi_1(x - ct)$ must have a period $(c - u)P/c$ from elementary considerations. This gives the normal Doppler expression

$$P' = \left(1 - \frac{u}{c}\right) P$$

The Relativistic Doppler Effect

In the elementary theory given so far the motions of transmitter and receiver were considered relative to the medium which conveyed the signals from one to the other, and a frame of reference at rest relative to this medium is the logical one to use. However, in the case of electromagnetic radiation, the attempt to find a frame of reference at rest relative to the medium failed in a manner which was of considerable importance in the development of Physics. It is a basic concept of Special Relativity that no such frame of reference can be found and this implies that the preceding theory, in the case of electromagnetic waves, employs a meaningless concept. The work is not completely wasted, since Special Relativity also contains the proviso that all formulae derived correctly from a relativistic treatment of a problem, must reduce to the classical formulae, when all velocities involved are small compared with c, the velocity of light, and, as expected, it will turn out that the correctly derived relativistic formulae agree with the foregoing as far as the first order in v/c. Very rarely, if ever, are the relativistic Doppler formulae really needed in practical applications. Referring back to fig. 1, since there is no meaning to be attached to motion relative to the medium, it is permissible to put $v = 0$, i.e., the axes of reference are chosen at rest relative to the observer, and this is a natural and convenient thing to do. Then u will be taken as the velocity of the transmitter in this frame of reference. If, as before, r is the distance between T and R, then a signal emitted by T at time t' will be received by R at time $t'' = t' + r/c$, and, differentiating as before

$$\varDelta t'' = \varDelta t' \left(1 + \frac{1}{c}\frac{dr}{dt}\right) \tag{7}$$

It is necessary to emphasise that this is the perfectly correct expression for the Doppler effect in Special Relativity, bearing in mind *that all quantities are measured in R's frame of reference*. In practice, the quantity $\varDelta t'$, will be the period associated with the transmitter T and this is usually specified by its " proper " value, that is, its value in a frame of reference at rest relative to T. If this period be $\varDelta t$ then

$$\varDelta t' = \frac{\varDelta t}{\sqrt{1 - u^2/c^2}}$$

and formula (7) becomes

$$\varDelta t'' = \varDelta t \frac{(1 + 1/c \; dr/dt)}{\sqrt{1 - u^2/c^2}} \tag{8}$$

The quantities all being measured in the frame of reference of R except that Δt is the " proper " period of the transmitter. As before, this equation can be inverted to give the apparent change in frequency,

$$f'' = f \frac{\sqrt{1 - u^2/c^2}}{(1 + 1/c \; dr/dt)} \tag{9}$$

It should not be necessary to mention that, when using relativistic equations, it is not permissible to write

$$\left(1 + \frac{1}{c}\frac{dr}{dt}\right)^{-1} \approx 1 - \frac{1}{c}\frac{dr}{dt}$$

It is possible to treat the relativistic Doppler effect in a slightly more sophisticated manner, which has the advantage of simultaneously giving the change in direction of arrival of a wave due to a change in motion of the observer's frame of reference, i.e., the formulae for aberration.

Consider first how a physical quantity F which is a function of the coordinates x, y, z and t in a frame of reference S_0, is changed when it is measured in a parallel frame S_1 (x_1, y_1, z_1, t_1) moving parallel to the x axis with velocity v relative to S_0. Suppose that F_0 represents a plane wave being propagated with velocity c in S_0 then F_0 may be written

$$F_0 = F_0(lx + my + nz - ct)$$

where l, m, and n are the direction cosines of the direction of propagation. Then the wave as seen in S_1 will be

$$F_1 = F_1\left[l\beta(x_1 + vt_1) + my_1 + nz_1 - c\beta\left(t_1 + \frac{vx_1}{c^2}\right) \right]$$

$$= F_1\left[\beta\left(l - \frac{v}{c}\right)x_1 + my_1 + nz_1 - c\beta\left(1 - \frac{vl}{c}\right)t_1 \right]$$

$$\beta \equiv \left(1 - \frac{v^2}{c^2}\right)^{-\frac{1}{2}}$$

Now the nature of the transformation of F_0 to F_1 is such that if we put $g(F_0) = F_1$, the operator g cannot involve the coordinates x, y, z, or t but only v/c and is often simply a constant multiplier. From this it follows that if $F_0(u)$ has a period P in u, then $F_1(u)$ has the same period in u. It should also be remembered that if $F_1(u)$ has a period P in u then $F_1(\alpha u)$ has a period P/α in u. Applying these considerations to F_1 above, if F_0 has a period Δt in t, F_1 has a period $\Delta t/\beta \sqrt{(1 - vl/t)}$ in t_1. To find the direction of propagation in S_1, take the factor

$$\sqrt{\beta^2\left(l - \frac{v}{c}\right)^2 + m^2 + n^2} = \beta\left(1 - \frac{vl}{c}\right)$$

out of the argument of F_1. This gives

$$F_1 = F_1\left[\beta\left(1 - \frac{vl}{c}\right)\left(l_1 x_1 + m_1 y_1 + n_1 z_1 - ct_1\right)\right]$$

(Incidently confirming that, under Lorentz transformations the velocity c remains constant.)

where $l_1 = \dfrac{l - v/c}{1 - vl/c}$, $m_1 = \dfrac{m}{\beta(1 - vl/c)}$, $n_1 = \dfrac{n}{\beta(1 - vl/c)}$ (10)

giving the direction cosines of the direction of propagation in S_1. The formula

$$\Delta t_1 = \frac{\Delta t}{\beta(1 - vl/c)} \tag{11}$$

does not apparently agree with the expression obtained previously. The disagreement is only apparent; it is necessary to substitute for l from (10) since the direction of motion of the wave which one uses will normally be the direction as seen by the observer in S_1, i.e., in the frame of reference of R in the previous treatment.

$$l_1 = \frac{l - v/c}{1 - vl/c} \text{ is equivalent to } l = \frac{l_1 + v/c}{1 + vl_1/c}$$

so (11) becomes by substitution

$$\Delta t_1 = \Delta t \frac{(1 + vl_1/c)}{\sqrt{1 - v^2/c^2}} \tag{12}$$

in which vl_1 represents the component of v along the direction of propagation as seen in S_1 which is equivalent to dr/dt in the previous case. The possibility of confusion arising between l and l_1 was discussed by Riedel[1] who pointed out that Pauli made the mistake of using, in effect, l instead of l_1 in his treatment of the Doppler effect in his book on Relativity[2]. This was presumably merely a slip rather than a misunderstanding of the subject, and one which escaped detection because the result was not used again in the text. The two simple cases of $l_1 = 1$ and 0, lead, in the first case to

$$\Delta t_1 = \frac{\Delta t(1 + v/c)}{\sqrt{1 - v^2/c^2}} = \Delta t \sqrt{\frac{1 + v/c}{1 - v/c}}$$

and

$$\Delta t_1 = \frac{\Delta t}{\sqrt{1 - v^2/c^2}} = \beta \Delta t$$

in the second, the latter being the expression for the so-called " time dilatation ". When $l = 0$, $l_1 = -v/c$, being the simplest case of aberration, which coincides with the classical result. The classical expression for aberration and the Doppler effect can of course be obtained by applying the Galilean transformations $x = x_1 + vt_1$, $y = y_1$, $z = z_1$ and $t = t_1$, to the expression for a plane wave.

The Doppler Effect and the Ether Drift

The possibility of measuring the velocity of an observer relative to the ether using the Doppler effect might appear to have been an alternative to the Michelson–Morley experiment, since we have seen the non-relativistic Doppler effect does involve the velocity relative to the medium as well as relative motion between the transmitter and receiver. It should also be capable of yielding an effect of the first order in v/c rather than the second order. Such a possibility indeed occurred to Clerk Maxwell who suggested the possible use of the periods of Jupiter's satellites. Unfortunately the precision needed was, and still is, beyond physical possibility.

The principal of the method is as follows. Referring back to fig. 2 and equation (6) the transmitter T is replaced by the satellites whose regular periods can be observed. The receiver is the observer on the earth which as a rough approximation is near the centre of Jupiter's orbit. Then if V is the velocity of the solar system through the ether and the velocity of Jupiter in its orbit is U, the frequency of the signal, when Jupiter's velocity is directly opposed to the general velocity through the ether, will be $f(1 - UV/c^2)$ and on the other side of its orbit, it will be $f(1 + UV/c^2)$ so that if the frequencies are compared there will be a difference of $2fUV/c^2$. This turns out to be too small to be detected for any plausible ether drift velocity, although it is not beyond future possibilities that a man-made oscillator of sufficient stability might not be put into a suitable orbit. Of course, further confirmation of Special Relativity is becoming less and less a matter on which one is prepared to expend a large amount of time and money. It will be noticed that the effect is of the first order in V/c but this is rather an illusory gain since V/c is multiplied by U/c which is probably even smaller. Also, if it happened that the ether drift were perpendicular to the plane of the ecliptic no effect could be hoped for. This fault is shared by the Kennedy–Thorndike experiment, designed to eliminate the Fitz-gerald–Lorentz contraction as a full explanation of the Michelson–Morley experiment.

Recently, however, a group of American experimenters (Cedar-holm, Townes, and others) have devised a laboratory version of the Doppler ether drift experiment[3]. The vibrational oscillations of the NH_3 molecule provide a highly accurate and reproducible frequency standard. Two ammonia masers are set up in which the excited ammonia molecules travel in molecular beams and interact with tuned resonant cavities. The two masers are arranged so that their molecular beams travel in opposite directions and correspond to the two opposite positions of the transmitter in fig. 2. (The idea of a circular orbit is of course not essential to the argument.) The frequencies seen by the cavities each correspond to the frequencies of the molecule subjected to the transverse Doppler effect of equation (6).

The difference between the two will be $2fUV/c^2$, a difference readily displayed by beating the output of the two masers together. If now the directions of the two beams are reversed with respect to the ether drift, whatever way that is, the beat frequency will change by $4fUV/c^2$. The method is of very great sensitivity and the authors claim to have reduced the possible ether drift to about 1/30 km. per sec. or less. The value of the velocity of the NH_3 molecules in the beams is about 0·6 km. per sec., while the ether drift must at some time be at least 30 km. per sec., which gives UV/c^2 of the order of 2×10^{-10}. (The frequency f is $2·378 \times 10^{10}$ c.p.s.) The ether drift concerned is now that due to the earth's orbital velocity, not that due to the motion of the solar system as a whole, so that the possibility of a coincidental absence of drift need not be considered. It was found, on rotating the apparatus, that a small drift did occur but this was found to be due to laboratory effects, in particular magnetic fields, and was not a function of the time of the year, as an ether effect would be.

The Cedarholm experiment while precise and simple in conception seems somehow to fail to carry complete conviction. This feeling of lack of conviction is no real criticism of the experiment; it is however often a stimulus to a closer examination of the ideas behind the experiment. The feature of this experiment which raises some doubts is the close relation between the moving molecules and the stationary resonant cavities. The emission of radiation is stimulated by, and linked in phase with, the oscillations of the cavity to which the NH_3 molecules supply energy. Is this then a clear case of the Doppler effect, since the resulting output frequency is to some extent influenced, or " pulled " by the natural frequency of the cavity? The treatment of the ammonia maser by Townes and others suggests that these doubts are in fact groundless.

Two interesting problems are suggested by this experiment. One is the effect of motion through a medium on a resonant cavity, the other is the case of a system in which the oscillations are maintained by positive feedback between two parts of the system which are in relative motion. In the case of the acoustic vibrations the first might be visualised as an organ pipe through which a steady current of air is passing, while the second could be represented by an amplifier fitted with a microphone and loudspeaker, which are moved relative to one another. The first problem is in fact closely related to the Michelson-Morley experiment. Consider a simplified system in which a wave is transmitted from a source, reflected at a surface normally and returns to the original source, source and reflector being at rest relative to one another but in motion through the medium with velocity v, normal to the reflecting surface. It will be assumed that there is a resonance when the wave arrives at the source in phase with the wave being emitted. Obviously ordinary fixed standing waves are not possible under these circumstances since the wavelengths going and coming will not be the same. The time taken for the return journey is

$$\frac{l}{c+v} + \frac{l}{c-v}$$

where l is the distance between source and reflector and phase change on reflection is ignored. The frequency received will be the same as that emitted (otherwise no steady condition could ever be reached), so that

$$\frac{N}{\nu} = \frac{l}{c+v} + \frac{l}{c-v}$$

where N is an integer and ν is the frequency for which resonance occurs.

If a phase change of $2\pi/s$ occurs on reflection this expression becomes

$$\frac{N + 1/s}{\nu} = \frac{l}{c + v} + \frac{l}{c - v}$$

whence

$$\nu = \frac{c}{2l} \sqrt{1 - \frac{v_2}{c_2}} \left(N + \frac{1}{s} \right)$$

Similarly, a cavity operating transversely to the direction of motion of the medium may be considered. The modification of the resonant cavity frequency by the ether drift does not seem to have been considered in the Cedarholm Townes experiment. The calculation of the effect would be by no means simple, however it can be thought of as completely eliminated in the most important cases, i.e. when motion is either with or directly against the ether drift, and in these two cases, since the drift velocity appears only as a square, there will be no difference in frequency. It thus cannot act so as to mask the Doppler shift effect which would be present if there were a genuine ether drift velocity. In addition a change in cavity tuning does not exercise its full effect on the output frequency which is mainly controlled by the NH_3 vibration frequency.

The second problem falls into two cases, the first where the relative motion is so slow that the problem can be treated as a quasi-stationary one. The frequency in this case is such that a phase change of a multiple of 2π is produced over the path, allowing for various other constant phase changes. Even so the problem presents complications which lie outside our scope, for example, what will determine which particular mode, of the many apparently possible, will be excited; also, such a system may exhibit various instabilities. The case where the relative velocity is not negligible compared with the speed of transmission of the waves is even more complex.

An Apparent Difficulty

In Chapter IV the astronomical applications of the Doppler effect are introduced by a quotation from Dingle[4], which stresses the extent to which we are dependent on the Doppler effect for our knowledge of the remote parts of the universe. However, this quotation, while suitable as an introduction to the chapter concerned, does not convey a true impression of the article from which it is taken. This is better done by the following short quotation from the same article: " The original justification for supposing the effect to exist was purely theoretical, and the theory concerned is no longer acceptable ". Dingle justifies the foregoing statement partly by producing paradoxical results from the Doppler effect as commonly applied (considered with his general disapproval of Special Relativity). One of the paradoxes, somewhat modified in presentation, will now be considered, not as a serious obstacle to the acceptance of the theory of the Doppler effect, but as an illustration of simple but important points for consideration by anyone interested in a genuine understanding of the theory. A paradox must not be confused with a contradiction; it is a seeming contradiction, or a statement which differs from what we would normally expect, but which, on closer examination turns out to be true. If a theory predicts paradoxical results, this is a stimulus to further thought, and calls for clarification and explanation, while if a theory predicts a contradiction this calls for a revision of the theory. Thus one might say that the role of the paradox in science is concerned with teaching and understanding while the role of the contradiction lies in the advancement of science itself. For example, the famous " clock paradox " in Special Relativity is a genuine paradox, in that it is in striking contrast with what our everyday experience teaches, but, nevertheless embodies no self-contradiction, and should, if studied, lead to a better understanding of the theory. Thus the properties with which the ether was endowed during the 19th century were certainly paradoxical, but not necessarily self-contradictory, until the problem of motion through the ether was considered, when, in addition to elements of paradox, elements of contradiction appeared, and the stage was set for a major theoretical advance. It is hardly necessary to add that every paradox produced by scientific theory (experiment does not generate " paradoxes " or " contradictions " which are words applying to statements or theories), needs to be investigated and resolved, lest in fact it is a real contradiction.

While it is now axiomatic that physical theories do not need to conform to " commonsense " it is still a fact that a disagreement with " commonsense " or with our intuitive ideas of the world, makes a prima facie case for taking a closer and more critical look at a theory. One reason for this is that an important element in scientific commonsense is logic, and a logical contradiction in a theory must sooner or later manifest itself; in other words, a conflict with commonsense can either be a symptom of a serious defect in a theory, or merely our reaction to the unfamiliar. The first possibility must not be ignored in our overwhelming enthusiasm for the strange and paradoxical, or in a pragmatic disdain for the integrity of our theory.

The first part of the paradox may be simplified (in my opinion) into the following. An observer is watching a distant source such as a star which emits an identifiable spectral line. While both source and observer are at rest (i.e. relative to one another) no Doppler shift is seen. Suppose now that the source suddenly starts to move; the observer sees no change for some time, the time delay being in fact the time taken by light to reach him from the source. After this definite interval, the light will show a Doppler shift. So far, so good, but consider the case where, instead of the source moving, the observer starts to move. The Doppler shift due to this is seen at once, there being no delay. This fact presents no difficulties at all in the classical (i.e. non-relativistic) case, as might occur with sound waves, since it is clearly a case of deciding who is moving relative to the medium, and so on, all of which can be done unambiguously. The Doppler shift in the first case is caused by the generation of waves of different wavelength by a moving source, while in the second case the apparent frequency is changed by the motion of the observer, and this is clearly shown by the formulae developed at the beginning of this chapter. However it is with light, and with the relativistic picture, that we are concerned, and here it is claimed that all that enters into the picture is the relative motion between source and observer, and to ask which one moves is to ask an unanswerable question. The postulate of the undetectability of absolute uniform motion through space is a very powerful tool in the Special Theory of Relativity, but it is also a rather delicate one; that is, its use must be precise, and one must be clear as to what it actually means. The paradox of the two apparently symmetrical cases, becomes completely trivial if it is considered with due regard to the frame of reference in which the observations are made. Consider first the sudden motion of the source; here all observations are made in the observer's frame of reference and the time delay in seeing the Doppler shift is calculated simply on the basis of the distance travelled by the light. In the second case we are concerned with something quite different. The observer suddenly shifts himself to a new frame of reference, and must apply the Lorentz transformations to predict the result of observations made in the new frame. There is no reason whatsoever to expect any delay in seeing the

Doppler shift under these circumstances. As an illustration consider an analogous question where no element of paradox enters at all. Supposing the observer changes his conditions of observation in some other way than by transferring to another frame of reference, for example by inserting a filter in his optical system. The change is instantaneous. But if the source changes its emission in a corresponding way, the time delay is obviously necessary before the effect can be observed. When, in a later chapter, interpretation of the Doppler effect shown in the spectra of double stars is considered, it will be seen that the procedure adopted is to eliminate the effect of the earth's orbital motion at the time when the signal is received, in order to determine the velocity of the source at the time of emission (many years earlier), and that this procedure leads to no confusion or apparent inconsistency.

The next step is to consider the case where source and observer simultaneously give themselves identical impulsive accelerations, as might be done by firing identical rocket motors. According to Dingle, they remain at rest relative to one another throughout, but nevertheless, the observer sees a temporary Doppler shift (due to the finite velocity of light), and this appears to constitute a violation of one of the postulates of Special Relativity. What has been detected by this means is not the absolute motion of either source of observer, but the change in the observer's motion, first; and when the Doppler shift returns to zero, the fact that the source has also changed its state of motion, is made known to the observer. There is nothing in this which either contradicts Special Relativity, or, for that matter, commonsense. Of course if this motion were to cease in the same way as it started, there would also be seen a Doppler shift during the corresponding period. This paradox underlines a fact which will be considered again in Chapter V, namely, that the integration of the Doppler shift in order to derive the relative displacement of a receiver and transmitter needs to be carried out with some care.

It should perhaps be mentioned that Dingle, in the article in question, does not use the word " paradox " while discussing these problems, his aim is in fact ultimately to show that " there are inconsistencies in Einstein's theory which, whatever result the experiment might give, make it untenable, at least in its present form ". To this remark, clear enough as it stands, and suggesting that Dingle regards these problems, involving the Doppler effect as more than just paradoxes, is the footnote which seems almost self-contradictory.

" Inconsistencies, that is, in the sense that the theory requires incompatible observations when applied to possible physical situations. Considered as a mathematical theory alone, it shows no inconsistency . . . "

The second paradox, or perhaps the continuation of the first one, is more complicated. Suppose that, as before, an observer and a source of monochromatic radiation are initially at rest relative to one another. The source starts moving towards the observer with velocity u, at time $t = o$. The distance between the two is x so that during the interval from $t = o$ to $t = x/c$ the observer sees no Doppler shift. At time x/c the observer abruptly accelerates so as to move with velocity u relative to his original position, thus bringing himself to rest again relative to the source; and thus no Doppler effect is seen. The distance between the observer and source has been reduced by ux/c but no Doppler shift has been seen; and what is worse, this procedure may be repeated as often as desired, so reducing the separation of source and observer to as small a distance as may be specified, and no Doppler shift will be observed, constituting as it were the converse of the preceding example. Before attempting to clear up this problem it is of interest to note that the repeated, abrupt, changes in velocity are not an essential part of the problem. By reducing the duration of the steps in the process the motion of both source and observer may be made continuous as regards velocity. Consider first the case where the velocities of transmitter and receiver are both small compared with c when measured in a suitable frame of reference, which, when signals are transmitted by sound, for example, could be the medium. All that is necessary for no Doppler effect to be observed is that the time of flight of the signal from the transmitter to the receiver is constant. Because of the restriction to small velocities, it does not matter in which frame of reference this time is measured. This is illustrated in fig. 3 where the lines AA', BB' represent the paths of signals between transmitter and receiver, the slope of these lines representing the velocity c. Given the motion of the transmitter, the necessary motion of the receiver to show zero Doppler shift is readily obtained. If the motion of the transmitter is defined by $x = f(t)$, then the receiver's motion is given by $x - ca = f(t - a)$, a being a constant. An alternative way of expressing the condition is that the velocity of the transmitter when it emits the signal, shall always be equal to the velocity of the receiver when it is received. This condition is clearly satisfied by zero relative velocity, but may also be satisfied by accelerated motions. A consequence of the condition is that the displacement-time curves of transmitter and receiver are identical, except for displacement without rotation, the direction of the displacement depending on c while the magnitude of the displacement is determined by the initial separation. There is here, in fact, no paradox worthy of the name; there is, however, a reminder that the results obtained for the Doppler effect usually apply to steady conditions.

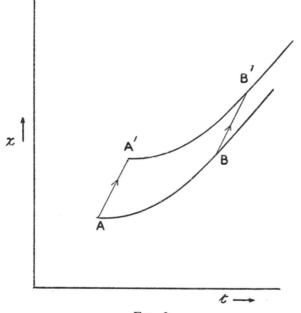

FIG. 3.

It is of interest to consider the relativistic treatment of this problem, and in doing so it will be possible to obtain a simple result for the Doppler effect in one case of non-uniform motion. Confining our attention to the case where transmitter and receiver move along the same straight line, let us choose an arbitrary inertial frame of reference, in which all measurements are to be made. If the observer's frame of reference were chosen, undesirable complications would be introduced as this is to be an accelerated frame. Let $x_R(t)$ and $x_T(t)$ be the coordinates of receiver and transmitter in this reference frame and let $v_R(t)$ and $v_T(t)$ be their velocities (all these quantities being functions of time). Suppose that at time t the transmitter emits a signal which reaches the receiver at time t', then the distance travelled by the receiver before it intercepts the signal is $\int_t^{t'} v_R(\tau)d\tau$, and the distance travelled by the signal itself is $c(t' - t)$, so that

$$x_T(t) - x_R(t) = \int_t^{t'} v_R(\tau)d\tau + c(t' - t) \qquad (13)$$

and differentiating with respect to t,

$$v_T(t) - v_R(t) = v_R(t') \frac{dt'}{dt} - v_R(t) + c\left(\frac{dt'}{dt} - 1\right)$$

whence

$$\frac{dt'}{dt} = \frac{c + v_T(t)}{c + v_R(t')} \qquad (14)$$

This is an expression for the Doppler effect as seen in the inertial reference frame. It is now necessary to find out how this Doppler effect will be interpreted by an observer moving with velocity $v_R(t)$. First, a time interval seen in the reference frame as dt will be seen, in a frame moving with velocity v_T in that frame, as

$$\frac{dt}{\sqrt{1 - v_T^2(t)/c^2}},$$

while a time interval seen in the reference frame as dt' will be seen in the frame moving with velocity $v_R(t')$ as

$$\frac{dt'}{\sqrt{1 - v_R^2(t')/c^2}}.$$

Calling these two time intervals Δt and $\Delta t'$ respectively it is possible to regard Δt as the proper period of an oscillation in the frame of the transmitter and $\Delta t'$ as the period as seen in the frame of the receiver. Thus the expression for the Doppler effect becomes

$$\frac{\Delta t'}{\Delta t} = \sqrt{\frac{[c + v_T(t)][c - v_R(t')]}{[c - v_T(t)][c + v_R(t')]}} \qquad (15)$$

When v_R and v_T are constant this formula may be compared with the expression obtained previously for the Doppler effect, namely,

$$\frac{\Delta t'}{\Delta t} = \sqrt{\frac{c + u}{c - u}}$$

u being the velocity of the transmitter in the frame of reference of the receiver. Expressing u in terms of v_R and v_T

$$u = \frac{v_T - v_R}{1 - v_T v_R / c^2}$$

and substituting in

$$\sqrt{\frac{c + u}{c - u}}$$

the result obtained is identical with equation (15). For no Doppler shift to be observed it is necessary for $\Delta t' / \Delta t$ to be equal to 1 in equation (15), i.e.

$$[c + v_T(t)][c - v_R(t')] = [c + v_R(t')][c - v_T(t)]$$

and therefore,

$$2[v_T(t) - v_R(t')] = 0$$

and so the requirement is $v_T(t) = v_R(t')$, the same condition as applies in the non-relativistic case. Now $v_T(t)$ and $v_R(t')$ are measured in an arbitrary inertial frame, but it is readily seen that if the condition $v_T(t) = v_R(t')$ holds in one inertial frame of reference it will hold in all such frames. If in equation (13), x_T is put equal to x_R, it is seen that

$$|c(t' - t)| = \left| \int_t^{t'} v_R(\tau) d\tau \right|$$

This cannot be true if v_R is always less than c, so that in the relativistic case the source and observer can never meet if they pursue zero Doppler shift trajectories.

REFERENCES

[1] RIEDEL, O. *Nuovo Cimento*, Vol. 25, p. 237 (1962).
[2] PAULI, W. *The Theory of Relativity* (Pergamon Press, London, 1958).
[3] CEDARHOLM, J. P. and TOWNES, C. H. *Nature*, Vol. 184, p. 1350 (1959). This work is also reported in *Phys. Rev. Letters*, Vol. 1, p. 342 (1958).
[4] DINGLE, H. *British Journal for the Philosophy of Science*, Vol. 11, No. 41, p. 11 (1960) and Vol. 11, No. 42, p. 113 (1960).

2

Inhomogeneous and Dispersive Media

The transmission of a ray in an inhomogeneous medium is governed by the vector equation

$$\text{grad}\,\mu = T\frac{d\mu}{ds} + N\kappa\mu \qquad (16)$$

where μ is the refractive index, N is the unit vector along the principal normal to the ray path, T is the tangential unit vector, κ is the curvature of the ray path and ds is the element of length of the ray. This result may be derived from the wave equation in the case where the wavelength is assumed very small compared with any other linear dimensions involved in the problem being considered, the unit vector T representing the normal to the wave front at any point. How the transition from wave optics to ray, or geometric optics may be made is outlined in the Appendix. Equation (16) can be reduced to a scalar equation by multiplying through by N.

$$\tan\psi\,\frac{d\mu}{ds} = \kappa\mu \qquad (17)$$

where ψ is the angle between the ray and the gradient of the refractive index, μ. Equation (17) can in turn be used to derive a differential equation, which, given μ as a function of position, enables the ray to be determined, subject to an initial condition. The form of (17) for a completely arbitrary μ leads to rather complicated expressions, so only two special cases will be considered here. These are firstly, when the medium is stratified, i.e. the gradient of μ is everywhere in the same direction and μ may be written $\mu(z)$ in Cartesian coordinates, or, what is the same thing, the surfaces of constant μ are parallel planes. The second special case is that in which the surfaces of constant μ are concentric spheres, i.e. the case of spherical symmetry. Perhaps the only really important applications of the Doppler effect to inhomogeneous media (to date) are in the study of the ionosphere, and both of these cases provide rough approximations to the state of affairs here. In the case of a stratified medium equation (17) becomes

$$\tan \psi \, \frac{d\mu}{ds} = -\mu(z) \frac{d\psi}{ds}, \text{ since } \kappa = -\frac{d\psi}{ds} \qquad (18)$$

whence $\mu(z) \sin \psi = \mu_0 \sin \psi_0$, i.e. a constant, μ_0 and ψ_0 being the values of μ and ψ at some arbitrarily chosen point on the ray. In our discussion, this point will be the point at which the ray is finally received by the observer. Since the refractive index for electromagnetic waves near the ground is very near to unity, μ_0 will be assumed to have this value. The path of the ray will in this case be a plane curve.

By a slightly more complicated procedure in the second case, that of spherical symmetry, the equation becomes

$$r\mu(r) \sin \psi = r_0\mu_0 \sin \psi_0 \qquad (19)$$

ψ still being the angle between the ray path and the gradient of the refractive index, that is, in this case the angle between the radius vector from the origin, and the ray path.

When examining the Doppler effect, the time of transmission of the signal is all important, but the foregoing expressions only give the geometrical form of the ray path between transmitter and receiver. To introduce the time it is only necessary to remember that the velocity is given by c/μ where c is the velocity in a vacuum. The time between transmission and reception of a signal, $t' - t$, as defined in Chapter 1 is given by

$$t' - t = \int_P \frac{\mu}{c} ds \qquad (20)$$

where ds is the element of length of the ray path and the integration is performed along the path of the ray, defined by equation (17), together with appropriate initial conditions. There need not of course be only one ray path between the transmitter T and the receiver R, it will be assumed here that only one need be considered, but if more than one were present, each would have its own appropriate Doppler shift. The existence of alternative paths of transmission is an everyday affair where long distance radio communication is involved but for the short wavelength radiation used in satellite observations it does not loom too large, but cannot be completely ignored.

Commencing with the second case (the surfaces $\mu =$ constant are concentric spheres), see figs. 4 and 5.

$$r\mu(r) \sin \psi = r_0 \sin \psi_0 \ (\text{putting } \mu_0 = 1)$$

and

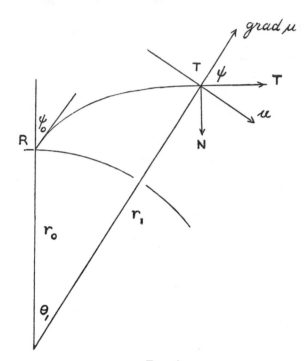

FIG. 4.

$$\cos \psi = \frac{dr}{ds} \ ; \ \sin \psi = r \frac{d\theta}{dr}\left[1 + r^2 \left(\frac{d\theta}{dr}\right)^2\right]^{-\frac{1}{2}} \ ; \ \tan \psi = r \frac{d\theta}{dr}$$

$$t' - t = \int_P \frac{\mu}{c} ds = \frac{1}{c}\int_{r_0}^{r_1} \mu(r)\left[1 + r^2 \left(\frac{d\theta}{dr}\right)^2\right]^{\frac{1}{2}} dr$$

$$= \frac{1}{c}\int_{r_0}^{r_1} \frac{\mu(r)}{\cos \psi} dr$$

$$= \frac{1}{c}\int_{r_0}^{r_1} \mu(r)\left[1 - \frac{r_0^2}{r^2}\frac{\sin^2 \psi_0}{\mu^2(r)}\right]^{-\frac{1}{2}} dr$$

and thus, proceeding as before,

$$\frac{dt'}{dt} = 1 + \frac{1}{c}\frac{d}{dt}\int_{r_0}^{r_1} \mu(r)\left(1 - \frac{r_0^2 \sin^2 \psi_0}{r^2 \ \mu^2(r)}\right)^{-\frac{1}{2}} dr \qquad (21)$$

whence the change in frequency can readily be derived provided that $\mu(r)$ is known over the range r_0 to r_1, and ψ_0 is known, this latter quantity being determined from equation (19) given the initial condition that the ray passes through the two end points (r_0, θ_0) and (r_1, θ_1). It is assumed that the receiver is fixed but that r_1 and therefore ψ_0 is a function of t. The equation (21) may thus be written

$$\frac{dt'}{dt} = 1 + \frac{1}{c}\frac{dr_1}{dt}\mu(r_1)\left(1 - \frac{r_0^2 \sin^2 \psi_0}{r_1^2 \ \mu^2(r_1)}\right)^{-\frac{1}{2}}$$

$$+ \frac{1}{c}\frac{d\psi_0}{dt} \cdot \frac{\partial}{\partial \psi_0}\int_{r_0}^{r_1} \mu(r)\left(1 - \frac{r_0^2 \sin^2 \psi_0}{r^2 \ \mu^2(r)}\right)^{-\frac{1}{2}} dr \qquad (22)$$

from which it is possible to proceed to various approximations or special cases. The simplest, but by no means least important, is the case, represented in practice by a vertical sounding rocket, where ψ_0 and $d\psi_0/dt$ are both zero. Then

$$\frac{dt'}{dt} = 1 + \frac{1}{c}\mu(r_1)\frac{dr_1}{dt} \qquad (23)$$

which, expressed in terms of frequencies gives

$$f \approx f_0\left(1 - \frac{\mu(r_1)}{c}\frac{dr_1}{dt}\right) \qquad (23a)$$

the Doppler shift being a function only of the refractive index in the region of the transmitter.

The complexity and the implicit nature of the expressions like equation (22) make it worth while to look at simplified treatments of the subject. The assumption, that a surface orthogonal to the ray paths from successive positions of the transmitter represents a constant time of transmission of the signal, is a reasonable one. We assume, in brief, that the transmitter which is always moving in a direction perpendicular to the ray which finally reaches the receiver, will show no Doppler effect. It will also be assumed that the ray lies in a vertical plane passing through transmitter and receiver, i.e. in a plane containing grad μ, T and R (see fig. 5).

B

Choose a set of axes such that the origin is at T, Oz is parallel to grad μ, and Ox and Oy are coplanar with and normal to the ray path respectively. As before, ψ will denote the angle between the ray path and the gradient of μ. The direction cosines of u will be denoted by $\cos \alpha$, $\cos \beta$ and $\cos \gamma$, while the direction cosines of the ray path at T will be $\sin \psi$, 0, $\cos \psi$, so that the cosine of the

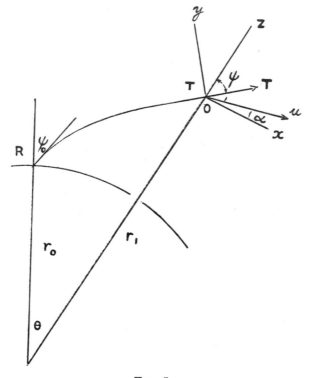

Fig. 5.

angle between the direction of u (the velocity of T) and the ray path will be

$$\cos \alpha \sin \psi - \cos \gamma \cos \psi$$

Thus under these conditions the component of u along the ray path will be $u(\cos \alpha \sin \psi - \cos \gamma \cos \psi)$. The Doppler shift will depend on the rate of change of " optical " path length, that is to say

$$\frac{dt'}{dt} = 1 + \frac{\mu u}{c}(\cos \alpha \sin \psi - \cos \gamma \cos \psi)$$

substituting $r\mu(r) \sin \psi = r_0 \sin \psi_0$ (and $r = r_1$)

$$\frac{dt'}{dt} = 1 + \frac{u}{c} \left\{ \frac{r_0}{r_1} \cos \alpha \sin \psi_0 - \cos \gamma \left(\mu^2(r_1) - \frac{r_0^2}{r_1^2} \sin^2 \psi_0 \right)^{\dagger} \right\} \quad (24)$$

In terms of frequencies this may be written,

$$f \approx f_0 \left\{ 1 - \frac{u}{c} \left[\frac{r_0}{r_1} \cos \alpha \sin \psi_0 - \cos \gamma \left(\mu^2(r_1) - \frac{r_0^2}{r_1^2} \sin^2 \psi_0 \right)^{\dagger} \right] \right\}$$
$$(25)$$

The case of vertical motion gives the same result as before. Two other special cases are worth noting, first, if the transmitter travels in a circular orbit, i.e. r is constant

$$f \approx f_0 \left[1 - \frac{u \, r_0}{c \, r_1} \cos \alpha \sin \psi_0 \right] \quad (26)$$

and if in addition the trajectory of T passes directly over R

$$f \approx f_0 \left[1 - \frac{u \, r_0}{c \, r_1} \sin \psi_0 \right] \quad (27)$$

If the details of the motion of T are known, then the Doppler shift will enable ψ_0 to be determined. If it is the ionosphere which is being studied, ψ_0 is not of any absolute significance in itself, it is the variation of μ with r which is normally of interest. The question is, in effect given ψ_0, what can be said about $\mu(r)$?

Reverting to equation (21), the form of this equation may be modified by making use of the geometrical relation

$$r \frac{d\theta}{dr} = \tan \psi,$$

θ and r being the polar coordinates of a point on the ray path. Integrating from the receiver to the transmitter,

$$\theta_1 = \int_{r_0}^{r_1} \frac{\tan \psi \, dr}{r}$$

$$= \int_{r_0}^{r_1} \frac{\sin \psi}{\sqrt{1 - \sin^2 \psi}} \frac{dr}{r}$$

$$= \int_{r_0}^{r_1} \frac{\sin \psi_0}{\sqrt{q^2 - \sin^2 \psi_0}} \frac{dr}{r} \quad (28)$$

where q has been written for $r\mu(r)/r_0$ and q_1 will be written for $r_1\mu(r_1)/r_0$

$$\frac{d\theta_1}{dt} = \frac{dr_1}{dt}\frac{\sin\psi_0}{r_1(q_1^2 - \sin^2\psi_0)^{\frac{1}{2}}} + \frac{d\psi_0}{dt}\int_{r_0}^{r_1}\frac{q^2\cos\psi_0}{(q^2 - \sin^2\psi_0)^{\frac{3}{2}}}\frac{dr}{r} \quad (29)$$

Equation (21) becomes, when the differentiation is carried out,

$$\frac{dt'}{dt} = 1 + \frac{1}{c}\frac{dr_1}{dt}q_1^2\frac{r_0}{r_1}(q_1^2 - \sin^2\psi_0)^{-\frac{1}{2}}$$

$$+ \frac{1}{c}\frac{d\theta_1}{dt}\int_{r_0}^{r_1}\frac{q^2 r_0}{r}\sin\psi_0\cos\psi_0(q^2 - \sin^2\psi_0)^{-\frac{3}{2}}dr \quad (30)$$

Equation (29) may now be combined with equation (30) since

$$\frac{d\psi_0}{dt}\int_{r_0}^{r_1}\frac{q^2\cos\psi_0}{(q^2 - \sin^2\psi_0)^{\frac{3}{2}}}\frac{dr}{r} = \frac{d\theta_1}{dt} - \frac{dr_1}{dt}\frac{\sin\psi_0}{r_1(q_1^2 - \sin^2\psi_0)^{\frac{1}{2}}}$$

and thus

$$\frac{dt'}{dt} = 1 + \frac{1}{c}\frac{dr_1}{dt}q_1^2\frac{r_0}{r_1}(q_1^2 - \sin^2\psi_0)^{-\frac{1}{2}}$$

$$+ \frac{1}{c}\sin\psi_0\left[r_0\frac{d\theta_1}{dt} - \frac{r_0}{r_1}\frac{dr_1}{dt}\frac{\sin\psi_0}{(q_1^2 - \sin^2\psi_0)^{\frac{1}{2}}}\right]$$

$$= 1 + \frac{1}{c}\left[\frac{r_0}{r_1}(q_1^2 - \sin^2\psi_0)^{\frac{1}{2}}\frac{dr_1}{dt} + r_0\sin\psi_0\frac{d\theta_1}{dt}\right] \quad (31)$$

This method of proceeding is due to Weekes[1], the result being essentially the same as equation (24) which is given by Hibberd[2]. In terms of frequency the result may be written

$$\frac{\Delta f}{f} \approx \frac{-1}{c}\left[\frac{r_0}{r_1}(q_1^2 - \sin^2\psi_0)^{\frac{1}{2}}\frac{dr_1}{dt} + r_0\sin\psi_0\frac{d\theta_1}{dt}\right] \quad (32)$$

Physically the Doppler effect in an inhomogeneous medium may be thought of as follows, the relation between the period of transmitted and received signals

$$\frac{dt'}{dt} = 1 + \frac{d}{dt}\int_{s_0}^{s_1}\frac{\mu}{c}ds$$

being regarded as consisting of two parts, even though these are not always explicitly separated in the formulae. Firstly there is the effect due to increasing path length, an effect depending on the refractive index in the neighbourhood of the transmitter, and secondly the effect due to the changing integral of the refractive index along the path as the path shifts or as the character of the medium changes with time. This latter is a possibility in the case of the ionosphere, which not only varies in its character with time owing to a number of causes but also contains moving inhomogeneities. The above comments can be summarised by writing the foregoing expression

$$\frac{dt'}{dt} = 1 + \frac{1}{c}\left[\frac{ds_1}{dt}\mu(s_1) + \int_{s_0}^{s_1} \frac{\partial}{\partial t}\mu(s)ds\right]$$

In a great many cases the second part of the expression in brackets is small compared with the first. A recent application of some interest[3] is an experiment in which the Doppler shift in radar signals reflected from the moon has been studied and as the line of sight velocity of the moon is small and well known, the effect of variations of the integrated refractive index of the intervening path can be isolated. This, as we will see later, amounts virtually to a study of the variations in total electron content of the intervening region.

If the exact orbit of a satellite is known from observations which are not seriously affected by the ionosphere, equation (32) will enable q_1 and $\sin \psi_0$ to be determined if two values of $\Delta f/f$ are known for accurately known positions of the satellite, thus giving the refractive index at a height $r_1 - r_0$. The true frequency of the transmitter must also be known, however, and since the variation in Doppler shift involved may be small, this needs to be known accurately. The determination of this is not necessarily a simple matter, although the Doppler shift is zero when the transmitter is moving in a direction normal to the ray path. However, a knowledge of $\Delta f/f$ is necessary to determine $\sin \psi_0$ and $\mu(r_1)$ which determine the ray direction relative to the transmitter. In addition there are various other uncertainties due to ionospheric motions and inhomogeneities. For this reason, the most satisfactory arrangement for studying ionospheric effects with rockets and satellites is to use, when possible, two transmitters whose frequencies are derived from a common source by multiplication, one frequency being relatively free from ionospheric influence, say above 100 megacycles, while the other is a submultiple of this, and influenced much more strongly by the ionosphere.

In reality even very high frequencies are influenced to some extent by the ionosphere, but for the present purpose it will be assumed that a frequency is available which shows no such effect. It is then possible to compare directly the frequency of a wave subject only to the normal Doppler effect in free space, with a wave of the same frequency (after suitable multiplication), for which the ionosphere has a refractive index substantially different from unity.

We will now consider the special case in which the transmitter travels in a circular orbit, defined by r_1 constant, and which, for simplicity, passes directly over the receiver, i.e. ψ_0 has the value zero, at some particular time. The frequency shift is given by

$$\Delta f = -\frac{f}{c} r_0 \sin \psi_0 \frac{d\theta_1}{dt}$$

and

$$\frac{d(\Delta f)}{dt} = -\frac{f r_0}{c} \left[\cos \psi_0 \frac{d\psi_0}{dt} \frac{d\theta_1}{dt} + \sin \psi_0 \frac{d^2\theta_1}{dt^2} \right] \tag{33}$$

and when $\psi_0 = 0$

$$\frac{d(\Delta f)}{dt} = -\frac{f}{c} r_0 \frac{d\psi_0}{dt} \frac{d\theta_1}{dt} \tag{34}$$

But from equation (29) $d\theta_1/dt$ may be written

$$\frac{d\psi_0}{dt} \int_{r_0}^{r_1} \frac{dt}{r^2 \mu(r)}$$

under the condition $\psi_0 = 0$ so that

$$\frac{d(\Delta f)}{dt} = -\frac{f}{c} r_0 \left(\frac{d\psi_0}{dt} \right)^2 \int_{r_0}^{r_1} \frac{dr}{r^2 \mu(r)} \tag{35}$$

in the zenith position. If now there are two frequencies f_1 and f_2 transmitted simultaneously, and, if it is assumed that $d\psi_0/dt$ will not be significantly different for these two frequencies,

$$\frac{\dfrac{d(\Delta f_2)}{dt} - \dfrac{d(\Delta f_1)}{dt}}{\dfrac{d}{dt}(\Delta f_1)} = \frac{f_2 \displaystyle\int_{r_0}^{r_1} \frac{dr}{r^2 \mu_2(r)} - f_1 \displaystyle\int_{r_0}^{r_1} \frac{dr}{r^2 \mu_1(r)}}{f_1 \displaystyle\int_{r_0}^{r_1} \frac{dr}{r^2 \mu_1(r)}} \tag{36}$$

The quantities $d/dt(\Delta f_2)$ and $d/dt(\Delta f_1)$ are known from the slope of the Doppler curves when the transmitter is overhead. The right-hand side of this equation may be written

$$\frac{d(\Delta f_2)}{d(\Delta f_1)} - 1$$

At this stage, rather than proceed further with the manipulation of the formulae it is worth while considering what quantity it is that is of interest in the Doppler observations of the ionosphere, or in other words, on what does $\mu(r)$ depend.

The refractive index, μ, is equal to

$$\left(1 - \frac{Ne^2}{\pi m f^2}\right)^{\frac{1}{2}}$$

where N is the number of electrons per unit volume, e and m the charge and mass of the electron and f is the frequency concerned. (This expression does not take into account the anisotropic nature of the ionosphere which is due in the main to the earth's magnetic field.) If $N(r)$ denotes the electron density at radius r, then

$$\mu(r) = \left[1 - \frac{N(r)e^2}{\pi m f^2}\right]^{\frac{1}{2}}$$

and

$$\frac{1}{r^2 \mu(r)} \approx \frac{1}{r^2}\left[1 + \frac{N(r)e^2}{2\pi m f^2}\right] = \frac{1}{r^2}\left[1 + \frac{\alpha N(r)}{f^2}\right]$$

when the refractive index is not too far from 1, a condition not always satisfied, particularly at lower frequencies.

Substituting for $1/r^2\mu(r)$ in equation (35)

$$\frac{d(\Delta f)}{dt} = -\frac{f r_0}{c}\left(\frac{d\psi_0}{dt}\right)^2 \int_{r_0}^{r_1}\left[1 + \frac{\alpha N(r)}{f^2}\right]\frac{dr}{r^2}$$

$$= -\frac{f r_0}{c}\left(\frac{d\psi_0}{dt}\right)^2\left[\left(\frac{1}{r_0} - \frac{1}{r_1}\right) + \int_{r_0}^{r_1}\frac{\alpha N(r)}{f^2}\frac{dr}{r^2}\right]$$

Substituting for $d(\Delta f_1)/dt$ and $d(\Delta f_2)/dt$ in equation (36) gives

$$\frac{d(\Delta f_2)}{d(\Delta f_1)} - 1 = \frac{(f_1 - f_2)(1/r_0 - 1/r_1) + (1/f_1 - 1/f_2)\int_{r_0}^{r_1}\alpha N(r)/r^2\, dr}{f_1(1/r_0 - 1/r_1) + 1/f_1\int_{r_0}^{r_1}\alpha N(r)/r^2\, dr}$$

Now

$$\int_{r_0}^{r_1} \frac{\alpha N(r)}{r^2}\, dr$$

may be written

$$\frac{\alpha}{(\bar{r})^2} \int_{r_0}^{r_1} N(r)\, dr$$

to a reasonable degree of approximation, particularly if most of the ionisation is concentrated in a narrow region, $\bar{r}$ denoting the effective mean distance of this region from the centre of the earth. The large value of r_0 compared with $r_1 - r_0$ also helps to make this a reasonable approximation. We may thus write, approximately

$$\frac{d(\Delta f^2)}{d(\Delta f_1)} - 1 = \frac{(f_1 - f_2)(1/r_0 - 1/r_1) + (1/f_1 - 1/f_2)\alpha N/(\bar{r})^2}{f_1(1/r_0 - 1/r_1) + \alpha N/f_1(\bar{r})^2}$$

where N denotes the *total number of electrons* per unit cross-section in the space between the transmitter and receiver. Consider for example $f_2 = 2f_1$, which was actually the case with Sputnik I, the first artificial satellite, the two frequencies in that case being close to 40 and 20 megacycles per second, both of which frequencies are substantially affected by the ionosphere. In this case, the expression

$$\frac{d(\Delta f_2)}{d(\Delta f_1)} - 1,$$

an observable quantity, is equal to

$$\frac{-f_1(r_1 - r_0)/r_1 r_0 + \alpha N/2f_1(\bar{r})^2}{f_1(r_1 - r_0)/r_1 r_0 + \alpha N/f_1(\bar{r})^2}\;; \qquad \frac{d(\Delta f_2)}{d(\Delta f_1)}$$

is the ratio of the rates of change of the two frequencies when the transmitter is overhead and from this ratio N may be calculated[4].

A further simplification may be made in calculations of this sort which is however only justified when ψ_0 is small. This is the assumption of a " flat earth ", i.e. the condition mentioned earlier, where the gradient of μ is everywhere vertical. This case follows very closely on the lines of the spherically symmetrical one and since, in the case of the ionosphere the spherical picture is usually closer to the truth, it is probably not worth while studying it in great detail. In this case $1/c \int_\rho \mu ds$ can be written

$$\frac{1}{c} \int_0^{z_1} \frac{\mu(z)}{\cos \psi} \, dz,$$

the lower limit of integration now being taken as zero without any loss of generality. Proceeding as before,

$$t' - t = \frac{1}{c} \int_0^{z_1} \frac{\mu(z)dz}{(1 - \sin^2 \psi)^{\frac{1}{2}}}$$

$$= \frac{1}{c} \int_0^{z_1} \frac{\mu^2(z)dz}{(\mu^2(z) - \sin^2 \psi_0)^{\frac{1}{2}}}$$

$\sin \psi_0$ having the same significance as before, and using $\mu(z) \sin \psi = \sin \psi_0$. Differentiating with respect to t,

$$\frac{dt'}{dt} = 1 + \frac{1}{c} \frac{dz_1}{dt} \frac{\mu^2(z_1)}{[\mu^2(z_1) - \sin^2 \psi_0]^{\frac{1}{2}}}$$

$$+ \frac{1}{c} \frac{d\psi_0}{dt} \int_0^{z_1} \frac{\mu^2(z) \sin \psi_0 \cos \psi_0 \, dz}{[\mu^2(z) - \sin^2 \psi_0]^{\frac{3}{2}}} \tag{37}$$

We now use the same method as that used by Weekes in the spherically symmetrical case, introducing the horizontal coordinate ρ, the receiver being located at the origin. (The azimuth angle is of no significance because of the symmetrical nature of the problem.) We have $\tan \psi = d\rho/dz$, so that ρ_1, the horizontal distance of the transmitter from the receiver is given by

$$\rho_1 = \int_0^{z_1} \tan \psi \, dz$$

$$= \int_0^{z_1} \frac{\sin \psi_0 \, dz}{\mu(z)[1 - \sin^2 \psi_0/\mu^2(z)]^{\frac{1}{2}}}$$

since $\mu(z) \sin \psi = \sin \psi_0$, μ_0 being taken as unity.

i.e.
$$\rho_1 = \int_0^{z_1} \frac{\sin \psi_0 \, dz}{[\mu^2(z) - \sin^2 \psi_0]^{\frac{1}{2}}}$$

and proceeding exactly as before,

$$\frac{d\rho_1}{dt} = \frac{dz_1}{dt}\frac{\sin\psi_0}{[\mu^2(z_1) - \sin^2\psi_0]^{\frac{1}{2}}} + \frac{d\psi_0}{dt}\int_0^{z_1}\frac{\mu^2(z)\cos\psi_0\,dz}{[\mu^2(z) - \sin^2\psi_0]^{\frac{3}{2}}} \quad (38)$$

This formula, and the formula (37) are almost identical with the Weekes' formulae, equations (29) and (30). The final formula corresponding to equation (32) thus becomes

$$\frac{\Delta f}{f} = -\frac{1}{c}\left[\frac{dz_1}{dt}(\mu^2(z_1) - \sin^2\psi_0)^{\frac{1}{2}} + \frac{d\rho_1}{dt}\sin\psi_0\right]$$

As might be expected, the case of vertical motion or horizontal motion are the simplest cases, the case of $d\rho_1/dt = 0$ and $\psi_0 = 0$ reducing to the same result as before. It also would be expected that the two formulae would give indistinguishable results for ψ_0 small enough, and this is indeed so, provided that r_1/r_0 is allowed to go to the limit unity.

When introducing the relation between μ and N the electron density, it was tacitly implied that the refractive index was unity where there were no electrons. This is, of course, not strictly true and the un-ionised regions of the atmosphere, which vary in density and therefore in refractive index with altitude, must make a small contribution to the Doppler effect. Some calculations have been made of the magnitude of the effect; for example, those of Hopfield[5] who calculates the extra Doppler shift produced by the troposphere for certain specified satellite orbits and frequencies. It will suffice to quote his figures for a satellite in a circular orbit 900 Km. above the earth, transmitting on a frequency of 300 megacycles per second. In this case the extra Doppler shift will be of the order of 2 cycles per second for 0° elevation and about $\frac{1}{4}$ cycle per second for 5° elevation, the effect becoming vanishingly small for elevations above about 30° or 40°. These figures are extremely small, but are they in fact negligible ? To answer this it is necessary to compare them with the Doppler shifts associated normally with ionospheric effects. The tropospheric effect is not very significant when considered from the point of view of satellite tracking but the ionospheric shifts themselves are often much smaller than the direct effect of changing path length in vacuum. The usual result obtained is that the total frequency shift in the presence of the ionosphere is only a few per cent different from that which would be observed in its absence; for example, round about 40 megacycles the maximum observed Doppler shift for a satellite like Sputnik I would be of the order of 1 kilocycle per second, of which the ionosphere would probably contribute something like 20 cycles per second and the troposphere something like 2 cycles per second. The small total effect of the troposphere could well be eliminated, if necessary, by calculated corrections of the nature of those given by Hopfield. The effect of the troposphere will not usually be greater than the various fluctuations, particularly so-called scintillations, due to ionospheric irregularities.

Weekes' equation [equation (32)] is, of course, applicable when there is no ionosphere present and it is of some interest to put this expression in a form which separates out the contribution from the ionosphere or other refracting medium. If ψ_v represents the actual angle between the vertical and the line joining the receiver and transmitter, the difference between the frequency shifts in the presence and in the absence of the medium is given by

$$\Delta f - \Delta f_v = -\frac{f}{c} \left\{ r_0 \frac{d\theta_1}{dt} (\sin \psi_0 - \sin \psi_v) \right.$$

$$\left. - \frac{r_0}{r_1} \frac{dr_1}{dt} \left[\left(\frac{r_1^2}{r_0^2} \mu^2(r_1) - \sin^2 \psi_0 \right)^{\frac{1}{2}} - \left(\frac{r_1^2}{r_0^2} - \sin^2 \psi_v \right)^{\frac{1}{2}} \right] \right\}$$

In practice $\psi_0 - \psi_v$ may be as much as 0·3 radian for 20 megacycles, but for 100 megacycles it will not exceed about 0·015 radian. A very interesting paper by Carru, Gendrin and Reyssat[6] may be consulted for a general discussion of ionospheric refraction. A rough expression for the ionospheric contribution to the Doppler effect may now be obtained by making two approximations. First, assume that the transmitter is " outside " the ionosphere, i.e. $\mu(r_1) = 1$ and secondly, that $\sin \psi_0 - \sin \psi_v$ is small. The assumption that $\mu(r_0) = 1$ has already been made. These approximations give,

$$\Delta f_v - \Delta f = \frac{\Delta \psi f}{c} \left[r_0 \frac{d\theta_1}{dt} \cos \psi_v + \frac{r_0}{r_1} \frac{dr_1}{dt} \frac{\sin \psi_v \cos \psi_v}{(r_1^2/r_0^2 - \sin^2 \psi_v)^{\frac{1}{2}}} \right]$$

The quantity $\Delta \psi$ is the " refraction ", i.e. the change in the angle of incidence produced by the refracting medium, and its calculation normally presupposes some knowledge of the variation of refractive index with height. This question has long been of concern in astronomical observations where the apparent displacement of

heavenly bodies near the horizon, on account of atmospheric refraction, is quite considerable, amounting to as much as 36′ in the
worst case, i.e. when the body observed is near the horizon.

In discussing atmospheric refraction in general the assumption
that $\mu_0 = 1$ is no longer possible but the necessary adjustments to
the formulae are readily made by going back to the derivation of
equation (21) and replacing the relation $r\mu(r) \sin \psi = r_0 \sin \psi_0$ by
$r\mu(r) \sin \psi = r_0\mu_0 \sin \psi_0$. The Hibberd formula, (25), becomes

$$f = f_0 \left\{ 1 - \frac{u}{c} \left[\frac{\mu_0 r_0}{r_1} \cos \alpha \sin \psi_0 - \cos \gamma \, (\mu^2(r_1) - \frac{r_0^2}{r_1^2}\mu_0^2 \sin^2 \psi_0)^{\frac{1}{2}} \right] \right\}$$

(39)

and in particular, equation (27) becomes

$$f = f_0 \left[1 - \frac{u}{c} \frac{\mu_0 r_0}{r_1} \sin \psi_0 \right]$$

(40)

and the modifications to the Weekes formulae are equally straightforward.

The case of refraction in a horizontally stratified medium is
almost as trival, in so far as the angle of incidence is concerned,
although the calculation of the actual ray path will involve the
integration of a more or less arbitrary function. Since $\mu(z_1) \sin \psi_1 = \mu_0 \sin \psi_0$ the angle of incidence at the " top " of the atmosphere
and the angle of incidence at the observer's level are very simply
related and only a knowledge of μ at the two levels is needed. The
case of the spherically symmetrical atmosphere is more complicated
and it is no longer possible to ignore the form of $\mu(z)$ or rather $\mu(r)$
as it now becomes. Equation (28), when μ_0 is given a value other than
unity becomes

$$\theta_1 = \int_{r_0}^{r_1} \frac{\mu_0 r_0 \sin \psi_0 \, dr}{r [r^2\mu^2(r) - r_0^2\mu_0^2 \sin^2 \psi_0]^{\frac{1}{2}}}$$

(41)

and in the case of an infinitely distance object, r_1 becomes infinite
and θ_1 becomes ψ_v the true zenith angle of the source or transmitter,
so that,

$$\psi_v = \int_{r_0}^{\infty} \frac{\mu_0 r_0 \sin \psi_0 \, dr}{r [r^2\mu^2(r) - r_0^2\mu_0^2 \sin^2 \psi_0]^{\frac{1}{2}}}$$

(42)

In principal, this relation permits ψ_v to be calculated, given ψ_0 and provided some suitable assumptions are made concerning $\mu(r)$. In the case of astronomical refraction the value of $\mu(r)$ is known with sufficient accuracy and tables have been computed giving the correction to be applied for various elevation angles.

Dispersive Media

So far it has been assumed, more or less tacitly, that the signals which are involved in the Doppler effect are transmitted unchanged through the medium with a velocity, the definition of which presents no problems. This will not be the case if the medium is dispersive, i.e. if the velocity of a sinusoidal wave is a function of its wavelength or frequency. It will be assumed that in all cases a sinusoidal wave is transmitted unchanged in form and with a constant velocity. This assumption is necessary for mathematical simplicity although in the case of the ionosphere it may break down for very large amplitudes. For the same reason, only one dimensional, or plane, waves will be discussed. Solutions of the wave equation

$$\frac{\partial^2 \Phi}{\partial x^2} = \frac{1}{c^2} \cdot \frac{\partial^2 \Phi}{\partial t^2}$$

represents waves in a non-dispersive medium, i.e. there is a constant velocity c with which any wave is propagated, irrespective of its form or frequency. However, every and any disturbance cannot be regarded as a wave in the ordinary sense, and one feature which seems intuitively necessary before one can speak of a wave is a velocity of propagation. This concept can be uniquely and unambiguously defined only in the case of a plane wave in a non-dispersive medium. The general definition of the velocity of a wave is as follows. Suppose that a disturbance occurs in a " medium " such that the quantity Φ is given by $\Phi(x, t)$, then a velocity of propagation is defined by dx/dt, subject to some condition imposed on Φ. For example, when looking at water waves the velocity one normally thinks of is the velocity of the crests, i.e. the condition imposed on Φ is $\partial\Phi/\partial x = 0$ (and perhaps also $\partial^2\Phi/\partial x^2 < 0$). The velocity so defined will not necessarily be the same if different conditions are impose on Φ, i.e. if different features of the waves are used to define the velocity. To illustrate this point, consider the spherically symmetrical wave, $\Phi = (a/r) \cos k(r - Vt)$ (which is in fact a solution of the wave equation). The condition $\Phi = 0$ is readily seen to lead to the result $dr/dt = V$ but the condition $\partial\Phi/\partial r = 0$ leads to

$$k(r - Vt) = -\frac{1}{kr}$$

and this gives

$$\frac{dr}{dt} = V + \frac{1}{1 + k^2 r^2}$$

A sinusoidal wave, propagating in a medium of the type postulated above, i.e. a medium possessing linear properties, can be described by the relation $\Phi = a \cos [k(x - Vt) + \phi_k]$.

The velocity of propagation is defined in this case by the condition $\Phi = $ a constant, which is equivalent to $k(x - Vt) + \phi_k = $ a constant, so that the velocity is V. Almost any reasonable condition imposed on Φ gives the same result, and this velocity V is called the phase velocity in the medium for propagation constant k (or angular frequency kV). It can be readily shown that in some cases governed by quite simple linear partial differential equations, the phase velocity V is a function of k. The wave propagating properties of the medium are in fact described by expressing V as a function of k.

It is possible to define another velocity, but, in this case instead of imposing a condition, such as $\partial\Phi/\partial x = 0$, on Φ, a condition is imposed on the phase $k(x - Vt) + \phi_k$. A condition which is of particular interest is that the phase should be stationary, with respect to the variation of k, i.e.

$$\frac{\partial}{\partial k}[k(x - Vt) + \phi_k] = 0$$

and so

$$\frac{dx}{dt} = V + k\frac{dV}{dk} \equiv U$$

(If V is not a function of k, then $dV/dk = 0$ and $dx/dt = V = U$.) U is termed the group velocity, and instead of defining the properties of the medium by expressing V as a function of k, this may be done by expressing U as a function of V, which leads to a differential equation

$$f(V) = V + k\frac{dV}{dk}$$

which apart from an arbitrary constant, is equivalent to expressing V as a function of k.

The reason why the velocity derived from the condition of stationary phase is especially significant may be seen from the following. The most satisfactory way of dealing with the propagation of a non-sinusoidal disturbance in a dispersive medium is to express it as either a Fourier series, if it is periodic, or as a Fourier integral if not. This can be done because of the linear character of the medium, a feature which is implied by the statement that any sinusoidal wave is transmitted without change of form or frequency. When one speaks of the " linear character " of the medium this is, in this instance, intended to mean that the quantity whose variation constitutes the wave satisfies a linear partial differential equation, having, in the cases usually met with, constant coefficients. This latter proviso ensures, in general, the homogeneity of the medium. A " group " is defined in this context as a wave whose Fourier integral covers only a very small frequency range and it may be represented by

$$\Phi = \int_{k_0 - \epsilon}^{k_0 + \epsilon} a(k) \cos \{k[x - V(k)t] + \phi_k\}dk \qquad (43)$$

ϕ_k being possibly a function of k.

Assuming that $kV(k)$ may be expanded in a Taylor series about k_0 and neglecting squares and higher powers of $(k - k_0)$, permissible if ϵ is not too large,

$$kV(k) = k_0V(k_0) + (k - k_0)[V(k_0) + k_0V'(k_0)]$$

$$= k[V(k_0) + k_0V'(k_0)] - k_0^2V'(k_0)$$

so that

$$\Phi = \int_{k_0 - \epsilon}^{k_0 + \epsilon} a(k) \cos [k(x - U_0t) + k_0^2V'(k_0)t + \phi_k]dk$$

$$= \cos [k_0^2V'(k_0)t] \int_{k_0 - \epsilon}^{k_0 + \epsilon} a(k) \cos [k(x - U_0t) + \phi_k]dk$$

$$- \sin [k_0^2V'(k_0)t] \int_{k_0 - \epsilon}^{k_0 + \epsilon} a(k) \sin [k(x - U_0t) + \phi_k]dk$$

$$(44)$$

where U_0 has been written for $V(k_0) + k_0V'(k_0)$, i.e. the group velocity for $k = k_0$. The above expression consists of two parts each of which can be regarded as a disturbance travelling with velocity U_0 and varying in amplitude with the frequency $k_0^2 V'(k_0)/2\pi$. The first term of the expression represents the original form multiplied by the slowly varying factor $\cos[k_0^2 V'(k_0)t]$. The above expressions would represent the exact state of affairs only if U were a constant, i.e. $V = a + b/k$ the limitation to a narrow band of frequencies then not being necessary.

A qualitative picture of the significance of the group velocity may be obtained by considering the fact that, what is propagated with this velocity, is the condition of stationary phase, i.e. phase independent of frequency over a small range. That is, the region in which waves of frequency $kV(k)/2\pi$ are reinforcing each other, will travel with a velocity $V + kV'(k)$, assuming that there is such a region. The question of the propagation of waves in dispersive media is treated very well in two books, one by Havelock[7] and the other by Brillouin[8]. One thing should be mentioned in passing, namely, that the group velocity, useful as it is, is not the only velocity besides phase velocity which may be significant; for example, the velocity with which the front of a disturbance is transmitted will not in general be either U or V, by " front " being understood the first disturbance detectable by an observer in the undisturbed region of the medium. Also, although the group velocity in many cases represents the velocity with which energy is transmitted, this would not necessarily always be the case. The reader is referred to the works mentioned above for a discussion of these and other interesting aspects of the subject.

When first considering the Doppler effect, the signal transmitted from T to R might well have been a sharp pulse, but in a dispersive medium this would very soon be resolved into a complex structure with no uniquely definable time of arrival. A key question which arises is this. Is it permissible to resolve the pulse into its Fourier components (either as an integral or a series), apply the Doppler formulae to each of these and then recombine them ? Let the assumption be made that this is indeed so, and proceed to consider the Doppler effect in relation to one of the sinusoidal components of a complex disturbance,

$$a_k \cos k_0[x - V(k_0)t]$$

Once the possibility of dispersion is brought in, then the concept of velocity relative to a medium becomes relevant. For simplicity consider the case of a transmitter and receiver moving along the x-axis with velocities u and v respectively, relative to the medium (fig. 6) and consider first the effect of the transmitter's motion on the frequency of a signal received by an observer at rest relative to the medium. The signal travels with velocity V relative to the medium and so, following the lines of earlier discussion on the relativistic Doppler effect, the frequency received will be

$$f = f_0 \frac{(1 - u^2/c^2)^{\frac{1}{2}}}{1 + u/V},$$

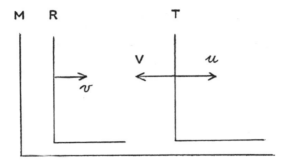

FIG. 6

the waves moving with velocity V relative to this observer, and f_0 being the " proper " frequency of the transmitter.

The next step is to take into account the motion of the receiver. The wave will be travelling with velocity

$$\frac{V + v}{1 + Vv/c^2}$$

in R's frame of reference and the frequency will be changed according to the relativistic Doppler shift by the factor

$$\frac{(1 - v^2/c^2)^{\frac{1}{2}}}{1 - v/V_R}$$

V_R being the velocity of the wave in R's frame of reference. Substituting

$$V_R = \frac{V + v}{1 + Vv/c^2},$$

the resulting frequency seen by R is finally

$$f_0 \left(\frac{1 - u^2/c^2}{1 - v^2/c^2}\right)^{\frac{1}{2}} \frac{V + v}{V + u} \tag{45}$$

The wave is thus seen by R as having a frequency

$$f_0 \left(\frac{c^2 - u^2}{c^2 - v^2}\right)^{\frac{1}{2}} \frac{V + v}{V + u}$$

and travelling with velocity

$$\frac{V + v}{1 + Vv/c^2}$$

The wave can thus be represented in R's frame by

$$a'(k_0) \cos \left\{2\pi f_0 \left(\frac{c^2 - u^2}{c^2 - v^2}\right)^{\frac{1}{2}} \left(\frac{V + v}{V + u}\right) \left[\frac{x(1 + Vv/c^2)}{V + v} - t\right]\right\} \tag{46}$$

or

$$a'(k_0) \cos \left\{2\pi f_0 \left(\frac{c^2 - u^2}{c^2 - v^2}\right)^{\frac{1}{2}} \left(\frac{1 + Vv/c^2}{V + u}\right) \left[x - \frac{(V + v)}{1 + Vv/c^2} t\right]\right\}$$

$$= a'(k_0) \cos \left[k'(x - V't)\right] \tag{47}$$

where

$$k' = k_0 V \left(\frac{c^2 - u^2}{c^2 - v^2}\right)^{\frac{1}{2}} \left(\frac{1 + vV/c^2}{V + u}\right) \tag{48}$$

and

$$V' = \frac{V + v}{1 + Vv/c^2} \tag{49}$$

The phase velocity as seen by R is the resultant of v and V taken according to the normal relativistic method. To determine the group velocity U' in R's frame of reference the relation

$$U = \frac{d}{dk}(kV)$$

is used, giving

$$U' = \frac{d}{dk_0}\left[k_0 V \left(\frac{c^2 - u^2}{c^2 - v^2}\right)^{\frac{1}{2}} \left(\frac{V + v}{V + u}\right)\right]$$

$$\times \left\{\frac{d}{dk_0}\left[k_0 V \left(\frac{c^2 - u^2}{c^2 - v^2}\right)^{\frac{1}{2}} \left(\frac{1 + Vv/c^2}{V + v}\right)\right]\right\}^{-1}$$

On carrying out the differentiation, the following result is obtained,

$$U' = \frac{k_0 \, dV/dk_0 \, (1 + 2u/V + uv/V^2) + (V + v)(1 + u/V)}{k_0 \, dV/dk_0 \, (v/c^2 + u/V^2 + 2uv/Vc^2) + (1 + vV/c^2)(1 + u/V)}$$

(50)

Two special cases are of interest, $u = 0$ and $v = 0$. For $u = 0$, the result is

$$U' = \frac{k_0 \, dV/dk_0 + V + v}{1 + v/c^2 \, (V + k_0 \, dV/dk_0)}$$

$$= \frac{U + v}{1 + Uv/c^2}$$

(51)

In this case the resulting group velocity is simply the relativistic sum of the group velocity and the velocity of the observer. This result is obtained quite simply by applying the Lorentz transformations to the wave as was done in deriving the relativistic Doppler effect in Chapter 1, and in fact this operation also provides the justification for assuming, as was done above, that the phase velocity is combined with the velocity of the observer in this way. The case of $v = 0$, i.e. the observer is at rest in the medium while the transmitter moves, is a case more likely to be of practical significance. Putting $v = 0$,

$$U' = \frac{k_0 \, dV/dk_0 \, (1 + 2u/V) + V + u}{k_0 \, dV/dk_0 \cdot u/V^2 + 1 + u/V}$$

$$= \frac{U(1 + 2u/V) - u}{1 + uU/V^2}$$

(52)

It should be emphasised that in the formulae,

$$V' = \frac{V + v}{1 + Vv/c^2}$$

etc., V' is the value of the phase velocity corresponding, in the receiver's frame of reference, to the quantity k', not k_0, while the velocity V corresponds to the quantity k_0 in the transmitter's frame of reference. The significance of this point is made clearer by considering the following question. Consider the case of the transmitter at rest in the medium and suppose that the medium has the property of having a constant group velocity a. This can readily be seen to imply that $V = a + b/k_0$ where a and b are constants.

($b = 0$ being the special case of a non-dispersive medium.) All that is necessary is to put

$$V + k_0 \frac{dV}{dk_0} = a$$

This type of dispersive medium (which is discussed at some length by Havelock) has the following interesting property. If a pulse is initiated in the medium its original form will be reconstituted at regular intervals with a frequency $b/2\pi$ and the pulse will travel with a velocity a while undergoing periodic changes in form. This can be quite readily seen by referring back to equation (44) where this particular case was in fact mentioned. Now the nature of the Lorentz transformations is such that the general form and topological character of a disturbance must be preserved although its dimensions may change. Thus if a wave repeatedly reassumes its "original" form in one frame of reference it must do so in all. This implies that the change from one frame to another must not alter the dependence of phase velocity on frequency in such a way as to destroy these qualitative features of a wave. In the particular case under discussion, $U = a$ and thus

$$U' = \frac{a + v}{1 + av/c^2}$$

which is obviously a constant. The condition $U' = $ constant rigorously implies that

$$V' = a' + \frac{b'}{k'}$$

This can be verified, if verification is necessary, by substituting

$$k' = \beta \left(1 + \frac{Vv}{c^2} \right) k_0 \text{ in } V' = \frac{V + v}{1 + Vv/c^2}$$

writing as usual, $\beta = (1 - v^2/c^2)^{-\frac{1}{2}}$

This is not quite as simple as it looks since, first $V(k_0) = a + b/k_0$ must be expressed in terms of k', using

$$k' = \beta \left[1 + \frac{vV(k_0)}{c^2} \right] k_0$$

$$= \beta \left[1 + \frac{v}{c^2} \left(a + \frac{b}{k_0} \right) \right] k_0$$

and solving for k_0. If this is carried through it is found that V' is indeed of the form $a' + b'/k'$. The determination of a' and b'

in terms of a and b may be carried out as follows. We have already seen that

$$U' = \frac{a + v}{1 + av/c^2} = a'$$

The result

$$k' = \beta \left[1 + \frac{v}{c^2} \left(a + \frac{b}{k_0} \right) \right] k_0$$

gives

$$k_0 = \left(k' - \frac{bv\beta}{c^2} \right) \left[\beta \left(1 + \frac{av}{c^2} \right) \right]^{-1}$$

and substituting in

$$V' = \frac{V + v}{1 + Vv/c^2}$$

the resulting expression of V in terms of k', namely,

$$V = a + \frac{b\beta(1 + av/c^2)}{k' - bv\beta/c^2}$$

leading to the relation,

$$V' = \frac{a + v}{1 + av/c^2} + \frac{b\beta(1 - v^2/c^2)}{(1 + av/c^2)k'}$$

$$= \frac{a + v}{1 + av/c^2} + \frac{b}{\beta(1 + av/c^2)k'}$$

(53)

whence

$$b' = \frac{b}{\beta(1 + av/c^2)}$$

So far, the formulae listed have been the relativistic ones but as a rule v will be very much less than c, but V need not be so, and may in fact be greater than c, which implies that, although v^2/c^2 may be neglected, the non-relativistic formulae for the combination of velocities cannot be used.

The expression given earlier for the refractive index of the ionosphere gives rise to the expression

$$V = c \sqrt{1 + \frac{K}{c^2 k^2}}$$

for the phase velocity, K being a constant proportional to the electron density. The group velocity is thus

$$V + k\frac{dV}{dk} = V - \frac{K}{ck^2\sqrt{1 + K/c^2k^2}}$$

$$= V - \frac{K}{k^2V}$$

$$= \frac{c^2}{V}$$

which is equal to zero when $K/k^2 = V^2$, corresponding to an infinite phase velocity. The condition of zero group velocity means that no propagation in any normal sense can occur for values of k less than $\sqrt{K}/V$ and the frequency at which this occurs plays a special part in the study of the ionosphere usually being called the critical frequency and is in fact the frequency at which a wave incident normally on the ionosphere is totally reflected. When dealing with the ionosphere, the case of a moving transmitter is perhaps more likely to arise than that of a moving receiver. The group velocity for the moving transmitter thus becomes

$$U' = \frac{V - K/k^2V + u - 2uK/k^2V^2}{1 + u/V - uK/k^2V^3}$$

$$= V \cdot \frac{c^2V + 2uc^2 - uV^2}{V^3 - uc^2} \tag{54}$$

For $U = 0$, the group velocity U' becomes $-u$. This is a reasonable thing to expect since a zero group velocity implies a disturbance which has no direction of propagation. Motion of either source or receiver can then impart to this pattern a new velocity.

If the group velocity does not vary rapidly with the frequency or if a narrow frequency range is involved, the envelope of a wave train moves with the group velocity. For example, in the case of a wave consisting of only two very close frequencies, the resultant sinusoidal envelope travels with the group velocity appropriate to the mean frequency. The group velocity may be expressed in terms of frequency by the relation

$$\frac{1}{U} = \frac{1}{V} - \frac{f}{V^2} \cdot \frac{dV}{df} \tag{55}$$

The time taken for the signal, now defined by the envelope which travels with the group velocity U, to travel over a path from s_0 to s_1 is

$$\int_{s_0}^{s_1} \frac{ds}{U} \tag{56}$$

where ds is the element of the path length. From (55),

$$\int_{s_0}^{s_1} \frac{ds}{U} = \int_{s_0}^{s_1} \frac{ds}{V} - \int_{s_0}^{s_1} \frac{f}{V^2} \frac{dV}{df} \cdot ds \tag{57}$$

The refractive index μ, which may be a function of both f and s is defined as c/V, so that (57) may be written,

$$\int_{s_0}^{s_1} \frac{ds}{U} = \frac{1}{c} \int_{s_0}^{s_1} \mu \, ds + \frac{f}{c} \int_{s_0}^{s_1} \frac{d\mu}{df} \cdot ds \tag{58}$$

$$= t' - t$$

where t is the time of transmission of the signal and t' the time of reception. If now we differentiate with respect to t

$$\frac{dt'}{dt} = 1 + \frac{1}{c} \frac{ds_1}{dt} \mu(s_1, f) + \frac{f}{c} \frac{ds_1}{dt} \cdot \frac{\partial \mu(s_1, f)}{\partial f} \tag{59}$$

where s_1 is taken as varying with t while s_0 remains constant, and also remembering that s is measured along the ray path, and not along the path followed by the transmitter. It has been assumed that $\mu(s, f)$ is not a function of t, apart from the time dependence introduced by the variation of s_1 due to the transmitter's motion. The added terms which are introduced if this is not so, or if s_0 is allowed to vary, are readily introduced if required. Consider now the simple case of motion in a straight line, parallel to the gradient of μ, as in equation (23) and write r_1 for s_1 and put $\mu = \sqrt{1 - f_0^2/f^2}$, f_0 being in general a function of r_1. Then

$$\frac{dt'}{dt} = 1 + \frac{1}{c} \frac{dr_1}{dt} \left(1 - \frac{f_0^2}{f^2}\right)^{\frac{1}{2}} + \frac{1}{c} \frac{dr_1}{dt} \frac{f_0^2/f^2}{(1 - f_0^2/f^2)^{\frac{1}{2}}}$$

$$= 1 + \frac{1}{c} \frac{dr_1}{dt} \left(1 - \frac{f_0^2}{f^2}\right)^{-\frac{1}{2}} \tag{60}$$

This result could just as easily have been derived from equation (56) by putting $U = c\sqrt{1 - f_0^2/f^2}$, the value of U being derived from equation (55).

REFERENCES

[1] WEEKES, K. *Journ. Atmos. and Terrest. Phys.*, Vol. 12, p. 335 (1958).

[2] HIBBERD, F. H. *Journ. Atmos. and Terrest. Phys.*, Vol. 12, p. 338 (1958).
HIBBERD, F. H. and THOMAS, J. A. *Journ. Atmos. and Terrest. Phys.*, Vol. 13, p. 376 (1959).

[3] HOWARD, H. T., LUSIGNAN, B. B., YOH, P. and ESHLEMAN, V. R. *Journ. Geophys. Res.*, Vol. 69, p. 540 (1964).

[4] ROSS, J. A. *Proc. First Internat. Space Science Symposium*, Nice 1960, p. 207 (Ed. H. Kallmann Bijl, North Holland Pub. Co.).

[5] HOPFIELD, H. S. *Journ. Geophys. Res.*, Vol. 68, p. 5157 (1963).

[6] CARRU, H., GENDRIN, R. and REYSSAT, M. *Proc. First Internat. Space Science Symposium*, Nice 1960, p. 286 (Ed. H. Kallmann Bijl, North Holland Pub. Co.).

[7] HAVELOCK, T. H. *The Propagation of Disturbances in Dispersive Media*, (Cambridge University Press, 1914).

[8] BRILLOUIN, L. *Wave Propagation and Group Velocity* (Academic Press, New York, 1960).

3

The Doppler Broadening
of Spectral Lines

The Doppler broadening of spectral lines, a very well known phenomenon, arises from the fact that the light emitted from a molecule of a gas will be shifted in frequency in a manner depending on the velocity of approach or recession of the molecule, and of course in a gas at any reasonable temperature this velocity varies widely. One of the basic problems of the kinetic theory of gases was to determine the number of molecules, which, at a given temperature, would have velocities lying within any specified range of velocities. The solution of this problem is usually referred to as the Maxwell-Boltzmann distribution. Although the term " molecule " is used, and in the context of kinetic theory this is correct, the applications of Doppler Broadening are most commonly concerned with spectral lines emitted from single atoms.

When discussing the Doppler effect it is the velocities along the line of sight which alone are of importance, so the form of the Maxwell distribution which is of use is that which applies to the components of molecular velocities in one direction. The distribution may be expressed as follows

$$N(o, u) = \int_0^u \frac{e^{-v^2/u_0^2}}{\sqrt{\pi}\, u_0}\, dv$$

or

$$\frac{dN}{du} = \frac{e^{-u^2/u_0^2}}{\sqrt{\pi}\, u_0} \tag{61}$$

where $N(o, u)$ represents the number of molecules having velocities (or more correctly components of velocity) between o and u in the one specified direction (the line of sight). The most probable value of the molecular velocity is u_0 and the root mean square velocity is approximately $1.22u_0$. The most probable velocity u_0 can be shown to be equal to $\sqrt{2kT/M}$ where k is Boltzmann's constant, T the

47

absolute temperature and M the mass of the molecule concerned. The quantity u_0 is the most probable velocity, *not* the most probable line of sight component of velocity. The most probable line of sight velocity is zero.

If now the frequency of a spectral line emitted from a molecule at rest is ν, the line being thought of as ideally monochromatic, the frequency observed when the molecule recedes from the observer with velocity u will be $\nu(1 - u/c)$ working only to the first order in u/c. This is justified as far as most applications go, as can be seen by considering the value of u_0 for an oxygen atom at several temperatures. At $T = 400°\text{K}$, $u_0 = 0·64$ km./sec., at $T = 4000°\text{K}$, $u_0 = 2·03$ km./sec., and at $T = 40,000°\text{K}$, $u_0 = 6·4$ km./sec., the last figure giving a figure u/c of the order of 2×10^{-5} so that u^2/c^2 is completely negligible. This argument is not completely sound, since from the nature of the Maxwell distribution there should be a certain percentage of molecules with extremely high velocities. (Molecules with $u > 10u_0$ will for most purposes make a negligible contribution.)

Consideration of the Maxwell distribution will normally show whether or not relativistic formulae need be introduced, and one would assume that if they are justified for the Doppler effect, then whether or not they need be applied to the Maxwell distribution itself, must also be considered.

The profile of the Doppler broadened line is immediately known if the relative number of molecules emitting each particular frequency is given. Suppose that in the final broadened line the number of molecules emitting frequencies between ν_0 and ν_1 is represented by

$$\mathcal{N}(\nu_0, \nu_1) = \int_{\nu_0}^{\nu_1} f(\eta) d\eta, \text{ or, } \frac{d\mathcal{N}}{d\nu_1} = f(\nu_1)$$

where the function $f(\nu)$ will represent the profile of the spectral line, since the intensity in a narrow spectral range will be proportional to the number of atoms emitting in that range. Consider now the spectral range ν_0 to $\nu_0(1 - u/c)$. The number of atoms emitting frequencies in this range will be

$$\mathcal{N}\left(\nu_0, \nu_0\left(1 - \frac{u}{c}\right)\right) = \int_{\nu_0}^{\nu_0 (1 - u/c)} f(\eta) d\eta$$

The number of atoms emitting in this range must obviously be the same as the number with line of sight velocities in the range o to u

so that it is possible to write,

$$N(o, u) = -\mathcal{N}\left(\nu_0, \nu_0\left(1 - \frac{u}{c}\right)\right)$$

or

$$\int_{\nu_0(1 - u/c)}^{\nu_0} f(\eta)d\eta = \int_0^u \frac{e^{-v^2/u_0^2}}{\sqrt{\pi}\, u_0}\, dv$$

Differentiate both sides with respect to u,

$$\frac{\nu_0}{c} f\left(\nu_0\left(1 - \frac{u}{c}\right)\right) = \frac{e^{-u^2/u_0^2}}{\sqrt{\pi}\, u_0}$$

whence

$$f\left(\nu_0\left(1 - \frac{u}{c}\right)\right) = \frac{c}{\nu_0} \frac{e^{-u^2/u_0^2}}{\sqrt{\pi}\, u_0}$$

writing ν for $\nu_0(1 - u/c)$ and $u = c(\nu_0 - \nu)/\nu_0$

$$f(\nu) = \frac{c}{\nu_0 u_0 \sqrt{\pi}} \exp\left[-\frac{c^2(\nu_0 - \nu)^2}{\nu_0^2 u_0^2}\right]$$

which has a maximum at $\nu = \nu_0$.

This expression gives a *relative* intensity distribution in the spectral line, the absolute values being of no importance in this context, the result being readily normalised if necessary. The half width of the spectral line is obtained by putting $\frac{1}{2}f(\nu_0) = f(\nu_0 \pm \Delta\nu/2)$, $\Delta\nu$ being defined as the half width. This gives

$$\tfrac{1}{2} = \exp\left[-\frac{c^2}{4}\frac{\Delta\nu^2}{\nu_0^2 u_0^2}\right]$$

whence

$$\frac{\Delta\nu}{\nu_0} = \frac{2u_0}{c}\sqrt{\log 2} \tag{62}$$

In wavelength units this becomes

$$\frac{\Delta\lambda}{\lambda_0} = \frac{2u_0}{c}\sqrt{\log 2}$$

and, substituting for u_0

$$\frac{\Delta\lambda}{\lambda_0} = \frac{2}{c}\sqrt{\frac{2kT \log 2}{M}} \tag{63}$$

Putting in numerical values for k, $\log 2$, etc.,

$$\frac{\Delta\lambda}{\lambda_0} = 7 \cdot 16 \times 10^{-7} \sqrt{\frac{T}{w}} \tag{64}$$

where w is the molecular weight expressed in the usual manner (i.e. $0 = 16$, etc.).

Molecular Beam Methods

The Doppler broadening is in the nature of a hindrance in much spectroscopic work, where it may obscure fine structure of a spectral line, but on the other hand it provides a means of measuring temperature, under circumstances where other methods may fail. The present standard of length is defined by the wavelength of a certain Krypton line (6056A). Krypton 86, apart from providing a suitable line, is free from undesirable fine structure, has a reasonably high molecular weight and is a gas at quite low temperatures, both features favouring a small Doppler broadening [equations (62), (64)]. In gases at pressures of a few millimetres of mercury or less, the Doppler broadening predominates over collision broadening and, apart from fine structure, over the natural line width as a rule. Where an extremely fine line is required the molecular beam technique may be employed to reduce the effect of Doppler broadening, a method apparently first devised by Dobrezov and Terenin[1]. The principle of the method is shown in fig. 7 where F is an oven or heated chamber containing a supply of material whose spectrum is to be studied, s_1 and s_2 are slits, G represents one or more electron guns capable of producing a copious supply of electrons of, say, several hundred volts energy, the purpose of which is to excite the atoms of the beam. The beam is viewed from a direction perpendicular to the direction of motion of the atoms in the beam, and because of the collimating slits, there should be no atoms in the beam which possess large velocity components at right angles to the plane defined by s_1 and s_2 and thus the Doppler broadening of the emitted lines should be substantially reduced. Care must be taken in the design of the electron gun so that no large fields which might introduce Stark or Zeeman effects, are produced, although, once recognised, this danger is not a great one. (Reference [2] contains some discussion of the functioning of the electron guns.) A more serious source of trouble could be the presence of atoms scattered from the beam or diffusing back after collisions with walls, slits, etc. For this reason the material in the beam must be condensed out on a cold surface, or, if a gas like helium, removed by efficient pumping. In principle there would appear to be no limit to the degree of collimation which could be achieved. However this obviously would be accompanied by a corresponding loss of available light, and in fact, until the invention of the laser, it was axiomatic that extreme spectral purity and high intensity were virtually incompatible.

FIG. 7.

The question of the width of a spectral line emitted from a molecular beam has been studied in particular by Minkowski and Bruck[3] who also studied the structure of the Cd red line, at that time favoured as an international length standard. In one particular result which they obtain, the slits s_1 and s_2 are of equal length s (an optimal arrangement), and of width a, l is the distance of the observed part of the beam from the slit s_1, h is the distance between the slits. In this case the spectral distribution of the light from the beam is given by

$$J(\nu)d\nu = C \cdot \frac{na}{2\pi^{\frac{3}{2}}} \frac{h}{l} e^{-(\nu-\nu_0)^2/b^2}$$

$$\times \left\{ \frac{s}{h} e^{-h/s(\nu-\nu_0)^2/b^2} + \frac{\sqrt{\pi}|\nu - \nu_0|}{b} \left[\Phi \left(\frac{h}{s} \frac{|\nu - \nu_0|}{b} \right) - 1 \right] \right\} \frac{d\nu}{b}$$

(65)

where

$$\Phi(x) = \frac{2}{\sqrt{\pi}} \int\limits_0^x e^{-v^2} \, dv,$$

the error integral, and b has been written for $\nu_0 u_0/c$. The spectral distribution for the line before the collimation of the beam, in the above notation, is

$$J(\nu)d\nu = C \frac{n}{\sqrt{\pi}} \cdot e^{-(\nu-\nu_0)^2/b^2} \cdot \frac{d\nu}{b}$$

The quantity n corresponds to the number of atoms per unit volume in the beam and C is a constant depending on a variety of factors.

The derivation of a half width from the equation (65) is rather complicated and must in practice be done numerically. Minkowski and Bruck have calculated the ratio of the normal Doppler broadening in the oven (in temperature equilibrium) to that in the beam, and find that for values of h/s greater than 1, the ratio of the two is proportional to h/s, and in fact

$$\Delta\nu_s = 0 \cdot 41 \frac{s}{h} \Delta\nu_G$$

where $\Delta\nu_s$ is the observed half width in the molecular beam while $\Delta\nu_G$ is the ordinary Doppler half width for the temperature concerned. Superimposed on this half width is an extra broadening caused by the finite angular aperture of the optical system used to observe the beam, which introduces extra line of sight components into the molecular velocities. The precise calculation of this effect is also best left to numerical methods but an upper limit is easily arrived at, since if θ is the maximum angle which the light makes with the perpendicular to the beam direction, the maximum shift introduced is given by

$$\frac{\Delta\nu}{\nu} = \frac{u}{c} \sin \theta$$

where u is the beam velocity. It will be readily seen that large apertures cannot be used without invalidating the use of the molecular beam technique, once again emphasising the generally reciprocal relation between spectral purity and intensity. Needless to say the optic axis of the observing system must be perpendicular to the mean beam direction, but this is not a difficult matter to achieve to the required degree of accuracy.

Barger and Kessler[2], using mercury, a substance which is favourable on account of its high atomic weight (the pure isotope of mass 198 is used for work of this kind), obtained interference fringes in a Fabry Perot interferometer with an order of interference of as much as 8×10^6, and this was by no means their limit. The value of $\Delta\nu/\nu$ which they arrived at, was about 4×10^{-8}, the mercury line being at 2537A. This half width would correspond, if it were a normal Doppler width, to a temperature of about $0\cdot6°K$, although when expressed in this way it perhaps conveys a rather exaggerated impression, because of the dependence of the half width on $\sqrt{T}$. The molecular beam method is probably essential if the finest details of atomic spectra are to be studied. The beams need not, of course, be excited by means of electrons, but light sources may be used; also it is possible to study the spectra in absorption instead of emission.

Upper Atmospheric Temperatures

There are two sides to every coin, and while the Doppler effect is an obstacle to the finest resolution of spectral lines, it may on the other hand provide a means of measuring temperature, and it is just in the case of gases at low pressures, where the Doppler broadening is best observed, that temperature measurement presents special difficulties. The most important gas at a low pressure, from many points of view, is in the upper regions of the atmosphere; and, of course, the sun and stars also possess regions of gas at low pressures and high temperatures. The measurement of the temperature of the earth's atmosphere, even at ground level, requires some care to ensure that the thermometer is not influenced by direct radiation from earth or sun, while at ionospheric heights the air temperature will play a negligible role in determining the equilibrium temperature of a thermometric device. The principle of determining temperature from Doppler broadening is extremely simple—the gas whose temperature is to be measured is caused to emit a spectral line, its profile is measured, its half width determined and from equation (63) the absolute temperature follows immediately. As is always the case, complications arise in practice. This method of measuring temperature is particularly attractive, however, since it is concerned in a very direct way with molecular velocities, and so gives a direct measure of what may be termed a kinetic temperature. Thus if an attempt is made to measure the temperature of a gas discharge by the method of line reversal (i.e. by placing a white light source behind the discharge and varying its temperature until the transition from bright gas discharge lines to dark absorption lines superimposed on the continuous spectrum takes place), a ridiculous result will normally be obtained, provided it is possible to make the white light source hot enough to observe the reversal. This is simply because the molecules of the gas are being excited by electrons travelling at velocities well above thermal velocities, in other words the system is not an equilibrium one. However since the Doppler effect depends only on the molecular velocities, and not on the mode of excitation, it should give a reliable result in a case like this, provided of course that it is the kinetic temperature which is required. There is a possibility which must sometimes, for example in the upper atmosphere, be considered (although it is very difficult to deal with), namely, that the excited atoms are not in equilibrium with their unexcited neighbours, because of some gain of momentum during the excitation process.

There are two other methods of temperature measurement which are applicable to the upper atmosphere, and which have been applied with some success. Both of these methods avoid the need to bring a massive body into temperature equilibrium with the rarified gases in the upper atmosphere. The first [4], [5] is to utilise the variation of the speed of sound with temperature, and is applicable up to about 90 km. or so, while the second [6] depends on the fact that in an atmosphere in equilibrium, the scale height of the atmospheric density is a function of temperature. (The scale height of the density is that vertical distance in which the density decreases in the ratio 1 : e.) The first method involves the explosion of grenades fired from a rocket at various heights above the earth, the arrival of the sound waves being timed at various points by an array of microphones. This experiment has been widely carried out in recent years and, as well as temperatures, it yields a picture of the atmospheric wind structure. In the second method, atmospheric density is measured by the drag on a suitable satellite, or balloon-like device ejected from a rocket. The method is capable of extension to very great heights, but suffers from some complications, as does the velocity of sound method, since both depend on a knowledge of the mean molecular weight. Of course the Doppler method also requires a knowledge of the molecular weight, but the recognition of a definite spectral line clearly identifies the molecule (or atom) emitting it.

To apply the Doppler effect to the measurement of upper atmospheric temperatures, it is essential to find a suitable emission line (in some circumstances an absorption line might serve), and also to locate in some way the region from which the line is being emitted. These conditions are satisfied in nature in a better way than one might have felt entitled to expect. The airglow or light emitted from the night sky apart from the light from the stars and other extraterrestrial sources, shows, when analysed, a number of prominent and very sharp lines as well as a continuous background and molecular band spectra. Worthy of special mention are the lines due to atomic oxygen (5577.345A and 6300.308A, etc.) and those due to sodium, in fact the two D-lines. These green and red oxygen lines as well as other airglow lines are also prominent features of the spectra of the aurora. The various so-called auroral lines can only be produced in the laboratory by special techniques, since they represent transitions from metastable excited states, the half lives of which are so long that, under normal discharge-tube conditions, the excited atoms give up their energy in some collision process before they have time to radiate it. In the upper atmosphere the mean free paths are very long and there are no containing walls so that these forbidden lines can in fact be radiated. This very long half life of the excited state is associated with an extremely sharp natural width for the spectral line, so that such lines should be satisfactory for Doppler broadening measurements. Also the emission of the green oxygen line (5577A) tends to have its maximum at a height somewhat above 90 km., possibly because of the opposing exponential decays in atmospheric density and various exciting agencies, such as solar radiation. In the case of aurora, the location of the emitting source can often be determined by triangulation from widely separated observing posts. Reliable information about the height of the 5577A emission has only been available since the advent of rocket soundings of the atmosphere. The red oxygen lines originate at higher levels and their source is extended over a great range of height.

c

The first attempt to measure an upper atmosphere temperature using the Doppler broadening was apparently made by Babcock[7] in 1923 and his method, in its essentials, has been employed in most, if not all, subsequent attempts. The method he used was simply to photograph the night sky through a Fabry-Perot interferometer of high resolution and attempt to estimate the width of the spectral line from the intensity profile of the fringes produced. By using five different orders of interference ranging from 3700 to 85000 he was able to make a very precise determination of the wavelength of this green line, obtaining a value 5577.350A $\pm$ ·005A. Unfortunately at the time the origin of the line was not known and Babcock does not seem to have suspected oxygen as the source: he was rather inclined to suspect helium or hydrogen. However he was able to infer, quite correctly, that the Doppler width of the line was less than 0·035A and in the light of various assumptions about the emitting atom this permits some upper limits to be set to the temperature. The actual Doppler width of this line is in fact about 0·015A which was beyond the resolving power of Babcock's instrument. Babcock used gold as the reflecting layer on his Fabry-Perot mirrors, but nowadays multiple dielectric layers are employed with lower absorption and correspondingly greater possible resolution, or finer " instrumental width ". In spite of all modern improvements, the method does not give a very precise figure for the temperature, but because of its direct character it gives an extremely useful check on other methods at a particular altitude. For details of determinations of temperature in this manner, reference should be made to the work, for example, of Wark[8] and Armstrong[9]. (The temperature of the layer emitting the oxygen green line is round about 180°K., quite a low temperature for this method.) Wark gives the temperature for the emission of the 6300A line as around 700° to 900°K. although, if the layer is of great depth, this would complicate matters. The type of apparatus used is shown schematically in fig. 8. The interferometer I is enclosed in a thermostatted box B and is placed in front of a camera lens L, the camera C being focussed for infinity in order to observe the Fabry-Perot fringes. The filter F, which is usually an interference filter, serves to reduce the intensity of unwanted lines and background. The photograph of the fringe pattern is then studied using a microphotometer and the half width is, of course, a combination of the instrumental width, the Doppler width and the intrinsic width of line, the last being negligible in the case of the oxygen green line, at any rate in this context. In order to estimate the instrumental width it is usually necessary to expose the system to radiation from some standard source, such as a mercury 198 lamp, and estimate the effective broadened width of this line. This process of estimating the true instrumental contribution to the width of the line is possibly the most difficult part of the operation. Because of the long exposures needed to obtain clear fringes from the airglow (of the order of hours), it is essential that the interferometer be thermostatted to avoid drift, and quartz or invar spacers are normally employed. While Wark used the photographic method of recording the fringes, Armstrong has employed photoelectric recording. The principle of the method is the same, except that instead of the photographic plate, a photo-multiplier tube is placed behind an aperture at the centre of the

FIG. 8.

fringe system. The interferometer is " scanned " by varying the pressure of the air in the box and a recording of the fringe profile obtained in this way, from the photomultiplier current. One possible source of error which affects both methods is the fact that the air-glow is uniform neither in time nor position, so that the intensity may vary slightly across the photographic plate or along the photo-multiplier record, thus slightly distorting the fringe profile. In practice this does not seem to have been very significant in the measurements made so far, but it is likely to be more significant in the case of the sodium vapour experiment which has been attempted recently by Armstrong and others[10].

This experiment, the result of a proposal by Bates, involves the liberation of sodium vapour in the form of a trail from a rocket at heights above about 60 km. The vapour is illuminated by sunlight while the earth's surface below is in darkness and the sodium trail glows, excited by the sunlight to emit the D lines. This experiment has been repeated many times in various countries, mainly with a view to determining wind speeds and diffusion rates. The measurement of temperature should be possible using the same technique as applied to the airglow, but unfortunately there are a number of additional difficulties. First and foremost, the sodium lines are not clear-cut monochromatic lines like the oxygen green lines but show a rather complex hyperfine structure. This leads to a more empirical approach, involving a study of the sodium spectrum using the molecular beam method and the simulation of the actual experiment in the laboratory, i.e. a vessel containing sodium vapour is raised to various temperatures and excited optically and the fringe profiles studied. The relatively high density of the sodium trail produced in this way leads to self absorption and possibly other effects which may distort the line profiles. The trail is laid at a very high temperature, being evaporated from a thermite burner, so that measurements are meaningless until the trail has reached equilibrium with the surrounding atmosphere, i.e. until sodium-air collisions predominate over sodium-sodium collisions. This is not thought to be a very serious problem because of the relatively long time over which observations can be made on the trail, up to as much as 15 or 20 minutes after it has been produced.

A question of some importance when considering the effect of the Doppler broadening of the spectral lines is how in fact the effects of different factors, such as instrumental width, Doppler width, etc. may be either combined or disentangled.

The Combination of Line-widths

Minkowski and Bruck[11] whose work has already been mentioned have also discussed this problem. They consider a line having a Doppler half width, w given by $w = 2\sqrt{\log 2} \cdot q$ where $q = u_0 \nu_0 / c$ [equation (62)], and a Fabry-Perot instrumental half width a. The resulting intensity distribution in the line then becomes.

$$J(\nu) = \int_{-\infty}^{\infty} \frac{e^{-x^2/q} \, dx}{1 + 4(\mu + x)^2/a^2} \tag{66}$$

where $\mu = \nu_0 - \nu$, ν_0 being the original frequency of the (assumed) monochromatic line. For a Fabry-Perot interferometer, the half width

$$a = \frac{(1 - R)\nu}{\pi N \sqrt{R}}$$

ideally, where N is the order of interference, and R is the reflection coefficient of the mirrors. This relation and equation (66) lead to a half width g for the combined effect which is not expressible in a concise form, but a relation can be established when $w \ll a$, namely,

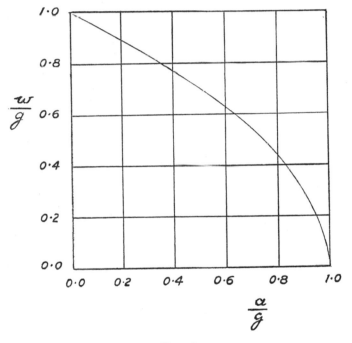

FIG. 9.

$g^2 = a^2 + 2 \cdot 5 w^2$. Minkowski and Bruck also provide a graph connecting w/g and a/g which is roughly reproduced in fig. 9. Pressure broadening or " radiation damping " both give rise to a different type of line profile from Doppler broadening, the frequency distribution being of the form

$$J(\nu) = \frac{1}{w^2/4 + (\nu - \nu_0)^2}$$

w being the half width as before. When this is combined with a Fabry-Perot line profile, we get

$$J(\nu) = \int_{-\infty}^{\infty} \frac{dx}{(w^2/4 + x^2)[a^2/4 + (x + \mu)^2]}$$

this expression, now being readily evaluated, giving the simple result $g = a + w$. The foregoing virtually summarises the content of this short but valuable paper of Minkowski and Bruck.

Absorption

Now, an absorption line, e.g. a Fraunhofer line in the sun's spectrum, will be broadened because of the to and fro motion of the absorbing atoms, in the same way as an emission line is broadened. It would seem to some to be intuitively obvious that absorption lines should undergo Doppler effects in exactly the same way as emission lines, nevertheless it is advisable to actually examine the case in some detail.

Consider an atom or other device, capable of absorbing radiation of one sharply defined frequency f_0, situated between the transmitter and receiver, which are at rest relative to one another. If the absorber is also at rest, and the transmitter emits a continuous spectrum an absorption line will be recorded by the receiver at frequency f_0. Suppose now, however, that the absorber is in motion with velocity u, taken as positive when towards the receiver. It will absorb, as before, the frequency which it sees as f_0. If this frequency is emitted as f in the frame of reference of the transmitter it will be seen by the absorber as

$$f \sqrt{\frac{1 - u/c}{1 + u/c}}$$

so that for frequency f to be absorbed

$$f_0 = f \sqrt{\frac{1 - u/c}{1 + u/c}}$$

and

$$f = f_0 \sqrt{\frac{1 + u/c}{1 - u/c}}$$

and, since the transmitter and receiver are not in relative motion, f will be the frequency at which the absorption is observed by the receiver. This frequency corresponds exactly to a Doppler shift applied to the frequency f_0, as if it were being emitted by the absorber, i.e. the Doppler shift is the same for absorption as for emission. It may be noted in passing that the factor

$$\sqrt{\frac{1 - u/c}{1 + u/c}}$$

has the property of changing into its reciprocal if the sign of u is changed, a property not strictly possessed by the first order approximation $1 - u/c$, and also a property which is essential if the medium is to play no significant part.

A new application of the Doppler effect has appeared in recent years (since 1958), in connection with the Mössbauer effect[12]. An atom in a crystal lattice which when excited emits a γ-ray, usually relatively soft (of the order of tens of KeV.), may under some circumstances emit this γ-ray both without the normal thermal Doppler broadening and without the systematic shift due to the recoil of the nucleus. For an explanation of this effect the reader should consult reference [12] which gives a general review of the effect and its applications, or some other parts of the voluminous literature on the effect which now exists. The interesting feature of the effect is that it renders observable a γ-ray emission line which has virtually only its intrinsic width, the value of $\Delta\nu/\nu$ being for example of the order of 10^{-12} in some cases. A width of this order in the visible spectrum would represent a matter of kilocycles per second bandwidth and it is indeed remarkable that, at much the same time as the Mössbauer effect was discovered, the laser, or optical maser, was also invented, giving for the first time, a coherent light source. The extreme sharpness of the γ-ray line emitted in the Mössbauer effect permits the Doppler effect to be observed for velocities of only a few centimetres per second, and in fact much less ($u/c = 10^{-12}$ gives $u = 0\cdot03$ cm./sec.).

The γ-rays may be absorbed by the same nucleus as emits them, provided they are both at rest. If, however, even the smallest relative motion exists, then the absorption falls off, and by varying the relative velocity of the emitter and absorber the profile of the γ-ray line can be explored in amazing detail. Apart from the applications to nuclear spectroscopy the Mössbauer effect has been exploited in attempts to verify the various frequency shifts predicted both by Special and General Relativity. So far, nothing inconsistent with either of these two theories has emerged and it may be safe to say that the importance of the effect will be in the study of the fine structure of nuclear energy levels and allied problems such as the nuclear Zeeman effect.

REFERENCES

[1] DOBREZOV, L. N. and TERENIN, A. N. *Naturwiss.*, Vol. 16, p. 656 (1928).

[2] BARGER, R. L. and KESSLER, K. G. *Journ. Opt. Soc. Amer.*, Vol. 50, p. 651 (1960). Also molecular beam methods are discussed by V. I. Odintsov in *Optics and Spectroscopy* (Translations), Vol. 10, p. 202 (1961).

[3] MINKOWSKI, R. and BRUCK, H. *Zeits. f. Physik*, Vol. 95, p. 274, p. 284 (1935).

[4] GROVES, G. V. *Space Research, Proc. First Internat. Space Science Symposium*, Nice 1960, p. 144 (Ed. H. Kallmann Bijl, North Holland Pub. Co.).

[5] STROUD, W. G., NORDBERG, W., BANDEEN, W. R., BARTMAN, F. L. and TITUS, P. *Space Research* (as in [4]), p. 117.

[6] KING HELE, D. G. and WALKER, Mrs. D. M. C. *Space Research II, Proc. Second Internat. Space Science Symposium*, Florence 1961, p. 918 (North Holland Pub. Co.).

[7] BABCOCK, H. A. *Astrophys. Journ.*, Vol. 57, p. 209 (1923).

[8] WARK, D. Q. *Astrophys. Journ.*, Vol. 131, p. 491 (1960).

[9] ARMSTRONG, E. B. *The Airglow and the Aurorae*, p. 63 (Ed. Armstrong and Dalgarno, Pergamon Press, London, 1956). Also *Journ. Atmos. Terrest. Phys.*, Vol. 13, p. 205 (1959).

[10] REES, J. A. *Space Research* (as in [4]), p. 207.

[11] MINKOWSKI, R. and BRUCK, H. *Zeits. f. Physik*, Vol. 95, p. 299 (1935).

[12] BOYLE, A. J. F. and HALL, H. E. *Reports on Progress in Physics*, Vol. 25, p. 441 (1962).

For general information on the airglow and related phenomena the reader may consult Chamberlain, *The Physics of the Aurora and Airglow* (Academic Press, New York, 1961), and for information on methods of interference spectroscopy, Jacquinot, *Reports on Progress in Physics*, Vol. 23, p. 267 (1960).

4

Astronomical Applications

" Most of our knowledge of Stellar Motions, including the characteristics of binary stars, the evidence for rotation of the galaxies, and the whole phenomenon known as ' the expansion of the Universe ', consists of deductions from this one principle ". This quotation is from Dingle[1], and it has been quoted, perhaps unfairly, apart from its context. The principle referred to is of course the Doppler effect, and it would seem that the quotation gives a true picture. In fact it is neither possible nor desirable here to discuss in detail every application of the effect to astronomy; the result would be in the nature of a catalogue. The importance of the Doppler effect in astronomy is that it gives a fairly direct and often easily interpreted measurement of the line of sight velocity of a remote and inaccessible object, and perhaps one needs sometimes to be reminded of the fact that the subjects of astronomical study are indeed as yet inaccessible.

All that the astronomer needs to do is to obtain a spectrum from a distant body, in which he can recognise certain spectral lines and then, from the shift in wavelength, the line of sight velocity is readily deducible. True, he must recognise the spectral line, and if only one line were observed, its wavelength altered, how indeed could it be " recognised " ? In practice, many more than one line may be observed, the lines likely to be present are known for other reasons, the Dopper shift $d\lambda/\lambda$ should be the same for all lines in the spectrum, and so on. It is not always a trivial matter, however, to identify a spectrum when only a few lines are present and the Doppler shift is large, particularly since those objects which show very great Doppler shifts are very distant and therefore very faint objects. Recently discovered objects, found as a result of attempts to identify astronomical radio sources, have shown very large red shifts and here identification of the much-shifted spectral lines is a key part of the investigation.

The Doppler shift immediately gives one component of the proper motion of a star, the other, at right angles to the line of sight requiring a relatively long time to become appreciable in the case of all but the closest stars and needing a knowledge of distance before it can be reduced to a velocity. It might be said of many astronomical applications of the Doppler effect that as applications of the effect, the interest is not very great, the determination of the velocity component is more or less a standard measurement of the deviation of the spectral lines from their normal positions; the real interest lies in the understanding and interpretation of the motions revealed. This is not invariably so, however, and the applications to be discussed are chosen as ones where the actual application of the Doppler effect is more than a trivial matter. Some other applications will be mentioned, merely because of their fundamental importance to the sciences of astronomy and physics. In this class comes the galactic red shift, associated with the name of Hubble. The spectra of distant galaxies show shifts to the red, indicating a velocity of recession which increases steadily and perhaps linearly (although this fact is questioned) with distance. This is the picture of the expanding universe. At a distance of some 10^{10} light years the velocity of recession should approach that of light and nothing further out should be observable. The proper explanation of this effect, and indeed whether it should be regarded as entirely the result of a motion away from us, is a key question in cosmology and it would seem to the non-specialist that solutions of the problem are favoured or rejected mainly on aesthetic grounds.

Many cosmologists look to radio astronomy to find a solution of the problem, and it must certainly play a major part. Here too, the Doppler effect finds some application, for example, in the exploration of the structure of our own galaxy. Together with the stars, whose proper motions give some picture of the swirling motion of the galaxy, there is a great deal of hydrogen dispersed throughout our interstellar environment. This hydrogen radiates a spectral line (an atomic line) on 1420·40 megacycles (about 21 cm.) which penetrates the earth's atmosphere and can be received by radio telescopes. As was expected, it shows a Doppler effect and from this a picture of the motion of the arms of the galaxy can be derived; it also gives a picture of the outline of the galaxy in a way which surpasses in some ways that given by the stars. Radiation of this wavelength has great penetrating powers where interstellar dust is present and radio astronomers can see deeper into the dense heart of the galaxy than can optical astronomers.

The application of the Doppler effect to the elucidation of the orbits of binary stars which is discussed more fully below, has an interesting sideline. The spectra of " Cepheid " variable stars show periodic Doppler shifts, or speaking more correctly, shifts which look like Doppler shifts. The initial interpretation of these shifts in terms of orbital motion led to extraordinary and even impossible orbits, until it was realised that what was being observed was a pulsating star whose surface rushed towards the observer as it expanded and then receded as the star more or less collapsed again. As there is no plausible alternative explanation of these spectral shifts and as the pulsation of stars is supported by other evidence, this explanation must be accepted. The Cepheid variables have played a very important part in fixing astronomical distances since they have been found to show a constant relation between their brightness and its period of variation, so that once the period is measured the distance may be computed using the inverse square law. Cepheid variables are among those peculiar phenomena which appear from time to time to provide a way across an apparently unbridgeable gap in scientific reasoning.

The subject of spectroscopic binaries is of particular interest for several reasons. These are stars whose double nature is revealed by a periodic Doppler shift of the lines in their spectra. The other classifications of binary stars are, visual binaries, whose motions are sufficiently great to be detected by the change in the stars' positions, eclipsing binaries in which the two stars eclipse one another producing a variation in brightness, and spectrum binaries where the double nature of the star is shown by the presence of two distinct types of spectrum. Any type of binary star may, of course, also manifest itself as a spectroscopic binary although those most suitable for study in this way are reasonably close pairs having high velocities of revolution about one another. The interest in binary stars lies primarily in the fact that it is only in these cases that any idea of the mass of a star other than our own sun can be obtained. Of course the great number of such stars is in itself an important feature of the universe which any cosmological theory must explain. The only information available in the case of a purely spectroscopic binary is the line of sight component of the velocity of the star relative to the earth. This can be thought of as made up of three parts, firstly that due to the earth's orbital velocity, secondly the velocity of the binary system as a whole relative to the centre of mass of the solar system, and finally the orbital velocity of the star. In some cases both stars yield satisfactory spectra, in others one may be too faint to give reliable results. In what follows attention will be concentrated on the case of a single star, whose spectrum can be observed and an accurate line of sight velocity calculated; and it will be assumed that the effect of the earth's own orbital motion has been subtracted from the calculated velocity. The type of velocity-time curve obtained will vary substantially with the eccentricity of the star's orbit, being a sine curve for uniform motion in a circle, and having a less symmetrical form for a more eccentric orbit.

Assuming that a velocity-time curve has been constructed (as in fig. 10), the non-periodic component, γ, of the star's velocity, is readily eliminated by finding a value for γ such that

$$\int_{t}^{t+p} (u - \gamma)dt = 0$$

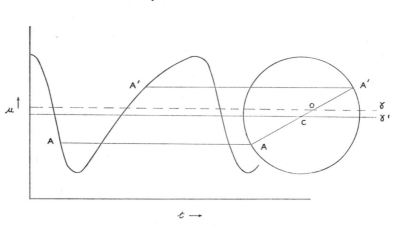

FIG. 10.

p being the period, t the time, and u the line of sight velocity. The motion of the star is thus referred to the centre of mass of its system, this being unable to execute any other than a uniform motion in a straight line, ignoring the very small influence of neighbouring stars and the galaxy as a whole. The whole problem can be approached analytically, but it is more instructive to use a semi-graphical method, and often the accuracy of the observations does not justify anything more. There is a very useful property of a Keplerian orbit which facilitates the procedure. This is the fact that the velocity of a body moving in such an orbit can be resolved into two components, one of constant magnitude V perpendicular to the radius vector to the attracting centre and the other of constant magnitude eV perpendicular to the major axis of the orbit, e being the eccentricity of the orbit. This result holds true for hyperbolic and parabolic, as well as elliptic, orbits, although only the latter are observed

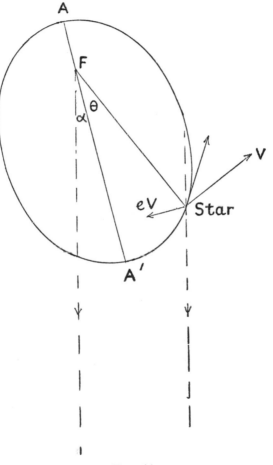

FIG. 11.

in the case of double stars. There does not seem to be any record of a " hyperbolic " encounter between two stars having been observed, not surprisingly perhaps when the vast distances between stars are considered. From fig. 11 it can be seen that the line of sight velocity u can be written

$$V \sin (\alpha + \theta) - eV \sin \theta \qquad (67)$$

It is assumed that the observer lies in the plane of the orbit, the effect of this restriction being considered later. If there are two

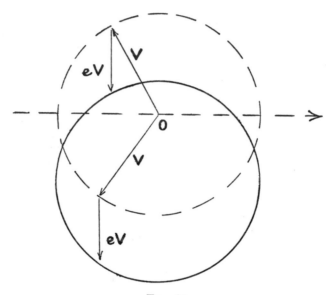

Fig. 12.

points which lie at the ends of a focal chord, and if θ_1 and θ_2 are the values of θ for these points, then $\theta_1 = \theta_2 + \pi$ and from (67)

$$u_2 = V[\sin (\alpha + \theta_2) - e \sin \alpha]$$

$$u_1 = V[- \sin (\alpha + \theta_2) - e \sin \alpha]$$

whence, $\dfrac{u_1 + u_2}{2} = - eV \sin \alpha$, a constant. (68)

Consider now the maximum and minimum values of u, these being found by differentiating (67) with respect to t, the time.

$$\frac{du}{dt} = V \cos (\alpha + \theta) \cdot \frac{d\theta}{dt}$$

Since $d\theta/dt$ is never zero (for an elliptic orbit), $\alpha + \theta = \pi/2$ or $3\pi/2$, that is, the maximum and minimum velocities u occur at the ends of a focal chord. We thus have

$$\frac{u_{max} + u_{min}}{2} = - eV \sin \alpha = \gamma'$$

which gives a value for the constant in (68) and this is readily found from the velocity-time curve (see fig 10). It can also be seen that $u_{max} - u_{min}$ is numerically equal to $2V$.

Using the preceding results it is possible to locate the periastron and apastron (the apses A and A') on the graph. (The periastron and apastron are the times of closest approach and greatest separation, respectively, of the two stars.) To do this one makes use of the fact that these points are separated in time by $p/2$ and since they are at the ends of the focal chord, (i.e. $(u_a + u_p)/2 = \gamma'$), they must be symmetrical about the line which is situated midway between u_{max} and u_{min}, i.e. γ'. It is necessary to find by trial and error two points which are the same distance from γ' (on opposite sides and separated by a turning point) and separated in time by $p/2$. As might be expected this process becomes indeterminate as the $u - t$ curve approaches a sine-curve.

To find the angle α, a graphical method is convenient, making use of the hodograph of the motion. The hodograph of the trajectory of a particle is defined as the locus of the end of a vector drawn from a fixed origin to represent the velocity of the particle at each instant. The hodograph of uniform circular motion, for example, is itself a circle, equal time intervals being represented by equal arcs of the circle. By using the property of a Keplerian orbit referred to above, namely, the possibility of resolving the motion into two velocities V and eV constant in magnitude but directed as described, it is easy to show, as in fig. 12 that the hodograph of a Keplerian orbit is always a circle, the origin however not in general being at the centre. Hyperbolic orbits are represented by only part of the circle but elliptic orbits, with which we are concerned, require the whole circle. The diameter of the hodograph circle is clearly $2V$, so it may be drawn on the graph using the same scale, as in fig. 10. The centre of the circle must lie on γ' since its radius is V. The position of the origin of the hodograph is for the moment undetermined. However the position of the apses on the hodograph may be found by drawing the horizontal lines AA and $A'A'$ to cut the circle. These should cut the circle at the ends of a diameter which thus cuts

γ' at the centre c. Since the ordinates from γ represent components of velocities parallel to the line of sight, the line of sight direction on the hodograph is parallel to the u axis. The intersection of γ with the line AA' will be the origin of the hodograph since this represents a zero line of sight component and thus it must pass through the hodograph origin. The sections OA' and OA are in the ratio $(1 - e)/(1 + e)$ (see fig. 12) whence e is known. The angle α is known since the angle between the line of sight and the direction of the velocity at the apses is the complement of α. Thus the period, eccentricity, and the angle α are known. The most important quantity remaining is the semi-major axis, denoted by a. If t_a and t_p are the times of the apastron and periastron respectively, then the length of the major axis, $2a$, is given by

$$2a \cos \alpha = \int_{t_a}^{t_p} (u - \gamma)dt,$$

$2a \cos \alpha$ being the projection of the major axis on the line of sight. Other points on the orbit can be filled in on the hodograph from the velocity-time curve, as desired. Points taken at equal time intervals will lie on the hodograph in a symmetrical arrangement about AA' but will be most closely clustered about the apastron position.

Two points, however, remain. We cannot from Doppler information alone derive any information regarding the way in which the orbit is oriented with respect to rotation about the line of sight. In addition it has been assumed that the line of sight lies in the orbital plane. The angle i between the normal to this plane and the line of sight cannot be found, unless some extra information is available. This can be seen by referring to the relation $u = V \sin (\alpha + \theta) - eV \sin \theta$, for the result of tilting the orbital plane is to multiply each term by the same factor $\sin i$ which could as well be interpreted as a different value of V. In practice the unknown $\sin i$ is left standing in the results unless some other evidence is forthcoming. If the spectroscopic binary is found also to be an eclipsing binary this sets a fairly definite limit to the values which i may assume. The fact that the orbit is so distant that our line of sight is constant in direction, while greatly simplifying the calculations, deprives us of a certain amount of information. In the case of a visual binary the orbits can be traced out and the angle i is determined from the fact that each star must be situated at the focus of the other's orbit, and although an ellipse when projected remains an ellipse, the focus does not in fact remain so when projected, as can readily be seen by considering the case of a circle.

Perhaps the most interesting information which emerges from a study of binary stars is the information regarding stellar masses. (Of philosophical interest only is the fact that Newton's laws seem to hold throughout the observable universe.) From the observational point of view spectroscopic binaries fall into two classes, those in which the spectra of both stars are suitable for Doppler measurements and those in which only one spectrum is observable or usable. Where two spectra are visible the ratio of the masses is the reciprocal of the ratio of the semi-major axes, i.e. $m_1/m_2 = a_2/a_1$. This result is simply due to the fact that the centre of mass of the system cannot describe any periodic motion, in other words, a consequence of the conservation of momentum. In addition, Kepler's laws lead to the relation

$$\frac{m_2^3 P^2}{(m_1 + m_2)^2} = a_1^3,$$

with a corresponding expression for a_2^3, the period obviously being the same for both component stars. This expression must be modified in view of the unknown $\sin i$, to read

$$\frac{m_2^3 \sin^3 i \ P^2}{(m_1 + m_2)^2} = a_1^3 \sin^3 i$$

where $a_1 \sin i$ is the quantity observed in practice. This results in our being able to determine m_1/m_2 and thus $m_1 \sin^3 i$ and $m_2 \sin^3 i$ when both spectra are usable. Then, either by a guess, from the existence of eclipsing, or by averaging over a large number of binary systems, star masses are determined. Astronomers appear to regard 0·67 as a suitable mean value for $\sin^3 i$. In arriving at such a mean value they take into account, together with other selective influences, the fact that small values of i will tend to be poorly represented, since a star system whose orbital plane is nearly normal to the line of sight is not likely to be recognised as a spectroscopic binary. In the cases when only one spectrum is seen, the ratio of the masses is not obtainable and only the quantity

$$\frac{m_2^3 \sin^3 i}{(m_1 + m_2)^2}$$

can be calculated. If now a mean mass is assumed for the visible star, allotted on the basis of its spectral class, then an estimate of the mass of the dark companion can be made (subject of course to the sin i uncertainty). The units used here are such that m_1 and m_2 are expressed in solar masses and a_1 and a_2 in terms of astronomical units, an astronomical unit being the mean distance of the earth from the sun. The period P is in years so that for the earth and sun $m_1 + m_2 = 1$, $P = 1$, $a = 1$.

The question of binary stars and in particular spectroscopic binaries is in many cases not as simple as is suggested by the foregoing. Thus, if the simple analysis above is applied in cases where the two stars pass sufficiently close to each other to raise substantial tides, or even eject material, anomalous results will be obtained. Stellar rotation also manifests itself by Doppler broadening, the wavelength of light from opposite edges of the star being displaced in different directions. A great many spectroscopic binaries however behave as gravitating particles, and, while not the most spectacular objects in some ways, help to provide a solid foundation for stellar mass determinations. A rather intriguing manifestation of the Doppler effect has been observed where a double star is itself in orbit around a third star, the latter orbit being large enough for the binary star to travel as a single unit. The period of the binary star shows a Doppler shift, analogous to that observed by Römer in the periods of Jupiter's satellites. Other anomalous and sometimes unexplained variations in the periods of double stars have been recorded, irregularities being perhaps commonest among eclipsing binaries, the latter, by the nature of things, being close partnerships and so liable to physical interaction.

A subject on which considerable speculation has taken place is the question as to whether planetary systems are at all common, the prevailing view at present favouring, on perhaps slender grounds, a very great frequency of occurrence of such systems. The natural question to ask is, how far can the Doppler shift be expected to provide an answer ? The observation of numbers of binary stars has revealed dark companions, but these are usually of considerably greater mass than, say, the planet Jupiter. For example, the radial velocity of the sun due to Jupiter's motion would be seen by an observer outside the solar system as about 1/100 Km. per sec., corresponding to a Doppler shift of $d\lambda/\lambda = 3 \times 10^{-8}$, i.e. a shift of about 0·0002A in the red part of the spectrum. The chances of observing a shift of this order can be ruled out completely. Probably something like a line of sight velocity of the order of a kilometre per second could be reliably detected, so that the detection of planetary system of as small mass as our own would hardly be likely by this method.

Among other astronomical applications of the Doppler effect the resolution of the nature of Saturn's rings is of historic interest. The fact that these rings consisted of small individual particles was determined by the fact that the parts of the rings nearest to the planet showed a greater Doppler shift in the Fraunhofer lines of reflected sunlight, than did those at the outside, in accordance with Kepler's laws for orbiting particles.

More recently the Doppler effect has been applied to the study of the Zodiacal light, a roughly elliptical zone of faint light, seen after sunset (or before sunrise) surrounding the sun, its maximum dimension lying along the ecliptic. Various considerations have led to the belief that this light is scattered by a large number of small objects in orbit around the sun, whose size is much greater than gas molecules, but too small to be resolved into individual objects even by the most powerful telescope. They shine in reflected sunlight, as is revealed by the presence of the tell-tale Fraunhofer lines in the spectrum of the zodiacal light. The investigation in question was carried out by Ring, Clarke and others[2] in 1962 from a post in the Andes at Chacaltaya. The only spectral lines visible in the zodiacal light are the Fraunhofer lines which are, of course, absorption lines. The spectral line chosen to study was the $H\beta$ line, and the system used was a Fabry-Perot interferometer having a useful diameter of 9 cm., plates flat to about 1/50 of a wavelength in the green, and coated with dielectric reflecting layers. Now the study of a single emission line with a Fabry-Perot interferometer is a straightforward matter; as was mentioned in Chapter 3, the recording of Fabry-Perot fringes from the emission lines in the airglow presents no real problems. However the interferometric study of an absorption line on a bright ground is more complicated. In principle, a continuous source with one single absorption line should show a set of dark interference fringes on a bright ground, but in practice if the total intensity of the background is large compared with the intensity of the absorption line, as it usually must be, the fringes due to the line are lost in the noise. It is therefore necessary to isolate the region of the spectrum in a band close to the absorption line, and this was done in this case by focussing the Fabry-Perot fringes into the slit of a spectrometer. The effective width of spectrum isolated was of the order of 20A, the Fabry-Perot interferometer had a spectral range of 30A and its instrumental half width was about

1·2A. From this it may be inferred that the main thing was light gathering power rather than high resolution. In order to determine the line profile and the position of its maximum, the Fabry-Perot interferometer was " scanned ". This was done by placing it in a container filled with propane, the pressure of which could be varied, thus varying the optical path difference in the interferometer, propane having a reasonably high refractive index. The fringe profile was measured by means of a photomultiplier using a pulse counting method. The current obtained was quite small, the zodiacal light being quite a faint object, and after the necessary dispersion of its light over the spectrum the resulting intensity is indeed small. The light sets or rises with the sun so that the time available for its observation is not unlimited. Each pressure of propane in the containing vessel corresponds to a particular wavelength centred on the photomultiplier aperture, provided the separation of the Fabry-Perot plates does not change, this latter being reasonably easy to ensure. As in airglow experiments a laboratory source is used to check on this point, and, in this case a hydrogen discharge was used as a comparison standard to determine the shift. Scattered sunlight from the sky also provided an $H\beta$ Fraunhofer line for comparison. The result was a blue shift corresponding to about twice that expected for circular Keplerian orbits. The precise explanation of this is not clear, although very elongated orbits, could of course give rise to quite large velocities at perihelion. Unfortunately, the escape velocity is only $\sqrt{2}$ times the velocity of a circular orbit, so that particles in orbit around the sun should not show such large velocities. The explanation lies presumably in the experimental error, which, chiefly because of the faintness of the source, is very large. The authors of this work plan further experiments and these should clear up this discrepancy. The existence of a *blue* shift and the absence of any significant red-shifted component implies that most if not all of the particles are revolving in the same sense around the sun. This sense is the same as that in which most members of the solar system revolve or rotate, this almost complete uniformity in the direction of rotation being a striking feature of our solar system. A moment's consideration will show that a direct rotation (i.e. in the sense of the general motion of the planets) will produce a blue shift if the observations are made after sunset. The velocity component due to the earth's rotation on its axis is quite negligible in comparison with orbital velocities near the sun (or even near the earth).

No attempt has been made to survey all the applications of the Doppler effect to astronomy, and the selection of topics must, to some extent, be arbitrary. The case of spectroscopic binaries does not fall into this class, however. It is of interest for a reason unrelated to its great importance to astronomical theory. To illustrate the point in question, consider a star describing a circular orbit about its companion, or rather about the centre of mass of the system. The velocity-time curve obtained from its spectrum will be a sine curve, the period, the period of rotation, and the amplitude proportional to sin i defined above. Now such a velocity-time curve would also be obtained if the star were executing simple harmonic motion along a straight line, or indeed moving in an elliptic orbit under the influence of a force whose magnitude was proportional to the distance from an attracting centre and directed towards the centre. This possibility cannot be entertained for a minute, since it is well known that stars, like everything else, are subject to the inverse square law of gravitation, which precludes a non-disastrous linear orbit, and in the case of a periodic orbit, permits only an ellipse as orbit with the attracting centre at the focus. Only in the case of a circular orbit, can the velocity-time curve be sinusoidal. Thus the observational data, alone insufficient, when combined with a knowledge of the laws of motion governing the system, enable an orbit to be determined, subject of course to certain limitations or ambiguities. If the orbits of double stars were governed by the linear force law mentioned above then the eccentricity of the orbits would not be ascertainable from the Doppler observations. The fact that the acceleration in an actual orbit is directed towards the focus and not the centre, and the velocity in the orbit is asymmetrical, is basically the reason why the loss of information due to the projected view, can to some extent be overcome. The general problem presented by spectroscopic and to some extent by visual and eclipsing binaries is this: The observational data is incomplete, i.e. we have only a projected view or a line of sight velocity, but to make up for this we are confident that we know the laws governing the motion. We have seen that in the case of spectroscopic binaries these laws are sufficiently restrictive to permit considerable inference to be drawn about the motions. The Doppler effect, by its nature, gives only partial information about a motion which it is used to study. The problem is to utilise all the other relevant information, in particular the general laws governing the motion, to combine with Doppler information to overcome the observational deficiencies. When the additional information consists of general laws governing the motion of a body, its combination with Doppler information is usually possible without much difficulty, although as is seen by the preceding example, the expressing of the law in the right form can make an enormous difference to the ease of the solution. The choice of the property of Keplerian motion whereby it can be resolved into two constant (in magnitude) velocities V and eV renders the problem fairly straightforward; it would be instructive to attempt the problem without using this fact, but instead, to go back to the inverse square law.

REFERENCES

[1]   See reference [4], Chapter 1.
[2]   RING, J., CLARKE, D., JAMES, J. F., DAEHLER, M., MECK, J. E. *Nature*, Vol. 202, p. 167 (1964).
      For information on binary stars, see Aitken, *The Binary Stars* (McGraw-Hill Book Co. Inc., New York, 1935) or, Hynek (Ed.), *Astrophysics*, Chapters 9, 10 and 11 (McGraw-Hill Book Co. Inc., New York, 1951).

5

Rocket and Satellite Tracking

A standard method of measuring the frequency of an incoming radio signal is to mix it with the output of a standard oscillator, and measure the resulting beat frequency, which will usually be quite a low frequency compared with that of the incoming signal. In measuring the line of sight velocity of a transmitter by means of the Doppler effect, it is obvious that very serious errors may be introduced if the transmitter's frequency varies in a manner unknown to the observer. In astronomical applications the transmitters are usually atoms of a substance with a known spectrum and atoms are not liable, as are electronic oscillators, to drift in frequency. Broadening or splitting of spectral lines occurs from several causes, but systematic shifts in frequency from causes other than the Doppler shift are rare, although not unknown. In applications to rocket and satellite tracking, oscillator stability is a practical question. The order of magnitude of the effect may be seen by the following:

The standard formula

$$u \approx \frac{f_0 - f}{f_0} \cdot c$$

is normally used to calculate u the line of sight velocity. Assuming that f the incoming frequency is measured with negligible error, but that f_0 is in error by Δf, then the fractional error in u, $\Delta u / u$ is $c/u \cdot \Delta f / f_0$. Since c/u may well exceed 10^5 in rocket work this implies that the oscillator stability should be of the order of 1 in 10^7 for 1 per cent accuracy in velocity measurement. While very stable oscillators can be produced, this problem is often eliminated in another way altogether. This is by using reflection or " transponder " Doppler, in which the moving vehicle does not generate a frequency of its own but merely reflects or retransmits a signal from a stationary transmitter. The reflected signal is then mixed with some of the outgoing signal and the beat frequency measured. The use of a receiver which amplifies and retransmits the signal, instead of passive reflection, has some advantages, particularly as regards reduction of transmitter power. When this method is adopted it is customary to multiply the frequency before retransmission, but this will be ignored for the moment since it does not significantly affect the theory. The stability of the oscillator frequency now becomes unimportant, at any rate as far as Doppler measurements are concerned, since an error in the transmitted frequency now only produces the same percentage error in the velocity determination, the frequency shift in transmitted and received signals compensating each other. Thus if the transmitted frequency becomes $f_0(1 + \epsilon)$ instead of the nominal f_0, the reflected signal will be $f_0(1 + \epsilon)(1 - 2u/c)$ to the first order in u/c as will be shown below, so that the beat frequency observed is $f_0(2u/c)(1 + \epsilon)$ instead of $f_0(2u/c)$.

The Doppler shift in a reflected signal may be calculated very simply from first principles as follows. Let T be the transmitter, and M a reflecting body moving in a frame of reference fixed with respect to T in such a way that the distance MT is a function of the time, $r(t)$. Let a signal be emitted from T at time t which after reflection from M arrives back at T at time t'. If we are dealing with electromagnetic radiation (or with a medium at rest relative to T) then the reflection occurs at time $(t + t')/2$. The time elapsing between emission and reception of the signal is

$$t' - t = \frac{2}{c} r \left(\frac{t + t'}{2} \right)$$

In order to find how a small interval between two transmitted signals is changed on reception it is necessary to differentiate with respect to t, as before.

$$\frac{dt'}{dt} = 1 + \frac{1}{c} \frac{d[r(t + t')/2]}{d[(t + t')/2]} \left(1 + \frac{dt'}{dt} \right)$$

giving

$$\frac{dt'}{dt} = \left[1 + \frac{1}{c} \frac{d[r(t + t')/2]}{d[(t + t')/2]} \right] \left[1 - \frac{1}{c} \frac{d[r(t + t')/2]}{[d(t + t')/2]} \right]^{-1}$$

which may be written

$$\Delta t' = \Delta t \frac{1 + 1/c \; dr/dt}{1 - 1/c \; dr/dt}$$

or, in terms of frequency

$$f' = f_0 \frac{1 - 1/c \; dr/dt}{1 + 1/c \; dr/dt} \tag{69}$$

or approximately

$$f' = f_0 \left(1 - \frac{2}{c}\frac{dr}{dt}\right)$$

When the situation does not permit dr/dt to be taken as constant over the range of time $t - t'$ taken for the signal to travel to and fro, then the value of dr/dt must be correctly evaluated at time $(t + t')/2$. A moment's consideration shows that for all normal applications an appreciable change in dr/dt during the time of flight of the light signal would imply impossibly large accelerations, for example, for $r = 300$ Km. $(t' - t = 2 \times 10^{-3}$ sec.) a variation of 1 metre per second in dr/dt implies an acceleration of about 50 g. The formula (69) has been derived so as to be in accord with the Special Theory of Relativity since all measurements have been made consistently in the frame of reference of T, and no reference to a medium has been introduced. It is, of course, essential to remember here that the frequency f_0 is measured in the frame of reference of the transmitter. Formulae (69) is in fact equivalent to a double transformation of axes. The same result applies if one assumes that the signal is received, amplified, and retransmitted, the lag introduced by this process being assumed constant.

It is sometimes convenient to approach the Doppler effect in another way, which might well be termed the " quasi-stationary picture ", and which is often very convenient in dealing with techniques of rocket tracking. Consider a transmitter emitting a signal of frequency f denoted by $\Phi_T = a_0 \cos 2\pi f t$ which will give rise to a wave which may be represented at the receiver by

$$\Phi_R = a_1 \cos 2\pi f \left(t + \frac{r}{c}\right)$$

both the receiver and transmitter being at rest, and r being, as usual, the distance between receiver and transmitter. A standard oscillator of frequency f can serve as a phase reference, i.e. we can, provided both local oscillator and transmitter remain fixed in frequency, determine a change in phase of the received signal by means of the change in amplitude of the signal obtained by mixing the local oscillator output with the received signal. The beat signal, the sum of Φ_R and Φ_T is

$$\Phi_B = a_1 \cos 2\pi f \left(t + \frac{r}{c}\right) + a_2 \cos 2\pi f t$$

where the local oscillator is regarded as being in phase with the transmitter, this assumption not leading to any loss of generality.

$$\Phi_B = a_2 \left[\cos 2\pi f \left(t + \frac{r}{c} \right) + \cos 2\pi f t \right]$$

$$+ (a_1 - a_2) \cos 2\pi f \left(t + \frac{r}{c} \right)$$

and therefore,

$$\Phi_B = 2a_2 \cos \frac{f\pi r}{c} \cos 2\pi f \left(t + \frac{r}{2c} \right)$$

$$+ (a_1 - a_2) \cos 2\pi f \left(t + \frac{r}{c} \right)$$

The intensity of the beat signal is the mean square value of Φ_B. This is equal to

$$2a_2^2 \cos^2 \frac{\pi f r}{c} + \frac{(a_1 - a_2)^2}{2}$$

$$= a_2^2 \cos \frac{2\pi f r}{c} + \text{constant terms.}$$

The intensity thus varies sinusoidally with frequency fr/c as r is varied, and if the transmitter is moved through a distance of c/f the beat signal shifts through one cycle. Now c/f is the wavelength of the wave emitted so that a displacement of the transmitter through a distance of one wavelength corresponds to one cycle of the beat frequency; and this is quite a convenient way of looking at the Doppler shift when the beat technique is actually being used. It also gives some idea of the very great potential precision of the Doppler method of rocket tracking. If no information is lost, and if initial conditions are given, a position should in principle be capable of being fixed to a fraction of a wavelength (perhaps a foot or so). The Doppler effect is thus thought of as a variation with time of the phase of the received signal due to the change in path length, and of course a continuously varying phase is indistinguishable from a frequency shift. An example of this method of looking at the Doppler shift is to consider a Michelson interferometer, illuminated with monochromatic light, one plate of which is being moved steadily. The illumination at a point in the field of view will vary sinusoidally, and this may be thought of as a beat frequency, produced by the interference of the beam from the stationary mirror, and the beam from the moving mirror, which has undergone a Doppler shift. Alternatively, and more usually, it is regarded as interference between two beams, the path difference being a function of time. The use of a quasi-stationary method is not uncommon in physics and is often the only method which is mathematically tractable.

The quasi-stationary picture is in fact only correct as far as the first order in u/c, the reason for this being, basically, the fact that the time for which a change in received frequency persists, is not the same as the time during which the receiver is in motion. If the transmitter is at rest with respect to the receiver at the beginning and end of observations the net distance moved must of course correspond to the resulting phase shift.

Doppler shift observations enable dr/dt to be calculated very simply, but even here there is at least one minor complication. Suppose the signal received from a moving body is observed to show a frequency shift $f - f'$, f and f' being given as functions of time, then the relation, using the first order approximation only is

$$\frac{dr}{dt} = \frac{c(f - f')}{f}$$

and if the signal is observed over a time interval t_0 to t_1 the distance travelled (along the line of sight) would appear to be

$$r_1 - r_0 = c \int_{t_0}^{t_1} \frac{f - f'}{f} \, dt$$

Unfortunately, however, the times t_0 and t_1 which must be used are those at which the transmitter considered begins and ends the emission of the part of the signal observed, and also f' must be converted into its value at the corresponding time. Thus if τ_0, τ_1 are the times of reception $t_0 = \tau_0 - r_0/c$, $t_1 = \tau_1 - r_1/c$ so that

$$r_1 - r_0 = c \int_{\tau_1 - r_0/c}^{\tau_1 - r_1/c} \frac{f - f'(t)}{f} \, dt$$

In the case of uniform velocity this becomes

$$r_1 - r_0 = c \left[(\tau_1 - \tau_0) - \frac{(r_1 - r_0)}{c} \right] \frac{(f - f')}{f}$$

$$\text{i.e.} \quad r_1 - r_0 = c(\tau_1 - \tau_0)\frac{\Delta f}{f}\left(1 + \frac{\Delta f}{f}\right)^{-1}$$

In brief, the time during which the signal is being sent, and not the time during which it is received, is the time over which integration of the velocity must be carried out. All time intervals are subject to the Doppler effect, and this may sometimes be overlooked if the Doppler effect is thought of only as a frequency shift.

Effects of this kind may be ignored as a rule in all practical applications, a possible exception would be an experiment designed to test the predictions of either Special or General Relativity.

The advent of the artificial earth satellite aroused some interest in the possibility of making further experimental tests of the Special and General Theories of Relativity, since the satellites travel at high speeds (by terrestrial standards) and also move into regions of varying gravitational potential. A frequency standard carried in a satellite should show the changes in frequency predicted by these theories. However the order of magnitude of the variations expected is of the order of a few parts in 10^{10}. While oscillators of the necessary stability should be achievable, the first order Doppler shifts at the velocities involved are some four or five orders greater. It is therefore interesting to consider a suggestion made by Badessa, Kent and others[1], whereby the first order Doppler shift may be cancelled out, leaving only second order effects, or effects not associated with velocity. The suggestion is made in the light of possible attempts to observe the gravitational red shift, but it is of some interest for its own sake.

A ground-based transmitter emits a signal of frequency f_0, derived from a stable frequency standard, and this signal is received by the satellite as a frequency f_1, given by

$$f_1 = f_0 \frac{[1 - (u/c)\cos\alpha]}{\sqrt{1 - u^2/c^2}}$$

where u is the satellite velocity in the observer's frame of reference and α is the angle made by the line of sight with the direction of the satellite motion, α *also being measured in the transmitter's frame of reference* (see Chapter 1 page 7).

In the satellite there is an oscillator of frequency f_0 derived from the same type of frequency standard as used by the transmitter and this frequency is doubled, and then mixed with the received frequency f_1. The resultant difference or beat frequency f_2 is given by

$$f_2 = 2f_0 - f_0 \frac{[1-(u/c)\cos\alpha]}{\sqrt{1 - u^2/c^2}}$$

The signal of frequency f_2 is amplified and transmitted to the ground where it is mixed with the original frequency f_0. The frequency f_2 is received at the transmitter as

$$f_2 \cdot \frac{\sqrt{1 - u^2/c^2}}{[1+(u/c)\cos\alpha]}$$

measurements still being made in the transmitter's frame of reference. When this frequency is mixed with the original frequency f_0 the resultant beat frequency Δf is given by

$$\Delta f = f_0 - \frac{\sqrt{1 - u^2/c^2}}{[1 + (u/c)\cos\alpha]} \left\{ 2f_0 - f_0 \frac{[1-(u/c)\cos\alpha]}{\sqrt{1 - u^2/c^2}} \right\} \qquad (70)$$

The expressions $\sqrt{1 - u^2/c^2}$, $[1 + (u/c)\cos\alpha]$ and $[1 - (u/c)\cos\alpha]$ may be expanded in powers of u/c since this quantity is decidedly less than unity. The result is

$$\Delta f = f_0 \frac{u^2}{c^2} + \left(\text{terms in higher powers of } \frac{u}{c} \right),$$

the terms in u/c having cancelled out. The authors of reference[1] discuss the question of oscillator stability in some detail, and in addition, the problem of variations in propagation time due to fluctuations in the properties of the ionosphere or troposphere. They suggest a frequency between 500 and 1000 megacycles per second as giving low refraction in both media. The analysis given above is somewhat simplified, in that the motion of the earth is neglected, the existence of this motion implying that the outward and return paths of the signal cannot coincide exactly. The demands on oscillator stability can probably be met, since the time for a frequency measurement of the desired precision need not be very long. However, in the above discussion the satellite's local oscillator is assumed to be exactly equal in frequency to the transmitter's standard. The effect of a constant difference Δf_0 between these is seen, if the satellite frequency f_0 is replaced by $f_0 + \Delta f_0$ when equation (70) becomes

$$\Delta f = f_0 - \frac{\sqrt{1 - u^2/c^2}}{[1 + (u/c)\cos\alpha]} \left\{ 2f_0 + 2\Delta f_0 - f_0 \frac{[1 - (u/c)\cos\alpha]}{\sqrt{1 - u^2/c^2}} \right\}$$

which reduces to

$$\Delta f = f_0 \left[\frac{u^2}{c^2} - \frac{2\Delta f_0}{f_0} \left(1 + \frac{u}{c}\cos\alpha + \ldots \right) \right]$$

which gives a constant shift in the beat frequency, apart from terms in u/c, u^2/c^2, etc. of which the greatest is

$$\frac{2\Delta f_0}{f_0} \frac{u}{c} \cos\alpha.$$

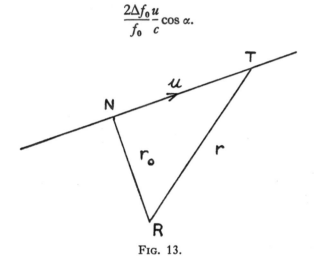

FIG. 13.

The product u/c. $\Delta f_0/f_0$ may well be negligible for quite realisable values of Δf_0. For example, if $\Delta f_0/f_0$ were reduced to 10^{-6}, a very modest requirement, a value of u/c of 10^{-4} would reduce the error to the order of 10^{-10}.

In Chapter 4 it was pointed out that apparently inadequate Doppler information might be combined with other information to permit the determination of a body's trajectory. The simplest possible law which can govern the motion of a body is that it be unacted on by any forces, i.e. it travels with constant speed in a straight line. Given this information, how much can be found from Doppler observations made from a single observation point? All that is obtained from observation is the value of dr/dt as a function of time, r being the distance of the transmitter from the observer. Suppose that r_0 is the perpendicular distance of the observer from the rectilinear trajectory and that u is the velocity of the transmitter. The geometry of the situation is shown in fig. 13 where the receiver is at R and the transmitter at T, RN is equal to r_0 and RT equal to r. Assume also that the transmitter is at the point N at time $t = t_0$ Obviously,

$$r^2 = r_0^2 + (t - t_0)^2 u^2 \qquad (71)$$

and so,

$$r \frac{dr}{dt} = (t - t_0)u^2 \qquad (72)$$

t_0, u and r_0 being the unknown quantities to be determined. It need scarcely be mentioned that no information can be obtained about the orientation of the trajectory. The quantity which is derived from the Doppler measurements is dr/dt which is equal to $(t - t_0)u^2/r$,

$$\text{i.e.} \quad \left(\frac{dr}{dt}\right)^2 = \frac{(t - t_0)^2 u^4}{r + (t - t_0)^2 u^2} \qquad (73)$$

Suppose now, as is suggested by this equation, a curve of the form

$$y = \frac{At^2 - Bt + C}{t^2 - Dt + E}$$

is fitted to the observed values of $(dr/dt)^2$. Taking three suitable values of t will permit A, B, C, D and E to be found; since they depend only on three quantites t_0, u and r_0, and are not independent. Thus $A = u^2$, $B = 2u^2 t_0$, $C = t_0^2 u^2$, $D = 2t_0$, $E = r_0^2/u^2 + t_0^2$ and if the curve in fact conforms to the theoretical shape the determination of the unknowns presents no difficulties. The determination of dr/dt involves at first sight a prior knowledge of the frequency of the transmitter. This added unknown is readily found by taking another point on the frequency-time curve and writing

$$\frac{dr}{dt} = \frac{c(f_0 - f)}{f_0},$$

the new unknown being f_0. There is, however, a slightly more elegant method of treating the data, which may be used. This depends on possessing a region of the frequency-time curve extending on either side of the point of inflexion [see fig. 14]. This is not a very great restriction in practice, since this is the position of closest approach and thus normally the position of strongest signals. We have

$$\frac{f_0 - f}{f_0} = \frac{1}{c}\frac{dr}{dt} \qquad (74)$$

remembering that when

$$f_0 > f, \frac{dr}{dt} > 0$$

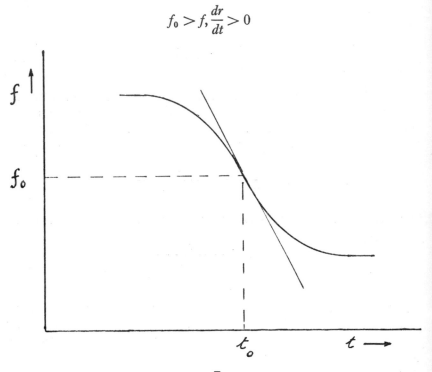

FIG. 14.

The time of closest approach is obviously the time at which $dr/dt = 0$ so that f_0 is immediately found and corresponds to the point of inflexion on the frequency-time curve. At this point the rate of change of frequency is a maximum. Differentiating equation (74) with respect to t gives

$$-\frac{df}{dt} = \frac{f_0}{c}\frac{d^2r}{dt^2} \qquad (75)$$

and differentiating equation (72) with respect to t

$$\frac{rd^2r}{dt^2} + \left(\frac{dr}{dt}\right)^2 = u^2 \tag{76}$$

Now when $t = t_0, r = r_0$, and $dr/dt = 0$, so that (75) becomes

$$\left(\frac{d^2r}{dt^2}\right)_{t=t_0} = \frac{u^2}{r_0}$$

Putting $t = t_0$ in (75) gives

$$-\left(\frac{df}{dt}\right)_{max} = \frac{f_0 u^2}{c \; r_0} \tag{77}$$

Thus or otherwise f_0 is known and this gives u^2/r_0 in terms of the observed quantity $(df/dt)_{max}$. The frequency of a signal from a moving source always falls in frequency as it approaches and moves past the observer. One more equation is needed to obtain the separate values of u and r_0 and a simple way of doing this is to use equation (71), $r^2 = r_0^2 + u^2(t - t_0)^2$, divide through by u^4 and substitute

$$r = \frac{(t - t_0)u^2}{dr/dt}$$

from (72). This gives

$$(t - t_0)^2 \left(\frac{dr}{dt}\right)^{-2} = \frac{r_0^2}{u^4} - \frac{(t - t_0)^2}{u^2} \tag{78}$$

from which by substituting for u^2/r_0, u is found. Various other methods of analysing such results are of course possible.

In brief, then, a single observer may, from a single frequency versus time measurement determine the velocity and distance of closest approach of a vehicle such as a satellite without precise prior knowledge of its transmitter frequency. This is a very simple and cheap method of satellite tracking and is within the reach of many amateurs, and it was in fact applied to the earlier Sputniks. The " flat earth " assumption of a rectilinear orbit is not completely justified, but it gives a reasonable result for a low altitude satellite. How great an error is introduced will be considered later. This method of tracking gives no information about the orientation of the orbit, a shortcoming which may be overcome by the use of optical or other directional tracking methods. The information from two stations leaves the trajectory with only one degree of freedom and

D

the addition of a third station fixes it completely, except for a possible ambiguity, usually trivial, or in the special case where the three stations are collinear or nearly so. A factor which has been neglected so far is the rotation of the earth, a satellite orbit remaining fixed (or only moving slowly), in space while the earth rotates under it. In the case of the simple rectilinear orbit, it will suffice to represent the earth's motion by giving the observer a uniform velocity. The velocity of the earth's surface relative to an orbit fixed in space would not exceed some hundreds of kilometres per hour, depending on the latitude. A value of 1000 Km. per hour would contribute only about 4 per cent to the observed Doppler effect in the case of

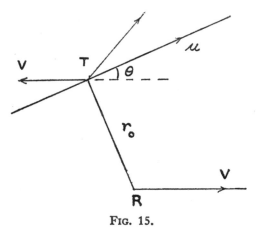

FIG. 15.

a low altitude satellite. For distant satellites showing small Doppler shifts the effect becomes more serious; and in no case is it really negligible if precision is required. Suppose that the earth is moving under the satellite orbit with velocity V at an angle θ to the direction of the trajectory. The problem as far as the Doppler shift is concerned is identical with the case in which the observer remains at rest but the transmitter has the velocity V added vectorially to its velocity u (see fig. 15). The new velocity will be $\sqrt{u^2 + V^2 - 2uV \cos \theta}$, the motion still being rectilinear and the calculations may be carried through in the new frame of reference as before. The velocity V will be known from the latitude of the observer and r_0 will be determined as before. Unless θ is known there remains some uncertainty as to the actual velocity although its *magnitude* in the observer's frame of reference is determined.

The next closer approximation to a real satellite orbit, after the rather crude assumption of rectilinear motion, is the assumption of uniform motion in a circular orbit, and because of the rapidly increasing complexity of the problem as more general orbits are permitted, this is as far is it is proposed to go in any detail. The case of the circular orbit is illustrated in fig. 16. Here R_0 is the

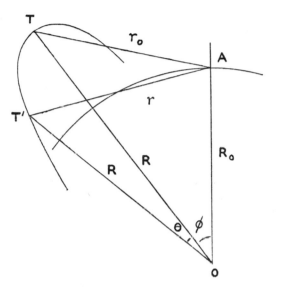

FIG. 16.

radius of the earth, R the distance from the centre of the earth to the satellite, ϕ the angle between the plane of the orbit and the vertical through the receiver, θ is the angle between the radius vector to the satellite from the centre of the earth and the same radius vector when the satellite is at maximum elevation as seen from A, the receiver. The angle θ may be put equal to $u(t - t_0)/R$, u being the constant speed of the satellite. As before, the distance between satellite and receiver is denoted by r. When $t = t_0$, r is a minimum and dr/dt will be zero. Now it can readily be shown that the cosine of the angle between OA and OT' is $\cos\theta\cos\phi$, and thus it is possible to write,

$$r^2 = R^2 + R_0^2 - 2R\,R_0\cos\theta\cos\phi$$

$$= R^2 + R_0^2 - 2R\,R_0\cos\phi\cos\frac{u(t-t_0)}{R} \qquad (79)$$

Differentiating,

$$2r \frac{dr}{dt} = 2uR_0 \cos \phi \sin \frac{u(t - t_0)}{R}$$

and

$$\frac{dr}{dt} = \frac{uR_0}{r} \cos \phi \sin \frac{u(t - t_0)}{R}$$

$$= \frac{uR_0 \cos \phi \sin u(t - t_0)/R}{\sqrt{R^2 + R_0^2 - 2RR_0 \cos \phi \cos u(t - t_0)/R}} \tag{80}$$

Since f_0 is known from the fact that when $dr/dt = 0$, $f = f_0$, and there is a maximum rate of change of frequency, dr/dt may be found as a function of time, as in the preceding case.

It is now possible to examine the error introduced by the assumption of a rectilinear trajectory. When $\theta = 0$, $r = r_0$ and so $r_0^2 = R^2 + R_0^2 - 2RR_0 \cos \phi$ and expressing equation (79) in terms of r_0, $r^2 = r_0^2 + 2RR_0 \cos \phi (1 - \cos \theta)$. Since the approximation of a linear trajectory is in any case only applicable if θ is small it is permissible to put $\cos \theta \approx 1 - \theta^2/2$, giving

$$r^2 = r_0^2 + \frac{R_0}{R} u^2 (t - t_0)^2 \cos \phi \tag{81}$$

If now this orbit is treated as a linear one, and the frequency-time curve near $r = r_0$ is studied, the value obtained for u^2 must be $u^2 R_0/R \cos \phi$. That is, if the analysis previously given [equations (71) to (78)] is applied to a circular orbit, a value is found for r_0 which agrees with the true value, but the velocity is in error by a factor $\sqrt{(R_0/R) \cos \phi}$, which may be approximately written, if ϕ is small, as $(1 - h/2R_0)$ where h is the satellite altitude. However the quantity $u^2(R_0/R) \cos \phi$ may be determined from the frequency-time curve near its point of inflexion, as may r_0.
We have,

$$\frac{dr}{dt} = \frac{uR_0 \cos \phi \sin u(t - t_0)/R}{\sqrt{r_0^2 + 2RR_0 \cos \phi [1 - \cos u(t - t_0)/R]}} \tag{82}$$

combining equations (80) and (81), in which r_0, R_0, t_0 and $u^2(R_0/R) \cos \phi$ may be taken as known. Equation (82) may be written

$$\frac{dr}{dt} = \frac{A \cdot R/u \cdot \sin u(t - t_0)/R}{\sqrt{r_0^2 + 2(R^2/u^2) A[1 - \cos u(t - t_0)/R]}}$$

where

$$A = u^2 \frac{R_0}{R} \cos \phi$$

In this expression u/R is the only unknown quantity remaining, so it may be found in terms of r_0, t_0, $u^2 (R_0/R) \cos \phi$, etc. The quantities determined are thus r_0, $u^2 (R_0/R) \cos \phi$, u, and u/R, whence the remaining R and $\cos \phi$ are found. Here the effect of the earth's rotation has been neglected. It is not a difficult matter to introduce its effect but the resulting expressions become rather involved and their manipulation somewhat laborious (see, for example, Williams [2]).

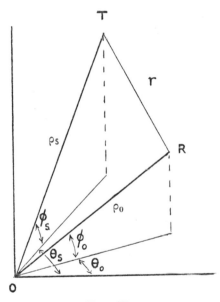

FIG. 17.

The general expression for the Doppler shift observed in the signal from an earth satellite is found, as follows, simply by differentiating the distance between transmitter and receiver with respect to time. If the coordinates of a satellite are ρ_s, θ_s, ϕ_s and those of the observer are ρ_0, θ_0, ϕ_0 in a set of geocentric, non-rotating, polar coordinates (fig. 17), the distance between observer and satellite is readily shown to be given by,

$$r^2 = \rho_s^2 + \rho_0^2 - 2\rho_s\rho_0[\sin \phi_s \sin \phi_0 + \cos \phi_s \cos \phi_0 \cos (\theta_s - \theta_0)] \tag{83}$$

The value of ϕ is taken as zero at the equator, and $d\theta_0/dt$ represents the angular velocity of the earth. Because of the choice of axes, $d\phi_0/dt$ is zero (as is, of course $d\rho_0/dt$). Differentiating with respect to t, and dividing through by r,

$$\frac{dr}{dt} = \frac{\rho_s}{r}\frac{d\rho_s}{dt} - \frac{\rho_0}{r}\frac{d\rho_s}{dt}\left[\sin\phi_s \sin\phi_0 + \cos\phi_s \cos\phi_0 \cos(\theta_s - \theta_0)\right]$$

$$- \frac{\rho_0\rho_s}{r}\left\{\frac{d\phi_s}{dt}\left[\cos\phi_s \sin\phi_0 - \sin\phi_s \cos\phi_0 \cos(\theta_s - \theta_0)\right]\right.$$

$$\left. - \left(\frac{d\theta_s}{dt} - \frac{d\theta_0}{dt}\right)\cos\phi_s \cos\phi_0 \sin(\theta_s - \theta_0)\right\} \qquad (84)$$

r being defined by equation (83). No restriction whatever is placed on the orbit, the case of a circular orbit being derived by putting $d\rho_s/dt = 0$ and also imposing the slightly more involved conditions that the orbit lies in a plane passing through the origin and describes the orbit with uniform angular velocity. These conditions may be expressed by, firstly,

$$l\cos\phi_s \cos\theta_s + m\cos\phi_s \sin\theta_s + n\sin\phi_s = 0$$

where l, m, n are the direction cosines of the normal to the orbital plane. Secondly,

$$\cos\alpha \cos\phi_s \cos\theta_s + \sin\alpha \cos\phi_s \sin\theta_s = \cos(\omega t + \beta)$$

where α is the angle between the line $\theta = \phi = 0$ and the intersection of the orbital plane with the plane $\phi = 0$, β defining the phase of the satellite in its orbit and ω is its angular velocity. The conditions for the more general elliptic orbit are more complex and the task of evaluating the various constants of the orbit given dr/dt as a function of t without electronic computing aids is formidable indeed. It is for this reason that considerable interest attaches to the simpler assumptions, since in these cases it is relatively easy to see how much can in fact be deduced from the Doppler observations.

It was mentioned, when spectroscopic binaries were under consideration, that the constant direction of the line of sight, arising from the great distances involved, while simplifying the mathematics, actually reduced the information available. How this arises is now seen from a consideration of the case of the circular orbit considered above. In particular, the angle ϕ in equation (79) which plays a similar role to the angle i in the binary star discussion, may now be determined. Equation (84) enables the Doppler effect from a satellite, in the absence of ionospheric effects, to be readily calculated once its orbit has been derived by other means. Such a procedure would be necessary in ionospheric studies in order to eliminate the " vacuum " Doppler shift which is normally considerably greater than the " ionospheric " shift. The inverse procedure, that is, determining the elements of the orbit from the Doppler shift at one or more stations, is more complicated. If very high precision is required, for example if the perturbations of the orbit of a satellite are to be used to investigate atmospheric density or the figure of the earth, the assumption of a strictly Keplerian orbit would defeat its own ends, and instead of assumptions about the laws of motion extra Doppler tracking stations are needed. This is also the case where guided missiles, particularly short range ones, are concerned since their trajectories are determined by more or less arbitrary guidance information. In this type of work there is often however an added piece of information, namely, the exact coordinates of at least one point on the missile's path are known, e.g. the launching point; and given this, dr/dt is readily translated into range, r, as a function of time. Thus if three stations are used and the launching point or some equivalent point is known, a completely arbitrary trajectory can be determined by Doppler observations, and if no information is lost, the precision will be very high indeed. In rocket work, the transponder method is very suitable, the frequency standard being located on the ground. Of course it is necessary that all the receivers are provided with the standard transmitter frequency in order to make the necessary comparison with the signals retransmitted from the rocket. It should be possible to use local stable oscillators, but a better scheme would obviously be, if possible, to transmit the original signal along a fixed path to all receiving stations.

As has been stated, when a fixed point on a rocket trajectory is known, then three Doppler stations will suffice to determine its subsequent path. This implies a reasonably continuous record, and for a number of reasons this is not always possible. Nevertheless a three station Doppler system is very valuable, particularly when combined with other methods of tracking (such as optical). The Doppler records even if insufficiently complete to give a trajectory, will often provide velocities at various points on the trajectory with a better precision than can be obtained by differentiating position information from radar or optical records. The question naturally arises as to how many Doppler stations are needed to determine an arbitrary trajectory when no initial data are given. It turns out that four stations will suffice, provided they are reasonably located; and in fact a prior knowledge of the transmitter frequency is not essential (see Carrara, Checcacci and Ronchi[3]). If $r_1(t)$, $r_2(t)$, $r_3(t)$, $r_4(t)$ are the ranges of the vehicle from the four Doppler stations at time t and $r_1(t_0)$, $r_2(t_0)$ etc. are the ranges at a time t_0 then

$$\frac{f_0 - f_i(t)}{f_0} = \frac{1}{c}\frac{dr_i(t)}{dt}; \quad (i = 1, 2, 3, 4)$$

where f_0 is the transmitter frequency, $f_i(t)$ is the frequency received at tracking station i at time t.
Thus

$$r_i(t) = r_i(t_0) + \int_{t_0}^{t} c\left(1 - \frac{f_i(\tau)}{f_0}\right)d\tau$$

$$= r_i(t_0) - c(t - t_0) + \frac{c}{f_0}\int_{t_0}^{t} f_i(\tau)d\tau \tag{85}$$

Suppose that x_i, y_i, z_i $(i = 1, 2, 3, 4)$ are the coordinates of the tracking stations in a cartesian system, and $x(t)$, $y(t)$, $z(t)$ are the coordinates of the vehicle (transmitter),

$$\left.\begin{array}{l} (x - x_1)^2 + (y - y_1)^2 + (z - z_1)^2 = r_1^2(t) \\ (x - x_2)^2 + (y - y_2)^2 + (z - z_2)^2 = r_2^2(t) \\ (x - x_3)^2 + (y - y_3)^2 + (z - z_3)^2 = r_3^2(t) \end{array}\right\} \tag{86}$$

and so x, y and z may be expressed in terms of r_1, r_2, and r_3, a not surprising result. However r_i may be expressed in terms of $r_i(t_0)$, and f_0, the other quantities in equation (85), c, t, $f_i(t)$ being known or observed. So that it is possible to write

$$\left.\begin{array}{l} x = x(t, f_0, r_1(t_0), r_2(t_0), r_3(t_0)) \\ y = y(t, f_0, r_1(t_0), r_2(t_0), r_3(t_0)) \\ z = z(t, f_0, r_1(t_0), r_2(t_0), r_3(t_0)) \end{array}\right\} \tag{87}$$

For the fourth station,

$$\frac{dr_4(t)}{dt} = c\left(1 - \frac{f_4(t)}{f_0}\right) \tag{88}$$

but $r_4(t)$ may also be expressed in terms of x, y, z, x_4, y_4, z_4 as in equation (86) and thus in terms of the four unknown quantities $r_1(t_0)$, $r_2(t_0)$, $r_3(t_0)$ and f_0 from equation (87).

$$r_4^2(t) = (x - x_4)^2 + (y - y_4)^2 + (z - z_4)^2$$

Differentiating with respect to t

$$r_4 \frac{dr_4}{dt} = (x - x_4)\frac{dx}{dt} + (y - y_4)\frac{dy}{dt} + (z - z_4)\frac{dz}{dt} \quad (89)$$

Substituting for dr_4/dt from equation (88),

$$\frac{1}{r_4}\left[(x - x_4)\frac{dx}{dt} + (y - y_4)\frac{dy}{dt} + (z - z_4)\frac{dz}{dt}\right] = c\left[1 - \frac{f_4(t)}{{}_0}\right] \quad (90)$$

Now we have seen that x, y and z and therefore r_4 are expressible in terms of $r_1(t_0)$, $r_2(t_0)$, $r_3(t_0)$ and f_0 and therefore dx/dt, dy/dt, and dz/dt may be similarly expressed. Equation (90) thus contains in essence four unknowns, and by taking four different values of t these four unknowns may be determined and from equation (85) further values of $r_i(t)$ may be found, and the complete trajectory plotted. Nothing has been said about the practical side of solving equation (86) for x, y and z and then substituting in (90) and, in the main, such tasks are best left to those equipped with suitable computers; the purpose here is to demonstrate that sufficient information is available from the four Doppler stations.

The analysis by Carrara and his colleagues is based on the simple assumption of a rocket borne transmitter, but is equally applicable to a transponder or reflection system. The transmitter for such a system may or may not be situated at one of the receiving posts. Instead of the dr_i/dt, being observed the quantities

$$\left(\frac{dr_i}{dt} + \frac{dr_T}{dt}\right)$$

are observed where r_T is the distance of the vehicle from the transmitter. It is readily seen that this modification does not change the minimum number of stations needed for complete determination of an arbitrary trajectory but the knowledge of f_0 introduces some redundancy, which is usually useful in such observations.

The fact that all Doppler tracking methods depend on the

measurement of frequencies counts very strongly in their favour since measurement and comparison of frequencies can be done with extremely high precision. For example, as discussed previously the incoming signal may be mixed with the output of a local oscillator, and the resulting beat frequency recorded on magnetic tape together with standard time and frequency signals. Under some conditions, such a tape may then be fed directly into a computer, which will usually count the cycles, and thus derive line of sight displacements as a function of time. If a frequency of about 100 megacycles per second is used for Doppler measurement (doubled to 200 for re-transmission, in transponder systems) a velocity of 1 Km. per second corresponds to about 1300 cycles per second, so that beat frequencies occur in a region where the electronic techniques are relatively simple and well established. Apart from the various rocket range installations, Doppler methods have been applied on a wide scale in the U.S. Doploc and Microlock systems[4]. As is common enough in the application of general principles to practical problems, the basic theory is not at all complicated or difficult, the main problems to be overcome lie in the field of techniques, for example, in automatic frequency recording, and in bridging the gaps in the record due to excessive noise, unfavourable vehicle attitude, etc. A minor effect should also be mentioned here. This is the introduction of variations in the Doppler frequency shift by motions of the vehicle about its own centre of mass (rolling, pitching, and yawing). In some cases these cancel out over a long period but in others, for example, a steady rolling motion, an extra progressive phase shift may be imposed on the returning signal. Just how this effects the results will depend on the actual system used, but in general it is safe to say that the worst effect expected will be the addition of the rolling frequency to the Doppler shift. This may reach a significant value, particularly in experiments concerned with ionospheric effects, where the changes in Doppler shift are of the order of cycles per second, rather than kilocycles per second. Fortunately the measurement of roll rate is a simple matter so that this effect can be eliminated if necessary.

The world-wide Minitrack satellite tracking system established by the United States is not a Doppler system but employs radio interferometers, i.e. the direction of a transmitter is deduced from the phase difference between radio waves arriving at different aerials spaced out in an array on the ground. It may be of some interest to enquire whether such a system is affected by the Doppler shift in the signals from a moving satellite. The basic principle of the system is shown in fig. 18 and the angle is deduced from the relation

$$\Delta\phi = \frac{2\pi A_1 B_1}{\lambda} = \frac{2\pi A_0 A_1}{\lambda}\cos\theta$$

where $\Delta\phi$ is the measured phase difference between the signals arriving at A_0 and A_1. By using large separations this phase difference may be made large and so a very high resolution obtained, the geometry of the system being analogous to that of the diffraction

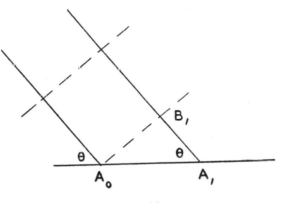

FIG. 18.

grating, but applied in reverse. Both Doppler change in λ and an abberation, or change in orientation of the wavefront are introduced because of the motion of the source, and both of these are first order effects in u/c. They are in fact opposite in sense, and tend to cancel out except where the motion of the transmitter is either along or perpendicular to the line of sight; the abberation or the Doppler shift respectively vanishing in these cases (to the first order in u/c). The error introduced by neglecting these effects turns out to be of the order of u/c in $\cos\theta$ which should not exceed about 3 parts in 10^5, and will normally be less. The error is not very serious and a very rough correction would eliminate it completely.

REFERENCES

[1] BADESSA, R. S., KENT, R. L., NOWELL, J. C. and SEARLE, C. L. *Proc. I.R.E.*, Vol. 48, p. 758 (1960).
[2] WILLIAMS, W. (Jr.). *Fifth National Symposium on Space Electronics and Telemetry*, 1960, Sec. 7, Inst. Radio Engineers, N.Y.

[3] CARRARA, N., CHECCACCI, P. F. and RONCHI, L. *Proc. Second Space Science Symposium*, Florence 1961, p. 215 (North Holland Pub. Co.).
[4] PATTON, R. B. and RICHARD, V. W., as [3] above, p. 218.
The problem of the minimum and optimum number of Doppler tracking stations is discussed from a mathematical point of view in two articles by C. H. Dawson, A.I.E.E. Trans. (Part I, Communications and Electronics), Vol. 81, p. 568 and p. 584 (1963).
A survey of Doppler methods applied to satellites is given by J. Mass and E. Vassy, in *Space Science and Technology*, Vol. 4, p. 1 (Academic Press, New York, 1962).

6

Doppler Navigation

In the preceding chapter the tracking of satellites or rockets was considered, the problem being the determination of the coordinates of the vehicle in the observer's chosen frame of reference as a function of time. The term navigation is used when this determination of a vehicle's position is made in the vehicle itself, and is thus most commonly used with respect to manned vehicles such as aircraft or ships. Of course an aircraft may be tracked from ground stations and the position relayed to the pilot who then adjusts his course if necessary. Whether this is described as navigation or a tracking system is a matter of taste. There are, in the most general sense, three types of navigation. The first, may be called the reference grid type and forms the basis of most practical systems of navigation by ships or aircraft. Here, two coordinates are fixed by observing quantities which may vary over the earth's surface in such a way as to uniquely determine a position if both are measured. Two rather than three coordinates are mentioned since the altitude of a ship is fixed (to a large extent) while that of an aircraft is usually independently determined and does not vary by more than a few miles. The traditional system of navigation, based on observations of the heavenly bodies is a system of this type, as are systems depending on fixed directional radio arrays. In the second type of navigation the velocity of the vehicle is measured as a function of time and then integrated to determine position, or rather displacement from the original, assumed known, position. This method of navigation has also been used extensively at sea and in the air, but since, unlike the first, its errors tend to be cumulative, it is usually customary to combine it with the first type. In the third type, which is a more recent development, the acceleration of the vehicle is measured, and integrated twice to determine displacement, this being generally referred to as inertial guidance or navigation. While the accumulation of errors is a serious problem, this method is being developed extensively for military purposes since it requires no contact with the world outside the vehicle and is thus incapable of being deliberately sabotaged or misled. It is perhaps not quite correct to describe it as a recent development, since the gyroscope, a form of inertial guidance, has been known for many years. The second two methods are vulnerable in three ways. Firstly, errors tend to accumulate, in contrast with the first type where each position determination is independent. Secondly, a gap in the recording of data, in theory, renders useless all subsequent observations, although in practice short gaps are bridged by " memory " devices which assume some continuity in the varying quantities. Also, if very short periods of high velocities or large accelerations are involved these, while contributing largely to the resulting displacement, may not be capable of being measured with sufficient accuracy on account of their short duration. For this reason one finds attempts being made to combine one or more type of navigation or guidance. It might be expected that navigation systems employing the Doppler effect would all be of the second type, since this effect measures velocity directly. There are, however, Doppler navigation systems which are of the first type, i.e. they depend on establishing a reference grid, and these will be considered first. The launching of artificial earth satellites has made possible the installation of new heavenly bodies and this has appealed to the imagination of those interested in navigation, in particular because such satellites may carry radio transmitters whose radiation will penetrate clouds and not be swamped out by sunlight, permitting an all weather navigation system. All satellite navigation systems share some common problems most of which are soluble however by practicable methods. Firstly, the orbits of such satellites must be computed and this information made available to the users of the navigation system before it has become obsolete because of various perturbations of the orbit. A very interesting suggestion is that the orbital data together with time signals be relayed from one or more master transmitters via the satellite itself. Secondly, enough satellites must be placed in suitably orientated orbits so that a twenty-four hour world coverage is given without a navigator having to wait too long for a set of observations. Systems in which satellites' angular positions are observed require precise directional aerials on the vessels and for this reason the Doppler systems are probably likely to be the most successful, and such a system has in fact been developed by the U.S.A. under the name " Transit ".

The way in which frequency measurements of the signal transmitted from a satellite can establish a reference grid may be seen by considering again the simple picture of a satellite moving in a straight line with constant speed as discussed in Chapter 5. Suppose now, that the problem is inverted, namely, all the details of the satellite's motion are known, including the orientation of the orbit, and the position of the observer is unknown. Let us suppose that the arrangement is as in fig. 19 and an observer is situated at (X, Y, O), the satellite travelling along the line $x = 0$, $z = h$ with constant velocity u being at $y = 0$ at time $t = t_0$. Then the observer

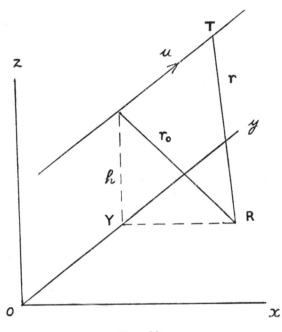

FIG. 19.

records a frequency-time curve and proceeding as in Chapter 5 determines the distance of nearest approach and the time at which it occurs, namely, r_0 and t_0', t_0' not being equal in general to t_0. His y-coordinate is thus immediately known, since $Y = (t_0 - t_0')u$ and his x-coordinate is found since $X^2 + h^2 = r_0^2$. His position on the plane is thus located except for one serious ambiguity, i.e. the sign of X is not determined and if X is small this ambiguity cannot be easily solved. However this ambiguity can be resolved by taking into account the rotation of the earth; this may be done by waiting for the next appearance of the satellite which the observer knows will be displaced by a definite amount to the west because of the earth's rotation. However this will take at least 90 minutes, so that for a practical system observations on a single passage of the satellite must suffice. That this can be done may be shown as follows. A knowledge of the observer's velocity in a non-rotating frame of reference will fix the latitude of the observer and this will resolve the ambiguity except in one or two special cases. It should be mentioned that this determination of latitude need not be done to the full precision with which the position is finally fixed.

Consider again the simple case of the rectilinear orbit discussed in Chapter 5, fig. 15, where the uniform motion of the observer is combined with that of the satellite. Using the same notation,

$$u'^2 = u^2 + V^2 - 2uV \cos \theta \qquad (91)$$

where u' is the velocity derived from the frequency-time curve by the method outlined in this chapter. This equation may be solved for V giving

$$V = u \cos \theta \pm \sqrt{u'^2 - u^2 \sin^2 \theta} \qquad (92)$$

Since equation (91) has two roots there is still an ambiguity in V but this may be removed, since if the positive sign is taken, V is greater than $u \cos \theta$. In practice $u \cos \theta$ will be many times greater than V, so that as long as θ is not close to $\pi/2$ the positive sign may be eliminated, and with it the ambiguity in V. Thus in choosing orbits for navigational satellites, polar orbits are eliminated. There remains the fact that V will have the same value for a given latitude either north or south of the equator. This ambiguity is resolved by the time of closest approach, t_0', unless the orbit is an equatorial one, which will be perfectly symmetrical as regards latitude. Orbits for navigational satellites thus have inclinations intermediate between the two extremes, so as to take advantage of the asymmetry introduced by the earth's rotation.

This simple picture of a rectilinear orbit shows how a single satellite can in fact establish a reference grid system provided the details of its orbit are accurately known. These may be found by various tracking methods, including Doppler methods, as well as optical and radio interferometer methods. A rather far-fetched extension of this idea might be conceived as a vast network of Doppler stations at known locations recording frequency-time curves from one or more satellites, and the navigation simply consisting of an interpolation between the known locations of these stations, the intermediate step of calculating the orbital parameters being unnecessary. Reasonable stability of the orbit is needed if the orbital calculations are to remain valid for a sufficiently long time. If the orbit has too high an altitude, the period will be long, the Doppler shift small, and the perturbations due to the moon and possibly the sun will complicate the calculations. On the other hand if it is too low, the perturbations due to atmospheric drag and the unsymmetrical form of the earth's gravitational field will become significant.

An expression for the Doppler shift in the frequency received from a satellite is given in Chapter 4, equation (84),

$$\frac{dr}{dt} = \frac{\rho_s}{r}\frac{d\rho_s}{dt} - \frac{\rho_0}{r}\frac{d\rho_s}{dt}\left[\sin\phi_s\sin\phi_0 + \cos\phi_s\cos\phi_0\cos(\theta_s - \theta_0)\right]$$

$$- \frac{\rho_0\rho_s}{r}\left\{\frac{d\phi_s}{dt}\left[\cos\phi_s\sin\phi_0 - \sin\phi_s\cos\phi_0\cos(\theta_s - \theta_0)\right]\right.$$

$$\left. - \left(\frac{d\theta_s}{dt} - \frac{d\theta_0}{dt}\right)\cos\phi_s\cos\phi_0\sin(\theta_s - \theta_0)\right\}$$

In this equation, the quantities ρ_s, θ_s, ϕ_s (and possibly ρ_0), are known as functions of t and the unknowns are ϕ_0 and θ_0. Equation (84) may be written, remembering that $d\theta_0/dt$ is known,

$$\frac{dr}{dt} = \frac{a_1 + a_2 q + a_3 p + a_4 pu + a_5 pv}{\sqrt{b_1 + b_2 q + b_3 pu + b_4 pv}} = \frac{c(f_0 - f)}{f_0} = \frac{c\Delta f}{f_0}$$

where a_1 to a_5 and b_1 to b_4 are known functions of t, and p, q, u and v have been written for $\cos\phi_0$, $\sin\phi_0$, $\cos\theta_0$ and $\sin\theta_0$ respectively. In principle it is now a straightforward matter to solve the simultaneous equations derived by putting in the values of the a's and b's and Δf for successive times. The a's and b's are derived from the central satellite tracking organisation via the satellite itself or otherwise; while Δf is observed directly. The calculation of f_0 if it is desired, is now not as simple a matter as in the case of a rectilinear or circular orbit, since the point of inflexion of the frequency-time curve does not correspond with $f = f_0$ in this more general case, although it will probably be fairly close if the orbit is nearly circular. This may be seen from the following. If the distance r between satellite and observer is a minimum at $t = t_0$, then r can be expressed as a function of $(t - t_0)$ in a Taylor series

$$r = r_0 + \alpha_2(t - t_0)^2 + \alpha_3(t - t_0)^3 + \alpha_4(t - t_0)^4 + \ldots$$

the term in $(t - t_0)$ being absent since $dr/dt = 0$ for $t = t_0$. Then

$$\frac{dr}{dt} = c\left(1 - \frac{f}{f_0}\right) = 2\alpha_2(t - t_0) + 3\alpha_3(t - t_0)^2 + 4_4(t - t_0)^3 + \ldots$$

If now this is differentiated twice

$$\frac{c}{f_0}\frac{d^2f}{dt^2} = 6\alpha_3 + 24\alpha_4(t - t_0) + \ldots$$

and d^2f/dt^2 does not vanish at $t = t_0$ unless $\alpha_3 = 0$. In the case of the rectilinear or circular orbit with stationary earth r is an even function of $(t - t_0)$ so that α_3 vanishes; but this will not, in general, be true for an elliptical orbit. The " Transit " system employs four satellites in circular orbits at altitudes of about 500 miles. This height is chosen so as to effect the best compromise between the disturbing factors mentioned earlier. The spatial arrangement is to have two orbital planes at angles of $67\frac{1}{2}°$ to the equator and two at angles of $22\frac{1}{2}°$[1]. Four satellites are required to give world coverage at all times and this together with the reasonably short periods means that positions can be determined at frequent intervals. The precision required for navigational satellites of this type is quite high, for example, it has been calculated by Wan[2] that to find a position to within one nautical mile presupposes a frequency stability of 1 in 10^9 over a two minute period. A very simple estimate of the degree of stability which is likely to be needed can be made using equation (77), which may be written

$$r_0 = \frac{u^2 f_0}{c^2}\left[\left(\frac{df}{dt}\right)_{max}\right]^{-1}$$

The value of r_0 may be about 1000 Km. and if an accuracy of 1 Km. in position is required the error permissible in r_0 will be of the same order of magnitude (actually less because of the angle involved). The fractional error in r_0 will be the same as the fractional error in $(df/dt)_{max}$. For a transmitter frequency of 100 megacyles per second $(df/dt)_{max}$ will be of the order of 10 cycles per second per second and a fractional error of 1 in 1000 in this is 10^{-2} cycles per second per second, giving a permissible rate of drift of 1 part in 10^{10} per second in the transmitter frequency, as against roughly 1 in 10^{11} per second estimated by Wan for a nautical mile. This discrepancy (less than an order) can be accounted for by the more complete analysis made by Wan, the determination of r_0 being only one factor. The value obtained here does give some idea however of the oscillator stability needed for accurate tracking as well as for Doppler navigation. The solution of the problem of position finding once the signals from the satellite are received and recorded implies that a suitable computer must be carried by the vessel which is navigating in this fashion. Whether the expense involved both in launching and tracking the satellite and providing the computers is justified by the advantages of precision and all-weather applicability is beyond the scope of this discussion. The economic advantages of improved navigation methods, under conditions where navigation is already reasonably efficient, presents a difficult problem, and the advantage for naval forces are not normally assessed in terms of straightforward economics. Once such a system is installed, however, it is available to all who wish to use it. The actual system is more complex than the foregoing might suggest, since, because of the high precision needed, ionospheric effects cannot be neglected. The fact that these effects are a function of f_0^2/f^2 where f is the frequency of transmission, and f_0 a critical frequency, enable them to be allowed for, by using two widely separated frequencies at the same time. The frequencies used are in the range from 50 megacycles per second up to 300 or more megacycles per second, so that the effects are not extremely large to start with, but even a matter of one cycle per second is significant in these applications. It has also been assumed that the navigating vessel is stationary, and a small correction will be needed on account of the velocity of the receiver relative to the earth, i.e. $d\theta_0/dt$ will need to be modified slightly and $d\phi_0/dt$ which was taken as zero will need to be replaced by an estimate derived from the " ground speed " of the vessel.

Since four Doppler stations provide sufficient information to track a vehicle, it follows that a vehicle carrying a receiver and a frequency standard could be navigated if it received signals from four suitably located transmitters operating on known frequencies. Such a system would, on paper at any rate, provide a means of interplanetary navigation, and in fact, as an interplanetary rocket must of necessity spend a large proportion of its time " coasting " in a Keplerian elliptic orbit, four transmitters would provide considerable redundancy. If only three transmitters were provided this would clearly be a system of the second type since an initial position would be needed in order to obtain the actual position of the receiver by integrating the velocity. When the fourth signal is added, an initial position need not be known, and one can think of a reference grid having been established, although it is not a simple one to visualise.

The second type of Doppler navigation has been applied to aircraft navigation, the basic principle being as follows (see reference[3]). The aircraft transmits a narrow beam of short radio waves, either ahead or astern and these are reflected back from irregularities in the ground beneath. The return, or echo, is mixed with some of the transmitted signal, and from the beat frequency the velocity of the plane relative to the ground may be obtained, and

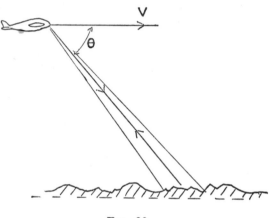

FIG. 20.

if this is then integrated with respect to time the distance travelled may be deduced. Normally there will be no reflecting surface directly ahead or behind an aircraft in flight, so the beam must be directed downwards at an angle θ so as to obtain a reflected signal, as shown in fig. 20. Working only to the first order the Doppler shift Δf is given by $\Delta f/f = 2(V/c) \cos \theta$. It is thus necessary to know $\cos \theta$ with some accuracy since, as $V = c/2 \, (\Delta f/f) \sec \theta$ a systematic error in θ will be cumulative and appear in the final value obtained for the distance. The choice of θ is not completely arbitrary since if θ is close to 90°, although the reflected signal is strong, a small error in θ will represent a large error in V, while if θ is close to 0°, the intensity of the reflected signal may be too small to permit its frequency to be measured. In practice a compromise value is adopted usually in the neighbourhood of 60° to 70°.

The actual attitude of the aerials as regards pitch obviously affects θ and for this reason the aerial system may need to be swung in a cradle which maintains a constant position with respect to the vertical, irrespective of the trim of the aircraft while rapid oscillations about the mean position will tend to cancel out. An alternative to this method of eliminating systematic errors in θ is to employ two transmitters, one facing forward and one backwards. How this works will be explained later.

A single radio beam directed along the axis of the aircraft will measure the component of the velocity along this line, but, as is well known, aircraft do not in general move in this direction, the velocity being the resultant of the velocity relative to the air, and the velocity of the air relative to the ground. The angle between the aircraft's velocity relative to the ground and its axis (to which angular measurements made in the vehicle are referred) will be called its " heading " or " heading angle ". Since wind speeds are often an appreciable fraction of airspeeds, this effect is quite large and cannot be neglected. It is therefore necessary to measure the speed of the aircraft in a direction perpendicular to its axis, and combining this with the component along the axis, arrive at the velocity relative to the ground. The direction of this ground velocity is measured, however, relative to the aircraft axis and in order to find the direction in which the aircraft is moving over the ground the actual direction of the plane's axis must be known. This cannot be obtained from Doppler information, and must be found by means of a compass of some sort. A system whereby the velocity relative to the ground may be found is illustrated in fig. 21. The aircraft is actually travelling in the direction XX' but its heading is β. Instead of a single beam directed along the axis two separate beams each making an angle α with the axis are used. The frequencies received, after mixing with the appropriate transmitter frequencies are given by

$$\left. \begin{aligned} \frac{\Delta f_p}{f_p} &= KV \cos (\alpha + \beta) \\ \frac{\Delta f_s}{f_s} &= KV \cos (\alpha - \beta) \end{aligned} \right\} \tag{93}$$

when f_p and f_s are the frequencies associated with port and starboard aerials respectively, V is the velocity and K is a constant involving the depression angle θ. The two equations may be used to determine both V and β.

$$V \cos \beta = \frac{\Delta f_s/f_s + \Delta f_p/f_p}{2K \cos \alpha}$$

$$V \sin \beta = \frac{\Delta f_s/f_s - \Delta f_p/f_p}{2K \sin \alpha}$$

Instead of computing β from these two frequencies Δf_s and Δf_p it is possible to arrange for the aerial to be rotated automatically

FIG. 21.

until they are equal, in which case its angular position relative to the aircraft gives β immediately. Radar frequencies (e.g. ca. 9000 mega-cycles per second) are employed for at least two reasons, firstly they give reasonably high Doppler beat frequencies, and secondly they can be directed in narrow beams (say 2–3°) with moderately sized aerials. Both pulsed and C.W. systems may be used but since the

C.W. system seems essentially simple it would appear to be preferable if no need for range information exists.

As is often the case with systems of this type, while the general principle is extremely simple, the attempt to eliminate various sources of error produces technical complications. We will limit ourselves to those which do not require a discussion of highly specialised (but often very elegant) electronic techniques. One solution of the problem of a systematic error introduced by the aircraft's attitude (in pitch) as mentioned above, is to employ two radio beams, directed fore and aft. We have seen how a two beam

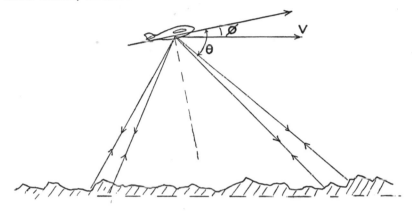

FIG. 22.

system enables the heading angle β to be determined and in a somewhat similar way, the problem of error in θ can be solved by using two beams. Assume that, as shown in fig. 22 the two aerials are supplied from one transmitter, and the reflected signals picked up by a single receiver. The two frequencies received will be given by

$$\left. \begin{aligned} \frac{f-f_F}{f} &= K'V \cos (\theta - \phi) \\ \frac{f-f_A}{f} &= - K'V \cos (\theta + \phi) \end{aligned} \right\} \tag{94}$$

The simultaneous reception of these two frequencies will produce a beat note in the receiver whose frequency will be

$$f_F - f_A = fK'V[\cos (\theta - \phi) + \cos (\theta + \phi)]$$
$$= 2fK'V \cos \theta \cos \phi \tag{95}$$

The fractional error introduced by ignoring the effect of the tilt ϕ in the aerial system is $\phi^2/2$ to a close approximation. A tilt of 3° (about 0·05 radian) will produce an error of only about $\frac{1}{8}$ per cent which is not serious compared with other sources of error. A system of this type cannot be expected to give accuracy of better than $\frac{1}{8}$ per cent in distance travelled. The use of this fore and aft system does not eliminate the need for two sideways-looking beams, but the added complication is not very great, and in fact a symmetrical system using four beams may be used. There is also another possible advantage in this system, in so far as it has certain possibilities where it is desired to use a pulsed system; but this will be discussed in Chapter 7 where the subject of pulsed Doppler is considered.

The beam transmitted covers a certain range of θ, the aerial also receives reflected waves through a finite angle, and since the frequency of the reflected signal is a function of θ, this signal will have a certain frequency spectrum rather than a single discrete frequency. By making some simplifying assumptions it is possible to calculate the magnitude of this effect and to estimate the systematic error which it introduces. Consider only a beam directed forwards (or backwards) at a depression angle θ with an angular beam width defined by the expression

$$I(\theta) = I_0 e^{-(\theta-\theta_0)^2/\sigma^2}$$

where $I(\theta)$ is the intensity in the direction θ, θ_0 the direction of the maximum intensity, i.e. the nominal beam direction, and σ is a constant whose value determines the angular half width of the beam. This latter quantity is found by putting $e^{-(\theta-\theta_0)^2/\sigma^2} = \frac{1}{2}$, solving for $\theta - \theta_0$, and multiplying by 2, the result being $2\sigma\sqrt{\log 2}$. The receiving aerial will be assumed to have a corresponding variation in sensitivity with direction, also centred on θ_0, and it will be assumed that the intensity of the received signal varies as $\sin^2\theta$. This assumption which is not always justified, represents a double application of the cosine law, firstly to the illumination of the ground by the transmitter, and secondly to the scattered radiation which is received by the aerial. The result is that the intensity of the signal received from the direction θ is given by

$$I(\theta) = I_0' \sin^2\theta \, e^{-2(\theta-\theta_0)^2/\sigma^2} \tag{96}$$

I_0' depending on the altitude of the plane, the nature of the ground surface, etc. The finite beam width produces two effects. One is a spread in reflected frequencies, and the other is a change in the frequency for which the intensity is a maximum; the latter effect representing a systematic error. Since the bandwidth of frequencies received will be augmented by random fluctuations arising from the aircraft pitching and rolling, irregularities in the ground, and at sea by wave motions, it will suffice to simply convert the angular beam width into frequency bandwidth. If $\Delta f = KfV \cos \theta$ the frequency bandwidth is given by

$$\Delta(\Delta f) = 2KfV\sigma\sqrt{\log 2} \sin^{\cdot}\theta$$

where $\Delta(\Delta f)$ represents the halfwidth of the frequency spectrum, and

$$\frac{\Delta(\Delta f)}{\Delta f} = 2\sigma\sqrt{\log 2} \tan \theta \qquad (97)$$

In practice this represents a spread of several per cent in the Doppler beat frequency or in the velocity, assuming as before that the half-width of the beam is about 0·05 radian. This width cannot be ignored and it is therefore essential that the velocity corresponding to the maximum intensity is used in calculating the distance travelled. Fortunately this maximum is not shifted by a great amount. The angle at which the reflected intensity is a maximum is obtained by differentiating $I_0' \sin^2 \theta\ e^{-2(\theta-\theta_0)^2/\sigma^2}$ and equating to zero. The result is the following equation for θ_{max}

$$\tan \theta_{max} = \frac{2(\theta_{max} - \theta_0)}{\sigma^2}$$

The systematic error introduced is $\theta_{max} - \theta_0$, and this may be put equal to η giving

$$\tan (\theta_0 + \eta) = \frac{2\eta}{\sigma^2}$$

which if η is assumed small gives

$$\eta = \frac{\tan \theta_0}{2/\sigma^2 - \sec^2 \theta} \qquad (98)$$

or even more roughly $= \sigma^2/2 \tan \theta_0$, if σ is assumed small and θ_0 is not close to 90°. This leads to the conclusion that for values of θ_0 near 60°–70° the systematic error introduced by beam width may be neglected if σ is of the order of 0·05 radian (aiming at an accuracy of 0·3 per cent). The assumption of the cosine law for the reflection of the radiation has been made on the grounds of simplicity. If, as might happen over the sea, there is a regularity of structure in the reflecting surface this might well give rise to a much greater systematic error than equation (98) would indicate. This is best studied experimentally by recording the frequency spectrum of the reflected signals when flying over various types of surfaces, and it appears that the error from the source may amount to as much as 1 per cent, which one might expect in most cases to be somewhat reduced if a fore and aft aerial system were used, since one would expect the angle to be shifted in the same sense from θ_0 in each case, but not necessarily by the same amount. Errors in velocity of a systematic kind would be introduced over the sea by wave motions and currents, these amounting to a few knots only, but becoming serious for long distances over the sea.

There exists a variety of methods of navigation both for ships and aircraft, mainly based on some form of grid system, and it is inevitable that eventually competition will result in natural selection among them. The satellite method described will no doubt eventually become widely used. The second method described has the advantage of being selfcontained, a feature which appeals to military users, but otherwise does not seem to possess clear advantages over reference grid systems based on radio.

REFERENCES

[1] KERSHNER, R. B. *Fifth National Symposium on Space Electronics and Telemetry*, Sec. 7.5, Inst. Radio Engineers, New York (1960).
GUIER, W. H. and WEIFFENBACH, G. C. *Proc. I.R.E.*, Vol. 48, p. 587 (1960).
WEIFFENBACH, G. C. *Proc. I.R.E.*, Vol. 48, p. 750 (1960).
[2] WAN, C. C. *Fifth National Symposium on Space Electronics and Telemetry*, Sec. 7.4. Inst. Radio Engineers, New York (1960).
[3] CLEGG, J. E. and THORNE, T. G. *Proc. I.E.E.*, Vol. 105B, Supp. No. 9, p. 235 (1958).
CLEGG, J. E. and CROMPTON, J. W. *Proc. I.E.E.*, Vol. 105B, Supp. No. 9, p. 258 (1958).
The supplement referred to here contains a number of general and specialised articles dealing with radio navigation methods and instruments.

7

Miscellaneous Applications

Radar Applications

The Doppler effect is of some importance in both civil and military applications of radar because of the opportunity which it offers of readily distinguishing between stationary and moving targets. In a normal radar system the carrier wave, usually at a frequency of some thousands of megacycles per second, is transmitted in a series of sharp pulses, the pulse repetition frequency (P.R.F.) being normally in the audio frequency range. The basic reason for this pulse modulation is to permit the range of the target to be determined, this being derived from the time taken for each pulse to reach the target and be reflected back to a receiver. If, in order to simplify the estimation of the Doppler shift, a continuous wave were employed, once the range exceeded half a wavelength ambiguities would arise, and so some form of modulation is essential, the period of repetition of this modulation being fixed by the maximum range which must be unambiguously determined.

However, when an attempt is made to measure the Doppler shift using a pulse modulated transmitter, a serious difficulty arises. In order to accurately measure distances the transmitted pulses need to be adequately separated in time in order that the echoes are received back in the clear spaces between pulses. But when a device like the magnetron is used, each time it is pulsed, the oscillations start up without any particular phase relation to the oscillations in previous or subsequent pulses, and there is no basis for comparing the phase of the waves in the echo with that of the transmitted waves. A simple and fairly obvious solution of this problem is to derive the pulses from a stable, steadily running, oscillator by pulsing a power amplifier. There will then be phase coherence from pulse to pulse and the reflected signal when mixed with the stable oscillator output will have the phase difference appropriate to its time of flight to and from the target. The output from the mixer will be a combination of pulses modulated with the Doppler beat frequency, and between these, the steady oscillator signal; and from this the former

113

can readily be extracted. There is, however, a further difficulty which is a matter of practical concern to radar engineers, namely, the possibility that the Doppler beat frequency may be equal to a multiple of the P.R.F. in which case the phase difference between transmitted and received signals is the same for each pulse and so the Doppler signal is lost. The " blind spots " which arise in this way are analogous to the effects which occur when the range is such that the return pulse coincides with a later transmitted pulse. It is almost impossible to eliminate ambiguities and " blind spots " completely, although they can be reduced in significance by selecting the most suitable P.R.F. or group of P.R.F.'s. In brief, C.W. radar gives no information about range but good and continuous information on the line of sight velocity, while at the other extreme a pulsed radar using a low P.R.F. is free from range ambiguities but cannot give useful Doppler information. Any form of modulating or " marking " the carrier wave will enable range to be determined, and one which is of some interest, although not nearly as important as the pulse method, is frequency modulation. To illustrate the principle of this method consider fig. 23 in which the continuous line represents the transmitted frequency as a function of time while the broken line represents the received frequency. The received signal will be delayed in time by an amount $2r/c$ and changed in frequency by an amount $(f/c)\ dr/dt$. In fig. 23 the resultant beat frequency is plotted as a function of time. The square wave frequency modulation has been chosen merely for simplicity in illustration, other forms could equally well be used. Both range and velocity may be readily found from such a frequency-time record; however, the diagram illustrates only the case where the Doppler beat frequency is high compared with the modulation frequency.

The beat frequency obtained by mixing a reflected signal with the transmitted signal, while it gives the magnitude of the line of sight velocity of the target, will not indicate whether the motion is towards or away from the observer. Frequency modulation permits this extra information to be obtained, provided the time taken for the echo to return is an appreciable fraction of the modulation period. This can readily be seen by substituting in fig. 23 a received signal of *higher* frequency than the transmitter frequency. If the target is too close and the delay in the return pulse is too short, this method may fail. This added information which frequency modulated radar provides is not of sufficient value to outweigh the advantages of the pulsed systems, since this information is usually derived in some other way. It (frequency modulation) has however been applied in radar altimeters in aircraft.

The method of modulating and amplifying the output of a stable oscillator in order to obtain coherence is not always practicable. Another method takes advantage of the fact that an oscillator with a relatively low Q can be pulled into phase with another oscillator

FIG. 23.

coupled to it. Thus the powerful pulsed oscillator, such as a magnetron, pulls a local oscillator into phase with it after a few cycles and when the pulse cuts off, this oscillator runs freely until the next pulse occurs. So when a return or echo pulse arrives during the interval between pulses there is available a frequency source maintaining the phase of the transmitted pulse, with which it can be mixed to give a Doppler beat frequency. Each successive transmitter pulse pulls the local oscillator into phase with it and so the phase relation between transmitted and received signals is preserved even though the actual transmitter phase varies in a random manner from pulse to pulse. The P.R.F. is such that the local oscillator does not drift significantly in phase during the pulse period. A schematic diagram of a system of this type is shown in fig. 24 (see reference[1]). The magnetron oscillator is pulsed by the pulse modulator and feeds the aerial, A. (The same aerial serves both transmitter and receiver.) The output of the standard oscillator of frequency f_0 is mixed with some of the pulsed signal supplied to the aerial at frequency $(f_0 + I.F.)$

Fig. 24.

and the difference frequency which will be called the intermediate frequency $(I.F.)$ is used to lock in phase another oscillator (phase-locked oscillator). The output of the standard oscillator is also mixed with the signal received after reflection from the target [at frequency $(f_0 + I.F. + \Delta f)$] and the new difference frequency $(I.F. + \Delta f)$ is mixed with the intermediate frequency to give the Doppler beat frequency Δf which will, of course, be superimposed on the received pulses.

Still another method of obtaining coherent radar, is to mix the signal reflected from the moving target with a signal reflected from a stationary object at nearly the same distance. Obviously this method will only be applicable in certain cases. One special case where it may be used is in the " fore and aft " system of Doppler navigation described in Chapter 6. Here the signals from the two beams will arrive back almost simultaneously and if the pulse length is not too short there will be some overlap and the two frequencies can be compared directly. The method demands the use of an adequate pulse length since the path lengths in the two directions will differ if the aircraft is pitching or if the terrain is uneven in altitude.

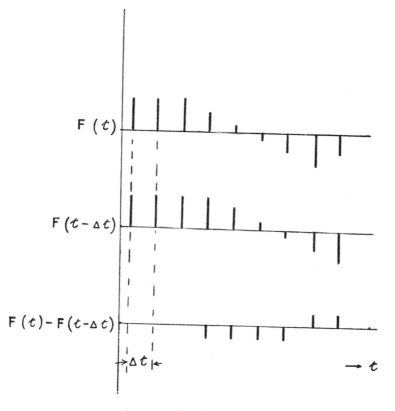

FIG. 25.

In certain types of radar installations, the regions near the horizon may be obscured by echoes from stationary objects, or in military applications, " window " may be ejected by a hostile target. Schemes have therefore been devised which suppress echoes which are not shifted in frequency by the Doppler effect. The straightforward use of a tuned filter to eliminate the original carrier frequency is ruled out by the smallness of the Doppler shift and the large band-width involved in the pulse modulated carrier wave. Discrimination between fixed and moving targets may however be achieved as follows. Consider the system illustrated in fig. 24. The output of this system is a series of pulses whose amplitude varies with the Doppler beat frequency. Suppose now that each pulse is sub-tracted from the pulse following it. If there is no Doppler shift the pulses are of constant amplitude and the result of the subtraction is no output, but if there is a Doppler shift the amplitudes of succes-sive pulses will be different and a signal will be detected. The subtraction is achieved by putting part of the signal through a line which causes a delay equal to one (or more) period(s) of the pulse modulation, and then subtracting this from the undelayed signal. This delay system is inserted between the output of the system depicted in fig. 24 and the display unit. The principle of the method is illustrated in fig. 25. Even without such a system as this, moving targets may sometimes be detected by the fluctuations produced by the beating of their echoes with echoes from stationary objects in their neighbourhood.

A very simple application of C.W. radar which uses the Doppler effect is in the measurement of motor vehicle speeds by traffic police. Here a radar beam is directed along the road from a fixed installa-tion, usually in a parked van, and the echo from a moving vehicle is mixed with the transmitted frequency and the resultant Doppler beat frequency measured to give the speed. The method is simple to operate and much more reliable than estimates by even the most experienced traffic experts. The speed may even be recorded simultaneously on a film with pictures of the vehicle involved.

Meteorites

Meteorites entering the upper regions of the atmosphere produce trails of ionisation which are sufficiently dense in many cases to reflect radio waves of suitable frequencies. These trails have been studied extensively[2] with a view to determining the speed with which the meteorites producing them enter the earth's atmosphere. The ionised region is " illuminated " by means of a radio trans-mitter and the reflected waves are received at one or more points, where the resulting signal will be a mixture of the reflected wave with the wave received directly from the transmitter. The trail grows in length as the meteorite plunges into the atmosphere, and as a result the signal strength at the receiver fluctuates. It might at first be thought that the fluctuating signal should be regarded as being due to the Doppler-shifted signal from the head of the meteor trail mixing with the ground wave, and producing beats. Apparently this is not entirely correct, except perhaps in the case of large meteorites. The fluctuating signal should rather be thought of as a moving diffraction pattern, rather analogous to the pattern produced by reflection at the edge of a plane mirror. The difference between this picture and the simple Doppler-shift one is the taking into account of the reflections from the part of the trail which is not growing, reflections which persist for some time after the meteorite has passed. While the determination of meteorite velocity by the direct application of the Doppler principle does not turn out to be practicable in most cases, the persistance of the ionised trails for a few seconds does afford an opportunity for another interesting application of the principle. These trails, consisting of ionised air molecules will move with the prevailing wind and so provide a means of measuring wind velocities. This method of measuring upper atmosphere wind speeds has been applied over a long period by Elford and his co-workers[3] and it is their technique which will be briefly described. It should be mentioned in passing that a great deal of work in connection with upper atmosphere winds has been carried out using irregularities in the ionosphere as reflecting targets, although most of these cannot be regarded as applications of the Doppler effect.

The region in which the ionised trails are produced is between 80 and 110 Km. altitude, and the frequency used is 27 megacycles per second, a frequency not reflected to any extent by the E-layer of the ionosphere in the neighbourhood of which the trails are produced. The arrangement used is shown schematically in fig. 26, the transmitter and receiver being separated by an appreciable distance (of the order of 20 Km.). If r_1 and r_2 are the distances of the reflecting point on the trail from the transmitter and receiver respectively, the Doppler shift in the received frequency is given by

$$\frac{\Delta f}{f} = - \frac{1}{c}\left(\frac{dr_1}{dt} + \frac{dr_2}{dt}\right)$$

A knowledge of dr_1/dt and dr_2/dt is not nearly sufficient, so the transmitter is pulsed, the pulses being superimposed on the C.W. transmission by increasing the transmitter power for a 10 micro-second interval every 0·01 second, the phase remaining coherent through the pulses. The time delay between the reflected and direct

E

pulses gives the quantity $r_1 + r_2 - r_0$. In addition it is necessary to know the direction of arrival of the reflected signal, and this is done by means of a radio interferometer, which instead of comparing the phase of the original carrier at two or more separate aerials compares the phase of the Doppler beats. It will be remembered that the phase relations are preserved in the process of beating with the direct signal. The use of both range measurement and direction finding fix the position of the reflecting trail. However, in spite of this there still remain uncertainties, the more serious of which may

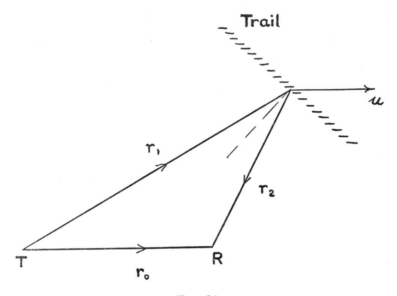

FIG. 26.

be illustrated as follows. An ellipsoid of revolution with the receiver and transmitter as foci will represent a locus of reflecting points with constant path length from transmitter to receiver. Any component of velocity tangential to this ellipse will not significantly affect the Doppler shift; the velocity determined will be the component normal to this ellipsoid at every instant. Since the position of the reflecting point is known, the direction in which the velocity component is measured is also known. However, in the work referred to, it has been assumed implicitly that the ellipsoid may be regarded as a sphere centred on the receiver, the transmitter and receiver not being widely separated. This merely simplifies the geometry of the situation but does not remove the ambiguity. There is no way in which this can be done using a single meteor trail; but when two or more trails are observed at about the same time but in different directions, two components of the wind velocity in different directions are then known, so that the actual velocity can be compounded from these. The matter is further simplified by the fact that the wind velocities do not as a rule have vertical components. On occasion a statistical analysis of the line of sight components may be carried out to derive the actual wind direction. One other ambiguity is worth mentioning. Since the Doppler beat frequency alone is recorded it is not possible to distinguish the sense of the velocity component observed unless some special device is employed. In this case a phase modulation is superimposed on the transmitted signal which carries out the sense discrimination in a manner analogous to that described earlier in the chapter. Ambiguities which arise in the discrimination of direction by the radio interferometer system are not inherent in the system and have been reduced to a level which can be tolerated.

There have been some applications of the Doppler effect to devices such as burglar alarms in which an ultra high frequency electromagnetic field, or a supersonic sound field, is set up in a region which is to be guarded. Any moving object in the area reflects a Doppler shifted wave which beats with the original signal and is thus detected; such devices can be made extremely sensitive, and, no doubt also have their military applications. Once again the question arises as to whether one should think of the Doppler effect or a moving interference pattern. This is largely a question of language and no doubt, in the last analysis the correct but pedantic approach is to speak of a solution of the wave equation with the appropriate (moving) boundary conditions. The pursuit of such linguistic or terminological arguments is only profitable in so far as it helps to throw light on real distinctions between different situations. Such a need for distinguishing may arise when the basic laws governing a phenomenon remain the same but the relative importance of various factors changes. In optics, for example, the ratio of the size of apertures to wavelengths may determine whether or not the concepts of geometrical optics are useful. In dealing with relative motion between transmitters and receivers, factors such as ratio of the dimensions of the system to the wavelength of the radiation, the importance of transient effects, etc., may well decide whether the phenomenon should be described in terms of the Doppler effect or

in some other way.   In some cases alternative descriptions are
rigorously equivalent, while in others, as in the quasi-stationary
approach to the Doppler effect dealt with in Chapter 5, one picture
is no more than a convenient approximation.

The laser, which has not yet achieved its maximum theoretical
possibilities, is capable of producing extremely monochromatic and
therefore coherent light. This makes possible the detection of small
changes in frequency and therefore the detection of small Doppler
shifts in a manner analogous to the use of the Mössbauer effect.

An early and historically important application of the Doppler
effect is illustrated in fig 27 (see reference[4]). An aircraft A flying

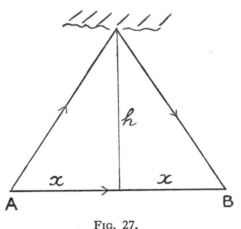

FIG. 27.

horizontally towards B carries a radio transmitter the signals from
which are received at B and it is observed that these signals show
periodic fluctuations in strength, or fading. The signals from A
reach B by two paths, one direct, and one after reflection from the
ionosphere, and both these paths are varying with time as the aircraft moves. The result is a steady variation in the phase difference
between the two signals which produces the fading. The lengths of
the direct and indirect paths are respectively $r_1 = 2x$ and $r_2 =
2\sqrt{x^2 + h^2}$, h being the effective height of the ionosphere and $2x$
the distance between receiver and transmitter. Each of the two
signals show a Doppler shift given by

$$\Delta f_1 = \frac{2}{c}\frac{dx}{dt} \text{ and } \Delta f_2 = \frac{2x}{c\sqrt{x^2 + h^2}}\frac{dx}{dt}$$

The beat frequency produced by the combination of the two signals will be the difference of these, namely,

$$\frac{2}{c}\left(1 - \frac{x}{\sqrt{x^2 + h^2}}\right)\frac{dx}{dt}$$

from which an effective height of the ionosphere may be calculated. This experiment may also be interpreted, if the transmitter is thought of as being at rest, as motion though a stationary interference pattern of standing waves, produced by reflection from the ionosphere. The interchangeability of the two approaches is permissible since the velocity is constant and therefore steady conditions prevail, and the ionosphere is at a reasonably constant height. This experiment was one of considerable importance among earlier investigations of the ionosphere.

REFERENCES

[1] GILLESPIE, N. R., HIGLEY, J. B. and MacKINNON, N. *I.R.E. Trans. Military Electronics*, MIL5, p. 131 (1961).
[2] LOVELL, A. C. B. *Meteor Astronomy* (Oxford University Press, 1954).
[3] ROBERTSON, D. S., LIDDY, D. T. and ELFORD, W. G. *Journ. Atmos. and Terrest. Phys.*, Vol. 4, p. 255 (1953).
ELFORD, W. G. and ROBERTSON, D. S. *Journ. Atmos. and Terrest. Phys.*, Vol. 4, p. 271 (1953).
[4] APPLETON, E. V. *Proc. Phys. Soc.*, Vol. 42, p. 321 (1930).

8

Black-body Radiation

Doppler's conjecture that the difference in the colours of the stars were due to their different velocities relative to the earth proved to be incorrect when their spectra were studied. It was not an absurd idea, however, in the absence of any information regarding the order of magnitude of stellar velocities. So far, in considering the Doppler effect it has been assumed that the source of radiation concerned emitted a single frequency; it is now opportune to consider the Doppler effect in relation to a continuous spectrum, and no better example exists than a black-body or perfect radiator. It is obvious that the spectral distribution of the energy radiated from a black body must be modified by the relative motion of source and observer, and the problem would be trivial but for one thing, namely, that the energy received from a monochromatic source, as well as the wavelength, varies with relative motion. Because of this it is necessary to define the conditions of observation more precisely than has been done hitherto. Let us assume that the observer receives and integrates the radiation received by a circular aperture A, the plane of which is perpendicular to the direction of the motion. The source will be on a line through the centre of the aperture and perpendicular to its plane. The arrangement is illustrated in fig. 28. The source of radiation, s, will be assumed to be small and to radiate uniformly in all directions. The radiation received by the aperture will be confined within a cone of half angle θ_0, this angle being measured in a frame of reference at rest relative to s. If $N(v)dv$ is the number of photons emitted per second in unit solid angle by s in a narrow frequency range dv, the number emitted in a conical element of solid angle defined by $d\theta$ will be $2\pi \sin \theta \, N(v)dv \, d\theta$. A consideration of the derivation of the formulae for the Doppler shift in Chapter 1 [equation (9)] will show that it is applicable to the emission of particles as well as waves, in fact no data were used except the relativistic transformation of time intervals and the finite velocity of transmission c. The number of photons per second received by the aperture in the element of solid angle defined by $d\theta$, and in a frequency range 0 to ν_0 thus

$$2\pi \sin \theta \left[\int_0^{\nu_0} N(\nu)d\nu \right] \beta \left(1 - \frac{v}{c}\cos \theta \right) d\theta$$

when the aperture A moves with velocity v relative to s, so that the total number of photons received per second by the aperture is

$$2\pi\beta \int_0^{\theta_0} \sin \theta \left(1 - \frac{v}{c}\cos \theta \right) \int_0^{\nu_0} N(\nu)d\nu \, d\theta \qquad (99)$$

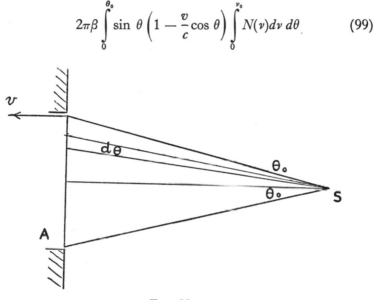

FIG. 28.

all the quantities being measured in a frame of reference at rest with respect to s. Suppose now that the observer ignores the motion relative to s and interprets the number of photons given by formula (99) as coming from a stationary source. The range of frequencies which he observes is not now 0 to ν_0 but 0 to $\nu_0(1 - v/c \cos \theta_0)\beta$ and the cone in which the radiation is received now has the half angle θ_0' given by

$$\cos \theta_0' = \frac{\cos \theta_0 - v/c}{1 - (v/c)\cos \theta_0} \qquad \text{[equation (10)]}$$

If now the observer interprets his observations in terms of a source emitting photons uniformly in all directions at the rate of $N'(\nu)d\nu$

photons per unit solid angle per second in a frequency range $d\nu$, the number of photons per second entering the aperture will be,

$$\int_0^{\arccos\left[\frac{\cos\theta_0 - v/c}{1 - (v/c)\cos\theta_0}\right]} 2\pi \sin\theta \int_0^{\nu_0(1 - (v/c)\cos\theta_0)\beta} N'(\nu)d\nu \, . \, d\theta \qquad (100)$$

The two expressions (99) and (100) represent the same number and so may be equated. Both (99) and (100) are readily integrated with respect to θ and the resulting equation is

$$\beta\left[1 - \cos\theta_0 - \frac{v}{2c}\sin^2\theta_0\right]\int_0^{\nu_0} N(\nu)d\nu$$

$$= \left[\frac{(1 + v/c)(1 - \cos\theta_0)}{1 - v/c\cos\theta_0}\right]\int_0^{\nu_0[1 - (v/c)\cos\theta_0]\beta} N'(\nu)d\nu \qquad (101)$$

so that

$$\int_0^{\nu_0[1 - (v/c)\cos\theta_0]\beta} N'(\nu)d\nu = \frac{\beta[1 - (v/c)\cos\theta_0][1 - (v/c)\cos^2\theta_0/2]}{(1 + v/c)} \int_0^{\nu_0} N(\nu)d\nu \quad (102)$$

Now differentiate with respect to ν_0, which gives,

$$N'\left(\nu_0\left(1 - \frac{v}{c}\cos\theta_0\right)\beta\right) = \frac{[1 - (v/c)\cos^2\theta_0/2]}{1 + v/c}N(\nu_0)$$

If now ν is written for $\nu_0(1 - (v/c)\cos\theta_0)\beta$,

$$N'(\nu) = \frac{[1 - (v/c)\cos^2\theta_0/2]}{1 + v/c} N\left(\frac{\nu}{[1 - (v/c)\cos\theta_0]\beta}\right) \qquad (103)$$

giving the apparent form of the spectral distribution as seen by the observer A moving with velocity v relative to the source. The quantity $N(\nu)$ the number of photons emitted per unit solid angle per unit frequency interval is given by the well known Planck radiation formula, expressed in photon numbers, namely,

$$N(\nu) = \frac{B\nu^2}{e^{h\nu/kT} - 1}$$

where B is a constant depending on the area of the source, T is the absolute temperature, h is Planck's constant and k, Boltzmann's constant. Substituting from equation (103)

$$N'(v) = \frac{B[1 - (v/c)\cos^2\theta_0/2]}{(1 + v/c)[1 - (v/c)\cos\theta_0]^2\beta^2} \cdot \frac{v^2}{(e^{hv/kT[1 - (v/c)\cos\theta_0]\beta} - 1)}$$

(104)

This is seen to correspond exactly to the spectral distribution of a black body at temperature $T' = T[1 - (v/c)\cos\theta_0]\beta$, except for a constant multiplier.

The case of θ_0 small is the only one likely to be of any practical importance, and in this case

$$N'(v) = \frac{Bv^2}{e^{hv/kT(1 - v/c)\beta} - 1}$$

(105)

the multiplying factor reducing to unity. The spectral distribution now corresponds exactly to that of a black body at temperature

$$T' = T\left(1 - \frac{v}{c}\right)\beta = T\sqrt{\frac{1 - v/c}{1 + v/c}}$$

The total energy received is found by integrating over all frequencies, and since the total energy is proportional to T^4, the energy will be changed in the ratio

$$\left(\frac{1 - v/c}{1 + v/c}\right)^2$$

[1]

The result then is very simple. The effect of the motion, provided observations are made in the manner described, is merely to produce an apparent change in temperature. For normal stellar velocities, the change will be of the order of a few degrees, well within the limits of observational error, even if stars could be regarded as black bodies with this precision. However, for the velocities shown by distant galaxies the situation is different, for example, a velocity of one-third of the velocity of light, causes the apparent temperature to change by a factor of $1/\sqrt{2}$ for a velocity of recession, and of course these large velocities are always velocities of recession. This gives rise to a definite reddening in the case of the most distant galaxies. Suppose now that somewhat different conditions of observation were adopted, namely, the radiation consisted of plane parallel waves instead of the divergent waves from a point source. The problem is now simplified as there is no need to consider the change in the solid angle sub-tended by the source. Thus if the range of frequencies received by the stationary observer is 0 to ν_0 the range of frequencies observed when he is moving with velocity v will be 0 to

$$\nu_0 \sqrt{\frac{1 - v/c}{1 + v/c}},$$

and if $N(\nu)d\nu$ represents the number of photons per second received by the stationary observer per unit area, and $N'(\nu)d\nu$ represents the apparent frequency distribution of photons when the observer is in motion, equation (101) can be rewritten

$$\sqrt{\frac{1 - v/c}{1 + v/c}} \int_0^{\nu_0} N(\nu)d\nu = \int_0^{\nu_0 \sqrt{(1 - v/c)/(1 + v/c)}} N'(\nu)d\nu \qquad (106)$$

Differentiating with respect to ν_0

$$\sqrt{\frac{1 - v/c}{1 + v/c}} N(\nu_0) = \sqrt{\frac{1 - v/c}{1 + v/c}} N' \left(\nu_0 \sqrt{\frac{1 - v/c}{1 + v/c}} \right)$$

so that

$$N'(\nu) = N \left(\nu \sqrt{\frac{1 + v/c}{1 - v/c}} \right)$$

$$= B \left(\frac{1 + v/c}{1 - v/c} \right) \frac{\nu^2}{e^{h\nu/kT \sqrt{(1 - v/c)/(1 + v/c)}} - 1} \qquad (107)$$

The spectral distribution is unaltered but a factor

$$\frac{1 + v/c}{1 - v/c}$$

has now been introduced. The significance of this factor may be illustrated in the following manner. If light is being received in a cone of half angle θ_0 from a point source, the solid angle in which the light is received is $2\pi(1 - \cos \theta_0) \equiv \Omega$. If now the source and observer are set in relative motion with velocity v, the angle θ_0 is transformed according to the equation

$$\cos \theta_0' = \frac{\cos \theta_0 - v/c}{1 - (v/c) \cos \theta_0}$$

so that the solid angle which is now observed as $2\pi(1 - \cos \theta_0')$ becomes

$$2\pi\left[1 - \frac{\cos \theta_0 - v/c}{1-(v/c)\cos \theta_0}\right] = \frac{2\pi(1 - \cos \theta_0)(1 + v/c)}{1 - (v/c)\cos \theta_0}$$

$$= \left[\frac{1 + v/c}{1-(v/c)\cos \theta_0}\right]\Omega$$

and when θ_0 becomes very small this may be written

$$\left(\frac{1 + v/c}{1 - v/c}\right)\Omega$$

If θ_0 were put equal to zero at the beginning, the calculation of the solid angle would be meaningless. There seems no doubt that the method of using a finite θ_0 and proceeding to the limit zero is the correct one.

In Chapter 3 a question was raised, but not answered, concerning the effect of the aperture of the optical system used to view a molecular beam source of light. (It may safely be assumed that the aperture of the observing system has no effect on the Doppler broadening effect for a source in which the molecular motions are random, since the motions will look exactly the same from whatever direction they are observed.) Suppose that a point on the beam is viewed by means of an optical system which defines a cone of half angle θ_0, and that the beam velocity is u (fig. 29). Let a point P in the plane of the circular aperture be defined by the angle θ measured from the optic axis OX and the angle ϕ measured from a line OY at right angles to the beam direction Xu and lying in the plane of the aperture. If it is assumed that a point on the beam radiates uniformly in all directions, an assumption which will be true to the first order in θ, the radiation received by an element of area of the aperture defined by $d\theta$ and $d\phi$ will be proportional to $\sin \theta \, d\theta \, d\phi$ or $\theta \, d\theta \, d\phi$ for θ sufficiently small, and no real loss of generality will occur if the constant of proportionality is taken as unity. Consider initially only the radiation received in the upper half of the aperture shown in fig. 29. The frequency received at a point (θ, ϕ) on the aperture will be

$$\nu = \nu_0\left(1 + \frac{u}{c}\sin \theta \sin \phi\right)$$

where ν_0 is the frequency of the source when at rest relative to the observer, the maximum frequency being $\nu_0[1 + (u/c)\sin \theta_0]$. To determine the frequency distribution of the energy received it is first

FIG. 29.

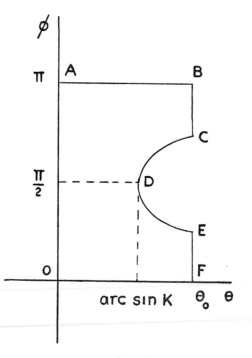

FIG. 30.

necessary to calculate the energy in the frequency range v_0 to v. The frequencies between v_0 and v will be confined to the area A, B, C, D, E, F, O in fig. 30 and the required energy is thus found by calculating the integral of $\sin \theta \, d\theta \, d\phi$ over this area. The curved part, $C\,D\,E$ of the boundary, is defined by

$$\sin \theta \sin \phi = \frac{v - v_0}{v_0} \frac{c}{u} \equiv K$$

The energy in this spectral range is thus

$$2 \left\{ \int_0^{\pi/2} \int_0^{\arcsin K} \sin \theta \, d\theta \, d\phi + \int_{\arcsin K}^{\theta_0} \int_0^{\arcsin (K/\sin \theta)} \sin \theta \, d\phi \, d\theta \right\}$$

$$= 2 \left\{ \frac{\pi}{2} \left[1 - \sqrt{1 - K^2} \right] + \int_{\arcsin K}^{\theta_0} \sin \theta \left[\arcsin \frac{K}{\sin \theta} \right] d\theta \right\}$$

The spectral distribution, $F(v)$ which gives the energy in a narrow spectral range dv, at frequency v is obtained by differentiating this expression with respect to v, and, carrying out this differentiation we obtain

$$F(v) = \frac{2c}{u v_0} \left\{ \frac{\pi K}{2\sqrt{1 - K^2}} - \int_{\theta_0}^{\arcsin K} \frac{d\theta}{\sqrt{1 - K^2/\sin^2 \theta}} - \frac{\pi K}{2} \right\}$$

$$= \frac{2c}{u v_0} \left\{ \frac{\pi K}{2} \left(1 - \frac{1}{\sqrt{1 - K^2}} \right) + \arccos \left(\frac{\cos \theta_0}{\sqrt{1 - K^2}} \right) \right\} \quad (108)$$

When θ_0 and K are both assumed small, this expression becomes

$$F(v) \approx \frac{2c}{u v_0} \arccos \left(1 - \frac{\theta_0^2}{2} + \frac{K^2}{2} \right)$$

$$\approx \frac{2c}{u v_0} \sqrt{\theta_0^2 - K^2}$$

$$\approx \frac{2c}{u v_0} \left[\theta_0^2 - \frac{(v - v_0)^2}{v_0^2} \frac{c^2}{u^2} \right]^{\frac{1}{2}} \quad (109)$$

giving the approximate frequency distribution. The half width $\Delta \nu$ is given by

$$\theta_0^2 - \frac{(\Delta \nu/2)^2}{\nu_0^2} \frac{c^2}{u^2} = \frac{\theta_0^2}{4}$$

$$\text{i.e.} \quad \frac{\Delta \nu}{\nu_0} = \sqrt{3 \cdot \frac{u}{c} \theta_0} \tag{110}$$

REFERENCE

[1] McCRAE, W. H. *Relativity Physics* (Methuen Monographs on Physical Subjects, London, 1949).

9

Experimental Verification

The first experimental verification of the Doppler effect appears to have been carried out by Buys Ballot, the Dutch meteorologist, in 1845, using the train whistles which to this day provide the most familiar everyday illustrations of the effect. Our concern is however mainly with electromagnetic radiation and it might well be asked whether there is any point in speaking of the experimental verification of a theory which has been so widely and successfully applied. There have been a number of experiments, the express purpose of which was to verify the Doppler theory for light, and these are of more than historic interest. The theory of the Doppler effect consists of mathematical deductions from a number of simple assumptions about the transmission of light signals, and an experimental check on the predictions of the theory tests these assumptions. For example, a naive ballistic theory of light would explain the null results of the Michelson-Morley experiment, and it is therefore of interest to ask what the Doppler effect would be, on the basis of such a theory, which assumes that the velocity of the light is the vector sum of the velocity of the source and the constant velocity of the light relative to the source. Obviously in calculating the predictions of such a theory the use of relativistic formulae would be an absurdity. Consider for simplicity the case of the transmitter and receiver moving along the same straight line, and referring back to the method of Chapter 1, the time of transmission of the signal is

$$t' - t = \frac{r}{c + u - v}$$

so that

$$\frac{dt'}{dt} = 1 + \frac{1}{c + u - v}\frac{dr}{dt}$$

$$= 1 + \frac{V}{c - V} \tag{111}$$

where V is the relative velocity of source and observer. This case differs from the classical case in so far as the medium is of no significance and from the relativistic case in so far as the velocity of transmission is not constant relative to the receiver. Equation (111) leads to the following relations for frequency and wavelength

$$\left. \begin{array}{l} f' = f\left(1 + \dfrac{V}{c-V}\right)^{-1} \\[2ex] \lambda' = \dfrac{c}{f} = \lambda \end{array} \right\} \qquad (112)$$

i.e. the wavelength is unaltered by the relative motion although the the frequency is changed in a manner which agrees with the normal Doppler formula to the first order.

The first attempt to verify the Doppler formula for light was made by Belopolsky[1] in 1901, who used an arrangement of two counter-rotating discs with mirrors arranged around the edges, the light undergoing six reflections in all, from either disc in turn. Each set of mirrors was moving at about 80 metres per second, so that dr/dt would be somewhat less than 960 metres per second, giving

$$\frac{1}{c}\frac{dr}{dt} \approx 3 \times 10^{-6}.$$

Belopolsky used the sun as a source of light, and measured the Doppler shifts in the Fraunhofer lines using a prism spectrometer. This experiment was repeated by Galitzin and Wilip[2] in 1907 who used a Michelson echelon combined with a spectroscope, and as a light source, a mercury lamp. The 5461A and 4358A lines were measured with an effective speed of about 250 metres per second, the direction of the motion being reversed, and the agreement with theory was within 10 per cent. It may be observed that while it is convenient in calculating the Doppler shift in reflection, to use the velocity of the image, this is not correct in principle, as can readily be seen if the case of a light source situated near the focus of a concave mirror is considered. Here a small velocity of the mirror (or source) can produce an enormous image velocity, but no correspondingly large Doppler shift is seen. About the same period, i.e. in the first decade of this century, a long series of investigations was being carried out by Stark, Paschen, and others[3] using canal rays. A great many problems were attacked by these workers including the precise nature of the particles which carried the charge in these rays. Stark and others clearly observed Doppler shifts in the lines emitted from the atoms in the canal rays and used these to estimate velocities. In this period Schott suggested the use of the rapidly moving atoms or ions in the canal rays to test the time dilatation predicted by Special Relativity, but it was some twenty years before a method of doing this was devised by Ives and Stillwell, and Otting. Before coming to this work however a number of other laboratory observations of the first order Doppler effect deserve consideration.

Fabry and Buisson[4], during the period from 1914 to 1919, performed some experiments using the Fabry-Perot interferometer to resolve the Doppler shift. Their apparatus was extremely simple in conception, consisting of a white paper disc mounted on a cream-separator which was rotated by hand at about 200 revolutions per second. This paper disc was illuminated by a mercury lamp and the light from the two edges showed maximum Doppler shifts when the disc was viewed edge on. The separation of the interferometer plates used was such that a shift of about 1/6 fringe was achieved for a speed of about 100 metres per second (order of interference about 240000). Such a shift can be measured with relative ease, although in this as in the previous cases mentioned, the precision is not nearly great enough for terms in v^2/c^2 to be significant. Another earlier but less successful attempt to examine the Doppler effect using a laboratory source was made in 1910 by Dufour who formed a mercury arc, under a pressure of about 1 mm. Hg., between two concentric circular mercury electrodes, the current passing in a radial direction. This whole arrangement was placed in a magnetic field directed at right angles to the plane of the circular electrodes, and this caused the arc to rotate at a very high speed, estimated by Dufour as about 17,000 revolutions per second. This rate of revolution was estimated by using a rotating mirror to view the arc and the light was analysed by means of a Fabry-Perot interferometer. Unfortunately the interpretation of the results was not simple since the gas in the discharge did not rotate at the same speed as the arc, the linear velocity of which was estimated at about 0·65 Km. per second while the Doppler shift observed, although in the right sense, corresponded to a speed of about 0·24 Km. per second. In order to eliminate the Zeeman splitting produced by the magnetic field, the light was passed through a Nicol prism. There was almost certainly considerable distortion of the fringe profiles since we are concerned with a source of light moving through an absorbing medium at non-uniform temperature and emitting in a region of anomalous dispersion.

In 1917 and 1918 Majorana[6] published accounts of two experiments designed to test the dependence or otherwise of the velocity of light on the velocity of its source. Equation (112) shows that if the simple ballistic theory of light were true, i.e. if the velocity of light simply added on to the velocity of source, the *wavelength* of light would not be changed by the motion of the source. If, however, light travels at a constant speed relative to either the medium or the observer then there would be a wavelength change. More sophisticated versions of the ballistic theory of light have been advanced since that day, but nevertheless these experiments clearly rule out one possibility. In fact the experiments of Fabry and Buisson and others, in so far as they show that light obeys the Doppler formulae we have discussed, demonstrated the impossibility of the simple ballistic theory. There is no basic difference between the experiments themselves but only in the emphasis which is put on their interpretation, and the light which new theories cast on their significance. In his first experiment Majorana essentially repeated the experiment of Galitzin and Wilip using mirrors fixed to the edge of a single rotating wheel. An effective value of 450 metres per second was obtained for dr/dt. The change in wavelength was observed by means of a Michelson interferometer. In the second experiment, instead of a moving mirror system two mercury discharge lamps were fixed to opposite edges of a wheel 2 metres in diameter and rotated at about 14 revolutions per second. The direction of motion was reversed to double the effect sought, producing a fringe shift of 0·238 fringe in the Michelson interferometer (path difference 232 mm.). The fringe shift which should have been expected from the rate of rotation was 0·226 fringe. The difference appears to have been due to a small systematic error, the nature of which does not seem to have been elucidated. The effect is not significant compared with the magnitude of the effect sought, however, and it is difficult to eliminate all systematic errors when using the Michelson or similar interferometers, as instance of which may be quoted the repetitions of the Michelson-Morley experiment by Miller, and more recently some experiments dealing with the very problem of the relation of the velocity of light to that of a medium through which it has just passed, which gave results in startling disagreement with accepted theory, but which have not been confirmed by further investigation.

It would seem that Majorana's second experiment was designed to make matters quite clear by actually moving the source of light and so avoid any theoretical difficulties which might be raised concerning reflection. This small point deserves some emphasis. In these experiments the point at issue was the mode of propagation of light and anything which had any bearing on the question called for examination. When the theory being tested concerned the manner in which light was emitted from bodies, to take for granted the laws governing reflection from moving mirrors would have introduced an unnecessary element of doubt. It is rarely if ever possible to test only one point of a theory at a time in an experiment but there is no doubt at all that some experiments carry more conviction because of their " directness " than others which are perhaps equally impeccable.

The Ives-Stillwell experiment[7] was the first published account of a laboratory experiment designed to check the predictions of special Relativity regarding a moving clock or oscillator. It should be mentioned that the work of Otting[8] was published only slightly later and must have been under way at much the same time. Although the Ives-Stillwell experiment agrees with the predictions of Einstein's theory, the authors did not support relativity but interpreted the results of the experiment in terms of an ether theory. For a concise expression of Ives' viewpoint the reader should consult reference[9].

The canal rays, or accelerated positive ions, provide a very rapidly moving source of light, and so give an opportunity of observing effects depending on v^2/c^2. There is also present the very much larger first order Doppler shift and although the effect of this may be greatly reduced by viewing the beam from a direction perpendicular to its direction of motion, as we have seen in Chapter 3, this cannot be done with the precision necessary to reduce the first order effects to the necessary extent. Not only is it hardly possible to align an optical system perpendicular to the ion-beam with the required accuracy, but the collimation of the beam to the desired precision presents an equally difficult problem. This problem, however, was overcome in a simple manner by Ives and Stillwell who abandoned any attempt to view the beam from a perpendicular direction, and instead adopted the scheme illustrated diagramatically in fig. 31. The region D is a gas discharge in which ions are produced, these being accelerated in region A and collimated by perforations in the electrodes. The atoms formed by recombination of ions emit light in region B, which is analysed by the spectroscope whose slit is shown at s the beam being viewed nearly end on. Ives and Stillwell used a grating spectroscope, and values of v/c of the order of 0·005; and the second order Doppler shifts were of the order of 0·01 to 0·05A, these shifts being quite measurable with care. Otting made what would seem to be a natural improvement, in that he used a Fabry-Perot interferometer to obtain the high resolution needed. The slit is placed at the centre of curvature of a spherical mirror M so that each element of the ion beam is viewed simultaneously from two exactly opposite directions. There are thus produced two symmetrically Doppler shifted lines, one seen directly and one by reflection, and an unshifted line due to stationary gas in the region B. At least this is the case if there is no Relativistic second order effect; in the

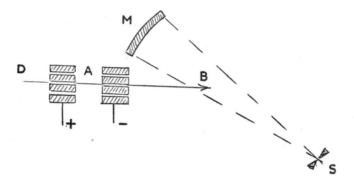

Fig. 31.

presence of this effect the two Doppler shifted lines will be asymmetrical, there being a general shift towards the red, or in other words the undisplaced line will lie to the blue side of the mean position of the two Doppler shifted lines. The velocity of the ions can be calculated from the potential through which they are accelerated so that this experiment gives a confirmation of the ordinary first order Doppler shift. In fact this provided a reliable way of calculating the atom velocities. The non-relativistic theory of this experiment may be outlined as follows. Referring back to equation (7), Chapter 1, the value of dr/dt is the ion velocity u, while v becomes the velocity of the observer through the ether. We have

$$f_1' = f \cdot \left(1 + \frac{u}{c - v}\right)^{-1}$$

for the receding view of the ions and, for the approaching view

$$f_2' = f \cdot \left(1 - \frac{u}{c - v}\right)^{-1}$$

The observed wavelengths are given by

$$\lambda_1' = \frac{(c - v)}{f_1'}$$

$$= \frac{c - v + u}{f}$$

and

$$\lambda_2' = \frac{c - v - u}{f}$$

so that the mean wavelength

$$\frac{\lambda_1' + \lambda_2'}{2} \text{ is } \frac{c - v}{f}$$

i.e. the value of λ corresponding to $u = 0$. The wavelength of the light from stationary atoms should thus be midway between the two Doppler shifted lines, according to the classical ether theory. The relativistic picture however gives

$$f_1' = f \sqrt{\frac{1 - u/c}{1 + u/c}}$$

v no longer being a significant quantity and

$$f_2' = f \sqrt{\frac{1 + u/c}{1 - u/c}}$$

and since the velocity of the waves is the same relative to all observers,

$$\lambda_1' = \lambda \sqrt{\frac{1 + u/c}{1 - u/c}}$$

$$\lambda_2' = \lambda \sqrt{\frac{1 - u/c}{1 + u/c}}$$

so that the mean value,

$$\frac{\lambda_1' + \lambda_2'}{2}$$

is

$$\frac{c}{f}\left(1 - \frac{u^2}{c^2}\right)^{-\frac{1}{2}} \approx \lambda \left(1 + \frac{u^2}{2c^2}\right) \qquad (113)$$

corresponding to the relativistic red shift. The above formulae have been simplified by the assumption that the emitting atoms are moving directly towards or away from the observer. The introduction of the angle between the line of sight and the direction of motion does not seriously change matters. The optical aperture and lack of beam collimation will cause some broadening of the lines. This is both small, and more important, symmetrical, in practice. The experiments of Ives and Stillwell and Otting agreed with the relativistic predictions within the experimental errors, and this experiment has been recently repeated by Mandelberg and Witten, agreement once again being achieved. The value derived for the coefficient of u^2/c^2 in equation (113) in this last experiment was $0 \cdot 498 \pm 0 \cdot 025$. While Mandelberg and Witten introduced some improvements and increased the precision of the measurements, their experiment is in essence the same as that of Ives and Stillwell, and Otting. In all these experiments the main object was the investigation of the relativistic red shift, but incidentally they may also be regarded as extensions of Fabry and Buisson's or Majorana's work.

One might attempt to summarise the situation regarding the experimental verification of Doppler theory as follows. The theory consists of a number of simple assumptions about the propagation of light, and straightforward mathematical deductions from these assumptions. The assumptions are those which are normally made in connection with the Special Theory of Relativity and, of course, in Optics generally. Thus any divergence between theory and experiment, other than that due to blunders, must call for a fairly fundamental change in our ideas about the propagation of light. The experimental evidence falls into two parts. There is first the vast amount of indirect evidence which results from the successful application of the Doppler effect to rocket and satellite tracking, and to astronomy. In the case of rockets or satellites, these are tracked simultaneously by other means and the correctness of the Doppler information is indisputable. In the case of astronomical objects, the confirmation is not quite so direct, but is derived from the generally self-consistent picture which results from the application of the theory. Both these regions however only give confirmation of the theory as far as the first order in v/c. Evidence for the correctness of the formulae to the second order in v/c depends on specially designed experiments which are few in number and not high in precision. Our conviction here rests only partly on actual experiments such as the Ives-Stillwell experiment, but in the main, on the general success of the Special Theory of Relativity, and the failure of rival theories.

One point may be worth mentioning in conclusion. An experiment such as Majorana's does not verify a particular theoretical idea, it distinguishes between two or more alternatives. That is why his accuracy of 5 per cent or so was adequate. In the same way, the Michelson-Morley experiment gave a null result in the context of the ether theories current at the time. In the light of some new and sophisticated ether theory the results obtained might become inconclusive. It might be argued with some justification that the repetition of the experiments of Majorana or Michelson and Morley to a higher precision would, if possible, be desirable, just in case some deviation from the predictions of theory might be observed. There is no reason at present to expect any such result and so the expenditure of effort would not be regarded as economical. No doubt, in some cases important facts lie undiscovered because no one will carry out or repeat an experiment where the result is a " foregone conclusion " but *on the average*, other activities will pay better and so are pursued. The theory of the Doppler effect can be regarded as established beyond reasonable doubt, the only possibility of its overthrow being bound up with the possibility of another revolution in Physics. To discuss the possibility or nature of an unforeseen or unforeseeable occurrence naturally contains certain elements of absurdity, so the matter will not be pursued. The only comment felt desirable is to the effect that the extent to which a theory is supported by experimental evidence is not an easy matter to judge, since every theory contains, as well as hypotheses or conjectures about the world, conventions and definitions and the prescriptions of a language for describing experimental results, which are intimately mixed with the genuine hypotheses but which are not refutable.

REFERENCES

[1] BELOPOLSKY, A. *Astrophys. Journ.*, Vol. 13, p. 15 (1901).
[2] GALITZIN, B. and WILIP, J. *Acad. Sci. St. Petersburg*, Bulletin 8, p. 213 (1907).
[3] STARK, J. *Ann. der Phys.*, Vol. 21, series 4, p. 401 (1906).
    PASCHEN, F. *Phys. Zeits.*, Vol. 7, p. 924 (1906).
[4] FABRY, C. and BUISSON, H. *Journ. de Phys.*, Vol. 8, p. 234 (1919).
[5] DUFOUR, A. *Comptes Rendus Acad. Sci.*, Vol. 151, p. 60 (1910).
[6] MAJORANA, Q. *Comptes Rendus Acad. Sci.*, Vol. 165, p. 424 (1917) and Vol. 167, p. 71 (1918).

[7] IVES, H. E. and STILLWELL, G. R. *Journ. Opt. Soc. Amer.*, Vol. 28, p. 215 (1938) and Vol. 31, p. 369 (1941).

[8] OTTING, G. *Phys. Zeits.*, Vol. 40, p. 681 (1939).

[9] IVES, H. E. *Journ. Opt. Soc. Amer.*, Vol. 27, p. 305 and p. 311 (1937).

[10] MANDELBERG, H. I. and WITTEN, L. *Journ. Opt. Soc. Amer.*, Vol. 52, p. 529 (1962).

Appendix

In dealing with the transmission of signals through inhomogeneous media it is convenient to speak in terms of rays rather than waves, although the actual transmission takes place by means of a wave motion, in other words we use the language of geometrical optics rather than physical or wave optics. Briefly a ray or ray path is a line everywhere normal to the wave fronts or surfaces of constant phase. The laws governing the geometrical form of ray-paths may be derived from the scalar wave equation in a relatively simple manner by allowing the wavelength to tend to zero. This, of course, corresponds to the possibility of neglecting diffraction in many optical problems where the dimensions of apertures, etc. are very large compared with the wavelength of the light. The equation

$$\frac{\partial^2 \Phi}{\partial x^2} + \frac{\partial^2 \Phi}{\partial y^2} + \frac{\partial^2 \Phi}{\partial z^2} = \frac{\mu^2}{c^2} \frac{\partial^2 \Phi}{\partial t^2} \tag{1A}$$

governs the motion of waves which move with velocity c/μ in a homogeneous medium. For it to be at all possible to use this equation it must clearly be assumed that μ cannot be a rapidly varying function of x, y and z.

Equation (1A) may be reduced to a time independent form

$$\frac{\partial^2 u}{\partial x^2} + \frac{\partial^2 u}{\partial y^2} + \frac{\partial^2 u}{\partial z^2} + k^2 u = 0 \tag{2A}$$

by writing $\Phi = ue^{i\omega t}$, and where k has been written for $u\omega/c$ and where ω is the angular frequency of the wave, assumed constant. In equation (2A) put $u = Ae^{ik_0 S}$ where $k_0 = \omega/c$ and where S is a slowly varying function of position, but nevertheless, the quantity $e^{ik_0 S}$ varies rapidly in comparison, since k_0 will be assumed to be large. The quantity A is assumed to be real, and determines the amplitude of the wave, while $k_0 S$ determines the phase. Let $u = e^{ik_0 S}$ now be substituted in equation (2A). We have

$$\frac{\partial u}{\partial x} = \frac{\partial A}{\partial x} e^{ik_0 S} + Aik_0 \frac{\partial S}{\partial x} e^{ik_0 S} = \frac{u}{A} \frac{\partial A}{\partial x} + ik_0 u \frac{\partial S}{\partial x}$$

and

$$\frac{\partial^2 u}{\partial x^2} = \frac{u}{A} \frac{\partial^2 A}{\partial x^2} + \frac{iu}{A} \frac{\partial A}{\partial x} \cdot \frac{\partial S}{\partial x} + \frac{iuk_0}{A} \frac{\partial A}{\partial x} \frac{\partial S}{\partial x} - uk_0^2 \left(\frac{\partial S}{\partial x}\right)^2$$

143

with similar expressions for $\partial^2 u/\partial y^2$ and $\partial^2 u/dz^2$. At this stage the quantities k and k_0 will be assumed to be sufficiently large for terms which do not contain one of them as a factor to be neglected, and taking the real parts of the equation resulting from substitution in (2A), we find

$$- k_0^2 \left[\left(\frac{\partial S}{\partial x} \right)^2 + \left(\frac{\partial S}{\partial y} \right)^2 + \left(\frac{\partial S}{\partial z} \right)^2 \right] + k_2 = 0$$

This may be written

$$(\text{grad } S)^2 = \frac{k^2}{k_0^2} = \mu^2 \tag{3A}$$

Since in the cases with which we are concerned here μ will be a real positive quantity it is permissible to write

$$\text{grad } S = \mu T \tag{4A}$$

where T is a unit vector in the direction of grad S, i.e. in the direction normal to the surfaces of constant phase, or tangential to the ray path. Differentiate (4A) with respect to s, s being the length of a ray path measured from some arbitrary point, ds thus being measured in the direction of T

$$\frac{d}{ds} \text{grad } S = \frac{d(\mu T)}{ds}$$

but

$$\frac{d}{ds} \text{grad } S = \text{grad } \frac{dS}{ds}$$

(since ds is measured in the direction of grad S)

$$= \text{grad } |\text{grad } S|$$

$$= \text{grad } \mu$$

i.e.

$$\text{grad } \mu = \frac{d}{ds}(\mu T) \tag{5A}$$

This equation becomes

$$\text{grad } \mu = T \frac{d\mu}{dS} + \mu \frac{dT}{ds}$$

$$= T \frac{d\mu}{ds} + \mu \kappa N \tag{6A}$$

where N is the unit vector in the direction of the principal normal to the ray path and κ is the curvature of the path. From this it follows immediately that T, N and grad μ lie in the same plane, namely, the osculating plane to the ray path. It is now possible to obtain simple expressions for the curvature and torsion of the ray path and thus establish conditions under which the path is plane or rectilinear. Take the vector product of T with both sides of equation (6A)

$$T \times \operatorname{grad} \mu = \kappa\mu T \times N$$

$$= \kappa\mu B \tag{7A}$$

where B is the binormal unit vector. This equation may be used to derive differential equations governing the form of possible ray paths once μ and therefore grad μ is known as a function of position.

Instead of doing this however, let us differentiate with respect to s

$$\frac{dT}{ds} \times \operatorname{grad} \mu + T \times \operatorname{grad}' \mu$$

$$= \frac{d\kappa}{ds}\mu B + \kappa \frac{d\mu}{ds}B + \kappa\mu \frac{dB}{ds} \tag{8A}$$

where grad$'$ μ denotes d grad μ/ds. Now $- dB/ds$ is defined as the torsion of a curve and it represents the rate at which the binormal at a point rotates about the tangent as the point moves along the curve. Since dB/ds is in the direction of N, dB/ds may be replaced by $- \tau N$ where τ is the numerical value of the torsion. In order to simplify (8A) take the scalar product of N with both sides

$$\frac{dT}{ds} \times \operatorname{grad} \mu \cdot N + T \times \operatorname{grad}' \mu . N = -\kappa\mu\tau$$

and since

$$\frac{dT}{ds} = \kappa N$$

$$T \times \operatorname{grad}' \mu . N = - \kappa\mu\tau \tag{9A}$$

If now T, grad$'$ μ and N lie in the same plane either κ or τ must be zero at the point concerned, i.e. either the curvature or torsion must be zero. Of more interest is the case when τ is zero everywhere, i.e. the ray path is plane. The exploration of the consequences of (7A) and (9A) as regards the possibility of rectilinear propagation may well be left to the reader.

It will suffice to show that in a spherically symmetrical medium the ray paths are planes passing through the centre of symmetry, since this fact is made use of in Chapter 2. A sufficient condition that all the ray paths are plane is that $\text{grad}'\,\mu$, $\text{grad}\,\mu$, and T are coplanar everywhere and this is satisfied if $\text{grad}'\,\mu \times \text{grad}\,\mu$. $T = 0$ at all points in the medium for all directions of T. Suppose that $\text{grad}'\,\mu$ is resolved in three directions at right angles, one of these lying in the direction of $\text{grad}\,\mu$, the other two in arbitrary directions denoted by unit vectors u and v, i.e. $\text{grad}'\,\mu = a\,\text{grad}\,\mu + bU + cV$. Then our condition becomes

$$(a\,\text{grad}\,\mu + bU + cV) \times \text{grad}\,\mu \,.\, T = 0$$

and therefore

$$bU \times \text{grad}\,\mu \,.\, T + cV \times \text{grad}\,\mu \,.\, T = 0.$$

It will in general be necessary that b and c are zero everywhere to satisfy our condition, since the directions of U, V and T may be chosen arbitrarily. This implies that $\text{grad}\,\mu$ cannot change at all for any infinitesimal displacement at right angles to its direction, i.e. $\text{grad}\,\mu$ must at all points be varying only in the direction of $\text{grad}\,\mu$. Such a condition can only be satisfied if the surfaces of constant μ are planes or concentric spheres. Clearly, in the spherical case the plane must pass through the centre of symmetry since the direction of $\text{grad}\,\mu$ passes through the centre and in addition must lie in the plane of the ray path.

REFERENCES

SOMMERFELD, A. *Optics* (Lectures in Theoretical Physics, Vol. IV), Sections 35 and 48 (Academic Press Inc., New York, 1954).

A full account of the derivation of the principles of geometrical optics from Maxwell's equations is given in Born, M. and Wolf, E., *Principles of Optics*, Chapter III (Pergamon Press, London, 1964).

Index

THE HERMIT KING

ALSO BY CHUNG MIN LEE

Fault Lines in a Rising Asia

Security Cooperation in Northeast Asia
(coedited with T. J. Pempel)

THE HERMIT KING

KING

THE DANGEROUS GAME OF KIM JONG UN

CHUNG MIN LEE

ALL
POINTS
BOOKS
NEW YORK

First published in the United States by All Points Books, an imprint of St. Martin's Publishing Group.

THE HERMIT KING. Copyright © 2019 by Chung Min Lee. All rights reserved. Printed in the United States of America. For information, address St. Martin's Press, 120 Broadway, New York, NY 10271.

www.allpointsbooks.com

Designed by Meryl Sussman Levavi

Library of Congress Cataloging-in-Publication Data

Names: Lee, Chung Min, author.
Title: The Hermit King : The Dangerous Game of Kim Jong Un / Chung Min Lee.
Description: First edition. | New York : All Points Books, 2019. | Includes
    bibliographical references and index. | Summary: "North Korea is poised at the
    crossroads of history. Which direction will its leader take? The answer concerns the
    whole world. Throughout the world, oppressive regimes are being uprooted and re-
    placed by budding democracies, but one exception remains: The People's Republic of
    North Korea. The Kim family has clung to power for three generations by silencing
    dissidents, ruling with an iron fist, and holding its neighbors hostage with threats
    of war. Under the leadership of Kim Jong Un, North Korea has come closer than
    ever to creating a viable nuclear arsenal, but widespread famine and growing resis-
    tance are weakening his regime's stability. In *The Hermit King*, Asian geopolitical
    expert Chung Min Lee tells the story of the rise of the Kim Dynasty and its atroc-
    ities, motivations, and diplomatic goals. He also discusses the possible outcomes of
    its aggressive standoff with the world superpowers. Kim Jong Un is not a crazed
    "Rocket Man" or a bumbling despot; he has been groomed since birth to take con-
    trol of his country and stay in power at all costs. He is now at a fateful crossroads.
    Will he make good on decades of threats, liberalize North Korea and gain inter-
    national legitimacy, or watch his regime crumble around him? Lee analyzes the
    likelihood and consequences of each of these possibilities, cautioning that in the
    end, a humanitarian crisis in the region is all but unavoidable. *The Hermit King* is
    a thoughtful and compelling look at the most complicated diplomatic situation on
    Earth."—Provided by publisher.
Identifiers: LCCN 2019021478 | ISBN 9781250202826 (hardcover) |
    ISBN 9781250202833 (ebook)
Subjects: LCSH: Korea (North)—Foreign relations—21st century. | Korea
    (North)—Politics and government—2011- | Korea (North)—History. |
    Kim, Chŏng-ŭn, 1984- | Kim, Chŏng-il, 1942-2011. | Dictators—Korea
    (North)—Biography.
Classification: LCC DS935.7778 .L44 2019 | DDC 951.93—dc23
LC record available at https://lccn.loc.gov/2019021478

Our books may be purchased in bulk for promotional, educational, or business use. Please contact your local bookseller or the Macmillan Corporate and Premium Sales Department at 1-800-221-7945, extension 5442, or by email at MacmillanSpecialMarkets@macmillan.com.

First Edition: November 2019

10 9 8 7 6 5 4 3 2 1

CONTENTS

LIST OF MAPS, FIGURES, AND TABLES

AUTHOR'S NOTE

Through *The Hermit King* I want the American public to understand that the North Korean story isn't just about nuclear weapons and long-range missiles that could potentially target the United States. It's about 25 million people incarcerated in the world's biggest jail: the Democratic People's Republic of Korea (DPRK). *The Hermit King* is about the wrenching dilemma facing Kim Jong Un: he badly wants to transform North Korea, but he can't, because the very system that created him—a communist state/family dictatorship hybrid that resembles an enormous Mafia enterprise—will die if he tries to reform it. At its heart, Kim's Catch-22 is simple: if he really wants to save the North Korean state, he has no choice but to enact wide-ranging economic and political reforms. Yet the moment he does so, the Kim dynasty is likely to collapse.

North Koreans from all walks of life are struggling to an extent not paralleled anywhere else, although the Kim Jong Un regime insists that its citizens are living in Earth's paradise. The world's last totalitarian state continues to be ruled by the Kim dynasty; a "people's power" uprising isn't around the corner. But seeds of change have been planted, and one day those seeds will grow into trees throughout the country that North Koreans can lean on as free men and women.

The Korean Peninsula is a land of stark contrasts. A famous picture taken from space shows the southern half ablaze in light while the northern half lies in pitch darkness. One day, many in both South and North Korea hope, the entire peninsula will be free from tyranny.

I was born in South Korea, but I have lived in ten countries since the age of four and have devoted my professional life to studying international affairs. As a political scientist, I've been privileged to observe Korea from Asian, American, and European perspectives, varied and wide-ranging as they are. Having worked at think tanks and universities in the United States, South Korea, Japan, and Singapore for thirty-four years, I've analyzed North Korea from multiple angles. My governmental experiences as South Korea's ambassador for national security affairs and as a foreign policy advisor to two South Korean presidents have also given me key insights.

There's no single school of thought on North Korea, and my perspective is one of many. Understanding North Korea depends on which lens you choose: a small nation standing up to giants, immensely powerful ethnocentrism, seven decades of socialism and mind-numbing political indoctrination, an intense love-hate relationship with China, or deeply rooted mistrust of the outside world mixed with the realization of the country's stark backwardness. The net result is an extremely impoverished country that has successfully developed nuclear weapons and other weapons of mass destruction (WMD). And its leader isn't deranged: Kim Jong Un is ruthless and sharp.

I've studied Korean security for more than thirty years, and my interactions with government officials, intelligence experts, and political analysts with direct experience in North Korean affairs stretch back to the late 1980s; many have of them shared their views in confidence with me as I was writing this book. North Korea is a hard target, as intelligence experts like to say, but it's not a total black box. While the regime remains firmly in control, more and more information is seeping out.

North Korea tries to exude a sense of mystery and plays its limited cards deftly. However, North Korea is breaking down in slow motion, choking on the fumes coming from its vast war machine. Kim Jong Un instinctively knows this, but he can't dismantle that machine, because that would also demolish the very mechanism that props up the Kim family.

Many North Korea watchers argue that Kim is going to follow China's path of structural economic reform; they see him as having no choice, since the economy continues to contract. They insist that since at present roughly 20 percent of GDP is allocated to defense, the only way Kim can dream of building a modern North Korea is by cutting military spending. The North Korean reformist school in South Korea and elsewhere believes that Kim Jong Un will be compelled to open up North Korea, much as Mikhail Gorbachev did with the Soviet Union beginning in 1985.

Only time will tell. But North Korea is nothing like the former Soviet Union, or any other prior or surviving communist state. It is, first and foremost, a family-run criminal cartel based on myopic delusions of grandeur and a belief in ethnic supremacy; that cartel helms a country with a massive army and nuclear weapons. Over time, however, a system characterized by multiple contradictions, massive corruption, corrosion in all institutions, fear and repression, and above all a ruling family and a super-elite who live like millionaires while the masses must fend for themselves can't last.

My ninety-two-year-old soldier-turned-diplomat father originally hailed from Anju, North Korea, and all of the events described in this book occurred during his lifetime. He lived through some of the more harrowing moments: the Soviet occupation of northern Korea, the division of the peninsula into the two Koreas, the outbreak of the Korean War, and diplomatic struggles between Seoul and Pyongyang during the Cold War. It is fitting that I continue the journey he began on foot in 1949 when he crossed the 38th parallel into the Republic of Korea as a penniless twenty-two-year-old.

NOTE ON KOREAN NAMES

This book uses the AP method in romanizing Korean names. For South Koreans, a hyphen is used between the first and middle names with the surname in front, that is, Park Chung-hee. Exceptions are made for those who prefer or preferred their own styles, such as Syngmann Rhee, South Korea's first president. For North Koreans, there is no hyphen between the first and middle names, that is, Kim Yo Jong, although names of North Korean officials contain hyphens in South Korean or other foreign sources. The transliteration of Korean names and places is based on the South Korean Ministry of Culture's guidelines issued in 2001, although other styles are used when they appear in original sources.

THE HERMIT
KING

INTRODUCTION

In February 2018, Kim Yo Jong, Kim Jong Un's only sister, stepped off Kim Jong Un's personal plane at Incheon Airport, outside Seoul. She had come to South Korea to participate in the opening ceremony of the 2018 Winter Olympic Games, held in Pyeongchang. Yo Jong was the first member of the Kim family to set foot in Seoul in sixty-eight years, since the outbreak of the Korean War. Her visit lasted only two days, but Korean and foreign media recorded every moment of her public appearances, including her handshake with President Moon Jae-in. The visit was a masterly display of public diplomacy, North Korean style, as will be explored at greater length in Chapter Three. Yet not even such a vivid, well-choreographed exhibition can hide the existence of the intense political-military struggle going on between the two Koreas.

South and North Korea have been locked in a deadly stand-off since the end of the Korean War. For sixty-six years, armed forces have been deployed along the 38th parallel, which cuts across the peninsula. When Kim Il Sung—the founding dictator of North Korea and Kim Jong Un's grandfather—failed to unify the peninsula by force, he resorted to guerrilla attacks, assassinations, and sabotage. His son Kim Jong Il masterminded the bombing of the Korean Air Lines jet in November 1987 that killed 115 passengers and crew members, as well as the bombing of President Chun Doo-hwan's entourage in Rangoon, Burma, that killed eighteen South Korean officials in 1983.

With more than 1.2 million troops, the Korean People's Army (KPA) is one of the most heavily armed militaries in the world. Because of the backwardness of the North Korean economy, the KPA is not as modernized as South Korea's 625,000-strong forces. Moreover, 28,000 American troops—the U.S. Forces Korea (USFK)—continue to be deployed in South Korea as a symbol of America's commitment to the South's defense. Still, since Seoul's ten million inhabitants live only 50 kilometers from the demilitarized zone (DMZ) that divides the two Koreas, North Korea has a geographic advantage if it wants to start another war.

In the fall of 2017, North Korea's Supreme Leader, Kim Jong Un, and U.S. president Donald Trump were exchanging increasingly harsh rhetoric. Kim had tested a thermonuclear bomb in September of that year and threatened to blast the United States if pressured. Trump retorted that his nuclear button was much larger than Kim's.

"This is what I have for Kim," Trump apparently said about Kim at the height of tensions between the United States and North Korea in October 2017, pointing to the "nuclear football"—the briefcase with the nuclear codes that always follows the president.[1] Given his tendency toward bravado and knee-jerk remarks, Trump was probably just venting his frustrations at Kim. But this episode illustrates the powder-keg nature of tensions on the Korean Peninsula.

Kim Yo Jong's visit to the South in February 2018 was designed to buy breathing room for Kim Jong Un, since he was in no position to begin a suicidal war. After ratcheting up tensions throughout 2017, Kim realized that if he played his cards right, he just might be able to get relief from international sanctions, which, while first imposed in 2006, had been crippling his country in earnest since 2016. South Korean president Moon Jae-in, who catapulted into office in May 2017 after the impeachment of former president Park Geun-hye, was more than willing to accommodate Kim's peace overtures. And Yo Jong was the perfect choice to make that first trip to the South. She and Kim Jong Un are portrayed as the young and dynamic brother-sister duo determined to modernize their backward country.

Prior to her meeting with President Moon in the Blue House (the president's office), Yo Jong wrote in the visitors' book, "I hope that in their hearts our people in Pyongyang and Seoul will become closer and that a prosperous future of unification can be expedited." It was signed, "Kim Yo Jong, High Level Delegation, Democratic People's Republic of Korea."

When Kim Jong Un made an unprecedented visit to Panmunjom, on the South Korean side, on April 27, 2018, Yo Jong was at his side. During his first meeting with U.S. president Donald Trump in Singapore on June 18, 2018, she was with him. She also joined her brother during his second meeting with Trump, in Hanoi on February 27–28, 2019. Although the South Korean press focused on her elegant demeanor, they were totally missing the point. Kim Yo Jong isn't merely a pretty face supporting her brother. She is an indispensable enforcer deeply integrated into the North Korean power structure.

More than anyone else in North Korea, Kim Yo Jong understands that serving the Supreme Leader comes with huge responsibilities and potential dangers. Her father's younger sister, Kim Kyong Hui, married her college sweetheart, Jang Song Thaek.

Kim Jong Il, the Great Leader, who was groomed as Kim Il Sung's successor beginning in the early 1970s, formally assumed power in 1994. Even though Jang was sent to reeducation camps intermittently to keep him in his place, he was one of Kim Jong Il's most trusted aides. Especially after Kim Jong Il suffered a debilitating stroke in 2008, Jang served as the gatekeeper. Most importantly, he was instrumental in ensuring Kim Jong Un's rise to power in 2011.

On December 12, 2013, however, Jang was accused of high treason and every other imaginable crime against Kim Jong Un and North Korea. Handcuffed and held by two armed guards, Jang was sentenced by a military tribunal and executed immediately by antiaircraft guns. The de facto number two under Kim Jong Il's reign was killed as soon as Kim Jong Un felt comfortable with his grip on power.

Four years later, on February 13, 2017, Kim Jong Un's older half-brother, Kim Jong Nam, was poisoned at Kuala Lumpur International Airport. The once heir-apparent Number One Son, who had lived in exile since 2001, died minutes after drops of the deadly nerve agent VX were applied to his face by two women trained by North Korean agents.

As gruesome as such killings are, they're not all that uncommon in dictatorships. What is important, however, is that Kim Jong Un is highly unlikely to have made such a momentous decision without involving his sister. Kim Yo Jong understands that even bloodlines are no guarantee of survival in North Korea's Game of Thrones.

This fact lies at the very heart of understanding North Korea under Kim Jong Un. High officials in the Moon administration believe that Kim is fundamentally different from his father and grandfather. Educated partially in Switzerland, Kim is more urbane, comfortable in his own skin, and supremely confident. He knows more about the outside world than the previous Great

Leaders—he apparently is fond of Swiss cheese, foie gras, and very expensive wines, and he is a basketball fan, as the South Korean and some foreign press like to emphasize. But that's not why Kim is holding on to power.

Kim Jong Un is a product not only of the Kim family dictatorship but also of a brutal political system. He was determined never to let his older half-brother become the next ruler, and fought mercilessly to become his father's successor. Kim's most important goal is to guarantee his hold on power and perpetuate the Kim dynasty; all else remains secondary. He knows that to do this he has to feed his lieutenants with hard currency and incentives; he must ensure that each accrues just enough power to balance, and if necessary destroy, other power brokers.

One of the errors many analysts make is mirror imaging—the belief that whomever you're trying to understand must share some traits with you. Many North Korea observers believe that because Kim Jong Un desperately wants to make North Korea into a modern economy and join the twenty-first century, he has no choice but to implement reforms. They think that because Kim invests so much money in defense—about 20 to 25 percent of GDP—he will reallocate scarce resources from the military into the economic sector.

There is every indication that Kim wants to modernize North Korea. The state economy collapsed in the mid-1990s during the great famine that killed as many as 1.5 million North Koreans. The *jangmadang*, or free markets, that have sprung up across North Korea are the de facto economy. Kim has legalized them because there is no viable alternative. Visitors to Pyongyang have noticed growing traffic jams, greater attention to fashion, people talking on cell phones, and taxis picking up customers. There are fast-food restaurants that serve North Korean versions of pizza and hamburgers. The city's apartment buildings have gotten fresh paint jobs. But the moment he crosses the Rubicon and allows structural economic reforms, as China and Vietnam have done, Kim enters a no-man's-land. The primordial dilemma for Kim is that in order to save the North Korean state, he has to reform the system, but the moment he reforms the system, the regime runs the risk of collapsing.

"We should properly plan and thoroughly implement the national operations aimed at maintaining, reinforcing, and re-engineering the national economy as a whole," said Kim during his New Year's speech in January 2019.[2] If China did it, why not North Korea? Why can't North Korea emulate Vietnam? These are fundamental questions.

When China embarked on economic reforms in 1978, Deng Xiaoping was able to do so because of the abject failure of Mao's social, political, and economic policies. The disastrous Great Leap Forward (1958–1962) and the Cultural Revolution (1966–1976) not only bankrupted China economically but set it back two generations. Deng embarked on reforms because China had no choice, but also because he wasn't tied to Mao Zedong's gargantuan failures. Kim Jong Un doesn't have that luxury, since the hand that he was dealt came from his father and grandfather.

Vietnamese analyst Huong Le Thu, based at the Australian Strategic Policy Institute, remarked that there are major differences between North Korea and Vietnam, including the power structure, despite the fact that they're characterized as communist regimes. "While North Korea is run in a dynastic manner, the VCP [Vietnamese Communist Party] has been faithful to the institutionalized collective leadership. There has never been a dynastic succession of power in Vietnam, and in fact, even the most charismatic leader of the party and its founder—Ho Chi Minh—revered as the founding father of independent Vietnam, never enjoyed such absolute power within the party as fellow communist leaders: the Kim family, Mao Zedong, or Josef Stalin in their respected parties."[3]

Since early 2018, Kim has entered the world at a furious pace. He met with South Korean president Moon Jae-in for three summits, in April, May, and September 2018. For the first time, Kim sat with a U.S. president, in Singapore in June 2018. Regardless of Donald Trump's clumsy diplomacy and his penchant for the limelight, he did what no other U.S. leader had done: He met face-to-face with a North Korean leader.

Trump pushed the envelope when he shook Kim's hand for the third time on June 29, 2019, at the 38th parallel. Both Kim and Trump are reality TV stars who share a yearning for the limelight and constant reaffirmation of their "genius" leadership skills. After the failed second U.S.–North Korea summit in Hanoi in February 2019, Trump and Kim needed fresh momentum to keep their reality TV show running. No one knows what a final agreement will entail, but all Kim and Trump need to do is to push denuclearization under the carpet in the guise of a nuclear weapons freeze agreement.

Chinese president Xi Jinping didn't allow Kim to visit Beijing until March 2018. Xi was upset that Kim continued to test nuclear weapons, including detonating a thermonuclear bomb in September 2017. It was essential for Kim Jong Un's legitimacy, however, to be officially blessed by President Xi. For the second summit with Trump in Hanoi in February 2019, Kim traveled sixty hours by train from Pyongyang through China and finally to Vietnam. Although he left empty-handed, that meeting also shifted Kim's international status, moving him away from being considered a pariah and toward being thought of as a young leader in a hurry. Kim had his first meeting with Russian president Vladimir Putin in Vladivostok on April 25, 2019.

The major stumbling block to normalized relations between the United States and North Korea is Pyongyang's nuclear weapons program. Estimates vary, but North Korea is thought to have between thirty and sixty nuclear warheads, with the ability to build three to five additional warheads annually. Ever since the first North Korean nuclear crisis erupted in 1993 when North Korea threatened to remove itself from the Nuclear Non-Proliferation Treaty (NPT)—which it subsequently did—all diplomatic efforts have failed to prevent North Korea from developing nuclear weapons.

As important as nuclear weapons are, however, other threats remain. North Korea has more than a thousand ballistic missiles, including intercontinental ballistic missiles (ICBMs) and submarine-launched ballistic missiles. It has chemical and biological weapons, and it is increasingly adroit at launching cyberattacks.

Can Kim Jong Un afford to give up nuclear weapons? The short answer is no. There are many, including those in the South Korean government today, who believe that Kim is committed to denuclearization. As Trump found out in Hanoi, however, North Korea's definition of denuclearization doesn't coincide with America's. Washington wants the total dismantling and destruction of all nuclear weapons. Pyongyang wants a phased reduction, and only after the U.S. nuclear umbrella over South Korea is removed—in other words, it really doesn't want to denuclearize at all.

The North Korean imbroglio is going to continue. There will continue to be high-level talks between the two Koreas and between the United States and North Korea. Given Kim's affection for showmanship, one can't rule out a trip to Seoul, but he will only do so when he is sure of getting major compromises and incentives from South Korea. And Kim's ultimate diplomatic prize would be an invitation to Washington, D.C., to ink a nuclear freeze accord.

The second U.S.–North Korea summit in Hanoi ended abruptly. Trump said that he had no choice but to walk away rather than sign a bad deal. The U.S. president was deeply disappointed because he thought he could charm Kim into giving up his nuclear weapons, and he badly needs a major foreign policy victory going into the 2020 presidential election. Kim isn't a seasoned leader, but he knows that without nuclear weapons, North Korea would not pose an existential threat to South Korea, Japan, or the United States.

Ultimately, "Mission: Impossible" best characterizes what Kim Jong Un wants to achieve: modernizing North Korea, without damaging his family-run dictatorship; luring South Korean investment and hard-currency earnings on the promise of greater inter-Korean exchange, without undertaking fundamental economic reforms; emulating his only patron, China, without making North Korea totally dependent on China; drawing South Korea much more closely into its orbit, without offering reciprocal measures; and normalizing relations with the United States, even while retaining his weapons of mass destruction.

He has, for now, a willing partner in President Moon, who also wants to ensure that the peace train remains on schedule. Kim is betting that despite Trump's rhetoric of never giving in to North Korea's nuclear blackmail, Trump will ultimately be tempted to go down in history as the president who brought lasting peace to the Korean Peninsula. Still, despite the seeming convergence of political interests between Kim, Moon, and Trump, a fundamental remaking of the Korean Peninsula can happen only if Kim Jong Un makes a strategic decision to save North Korea by dismantling the Kim dynasty. So long as he remains in power, however, Kim will never make that choice.

ONE

LIFE IN EARTH'S PARADISE

The Land of Avatars

Whenever a North Korean is asked by a foreign journalist or visitor what life is like inside North Korea, the reply is that the country's citizens live in an earthly paradise for one reason: the care given to them by the Supreme Leader. He is their father and provider. They lack for nothing, nor do they desire anything else. The Supreme Leader makes sure they are totally happy. Just like the Heavenly Father in Christianity, it is the living head of the Kim family that makes everything possible in North Korea.

This is a total lie. Except for the super-elites who are bound inextricably with the regime, including the crème de la crème of the party, armed forces, security agencies, and hard-currency-making enterprises, the vast majority of North Koreans must fend for themselves.

Life was not always like this in North Korea. While it's

impossible to imagine today, North Korea had a higher GDP than South Korea until the early 1970s. In 2017, South Korea's GDP was $1.5 trillion, whereas North Korea's was $33 billion; per capita GDP was $30,000 and $1,300, respectively.[1]

Still, North Koreans are routinely told that South Korea is filled with beggars and only a tiny percentage of corrupt capitalists live well; the rest of the population ekes out the barest of livings in squalid conditions. Because the country is a stooge of the American imperialists, South Korean women are constantly raped by American soldiers, Pyongyang's propagandists claim, and the people are yearning for liberation by North Korea. Even the government-funded Russian international television network RT, which has prided itself as a mouthpiece of the Putin regime, believes that North Korean propaganda has gone a step too far. A 2017 RT documentary called *The Happiest People on Earth: North Korea: The Rulers, the People and the Official Narrative* offers the outside world a peek into the nation.[2]

A factory manager recounts her emotions when Kim Jong Un made an on-site inspection visit in January 2016. "When the Great Marshal Kim Jong Un opened the doors and walked in, we beheld his sun-like image. It was like a dream, as if I was the only one who enjoyed this great honor." She continues with a straight face, "The entire factory and workshop filled with sunlight when the Great Marshal arrived!"

The film crew captures a scene of students studying in the famous Kim Chaek University of Technology. Since most North Korean men have to spend ten years in the army before they can enroll at a university, male students at Kim Chaek are typically in their late twenties or early thirties. One student says, "Thanks to the Great Leader and the Marshal General's revolutionary course, our country became the strongest country in the world!"

With a big smile, the student goes on to say, "All stooges who dare attack our sovereignty are our enemies."

Each year the nation busies itself preparing for the celebration of Kim Il Sung's birthday on April 15, called the Day of the Sun. The film crew captured citizens gathering in a plaza to pledge their loyalty to Kim Il Sung and Kim Jong Il. After they take their vows, first-grade children goose-step to martial music, and the child leading the formation raises her right arm in a 45-degree salute, just like the goose-stepping members of the armed forces.

A middle-school orphanage official tells the film crew that the Great Marshal Kim Jong Un spent two hours visiting the school. In the entrance, you see a giant mural depicting the floor plan of the orphanage. The point where Kim began his inspection is marked with a red star, and his footsteps are marked in red arrows. An entire room is devoted to pictures and relics of his visit. The red and yellow blanket that Kim touched and the white chair with a blue cushion he sat in are boxed in glass. Everything he touches is preserved as a holy remnant, just as was done with anything his father or grandfather touched.

This is how the state wants to portray the average North Korean: filled with undying love for the Kim family, finding truth only in the teachings of Kim Il Sung and Kim Jong Il, and receiving guidance in everything from the current Supreme Leader, Kim Jong Un.

The truth is, every North Korean has an avatar, because how the avatar behaves can mean the difference between life and death.

The avatar is for public consumption—what is shown to most friends, relatives, and co-workers. A North Korean can show his or her innermost secrets to just a handful of people, perhaps immediate family members, trustworthy relatives, and best friends who have committed a common crime—like watching a South Korean movie.

The dark side of North Korea, the state argues, is simply "fake news": conjured up by the capitalist West and enemies of the state. But right beneath the veneer of 25 million smiling North Koreans lies a darkness that fills every square meter of the DPRK.

There are at least four gulags in North Korea where between 200,000 and 300,000 political prisoners and their families are held. Officially the state says there are no political prisoners. Ahn Myong Chol was a guard in Camp 22 (no longer in operation) and one of the few guards who escaped to South Korea. He was trained to see prisoners not as human beings but as animals. In fact, prisoners got smaller rations than the dogs reared by guards.

"Prisoners shouldn't make eye contact with instructors," recalls Ahn ("instructor" is the euphemism used in the camps for guards). "If they do or look up, they will, again, be beaten but that isn't always the case. Depending on the day's mood, you can make up pretexts and be harsher on them."[3]

Camp 22 was a gulag for family members of those who had committed offenses. The individuals who were directly responsible were sent to even more dismal camps, like Camp 15 in Yodok. There prisoners died regularly, from forced labor, starvation, disease, torture, beating, or execution. In North Korea, families and relatives of political prisoners are also shipped off to be punished for crimes by association. If your cousin defects to the South, for example, not only is that person's immediate family sent to reeducation camps, prisons, or gulags, but you and other similarly distant relatives may also be caught up. If an office or factory worker is accused of a serious offense, his or her superiors and co-workers can also be carted off. Students are taught to watch their parents; they're supposed to report them for infractions or impure thoughts.

Deep inside, everyone in North Korea knows he or she must live a double life. The older a person gets, the more attention he must pay to his avatar. If he doesn't, the avatar will slip up somehow—perhaps tell a joke on a forbidden subject, tell a party apparatchik of alternative options, or simply nod off during a gathering of hundreds or even thousands of citizens.

The most serious crime a North Korean can be charged with is contravening one or more of the Ten Principles in the Establishment of the Monolithic Ideology of the Party (Table 1). Not by coincidence, these principles are like the Ten Commandments. First introduced by Kim Jong Il in 1974 just as the personality cult surrounding Kim Il Sung and the Kim family was reaching new heights, it was revised by Kim Jong Un in 2013. Every North Korean must memorize the principles and repeat them when asked.

Almost any act can be considered as violating one or more of the Ten Principles. In November 2017, the South Korean National Intelligence Service (NIS) reported to the National Assembly's Intelligence Oversight Committee that several members of the North Korean party daily newspaper *Rodong Sinmun* had been "revolutionized" (that is, reeducated) for not putting a story about the successful testing of a ballistic missile on the front page.[4] If Kim Jong Un saw that an official didn't write down his every word or if someone didn't bow her head to 45 degrees in front of his grandfather's or father's statue, that could be interpreted as going against one of the Ten Principles.

In his documentary *Under the Sun* (2015), Russian director Vitaly Mansky's goal was to provide the world with a glimpse of the life of an ordinary North Korean schoolchild, eight-year-old Ri Zin Mi. The North Korean government allowed only Mansky, his cinematographer, Alexandria Ivanova, and a sound assistant into Pyongyang, and Mansky was obliged to shoot just scripted scenes prepared by North Korean handlers. Unbeknownst to the North Koreans, however, the sound assistant was a Russian who was fluent in Korean, and Mansky left his cameras running all the time, not just during the scripted scenes. According to the *Los Angeles Times*, "At the end of each day, the North Koreans would go through the day's shoot, but in a risky move, in a country where foreigners who act out sometimes spend years in jail, the crew kept duplicate memory cards of all footage, that they then snuck out of North Korea."[5] Throughout Mansky's finished movie, one can hear North Korean handlers who shout "Action!" and then "Cut!"

In the film, Zin Mi is shown right before she joins the Children's Union on the Day of the Shining Star (the late Kim Jong Il's birthday), one of the holiest days in North Korea. The camera zooms in on her classroom. She is dressed in a well-pressed blue Mao suit. That day's lesson is about the anti-Japanese and anti-imperialist struggles of the Great Leader, Kim Il Sung.

"What did the Generalissimo Great Leader Kim Il Sung teach us about the wretched Japanese?" asks the teacher. All the students raise their right arm at a 90-degree angle with their left arm across their chest, a signal that they want to answer.

"To remember how much they mistreated the Korean people!" says one student.

"Yes, that's right!" the teacher responds.

From nursery school on, North Korean children are taught to worship the Supreme Leader and the two former Great Leaders. They sing songs praising the Kims' leadership, although at that age they don't have the faintest clue what they are singing about.

Zin Mi's father, in real life, is a print journalist. For the party handlers who were responsible for the film shoot, however, a print journalist was deemed too low in the social hierarchy, so they made him into an engineer at an exemplary garment factory. Her mother, who works in a cafeteria, is instead shown as working in a model soy milk factory. Of course, the three of them are shown living in a very nice apartment, one that Mansky was not sure actually belonged to them. In a scene in which the family sits

TABLE 1
NORTH KOREA'S TEN COMMANDMENTS

1. Fight, with all your strength, to make the whole society the Kimilsung-Kimjongilist one.

2. Venerate the Great respected comrades Kim Il Sung and Kim Jong Il as the Great Leaders of the Party and of the People, as the Eternal Suns of Juche.

3. Make the authority of the respected comrades Kim Il Sung and Kim Jong Il and of the Party the absolute one. Be ready to defend them.

4. Arm yourself with revolutionary ideas of the Great respected comrades Kim Il Sung and Kim Jong Il and with the fulfillment of their ideas: the line and the policy of the Party.

5. Defend the principle following unconditionally the commandments of the Great respected comrades Kim Il Sung and Kim Jong Il as well as Party line and its policy.

6. Reinforce further the ideological willful and revolutionary unity of the whole Party around the figure of its Leader(s).

7. Learn after the Great respected comrades Kim Il Sung and Kim Jong Il, have a high moral and ethical image, use the revolutionary methods of action and the people's model of action.

8. Venerate the political aspect of life, bestowed by the Leader and by the Party, respond to it by having a high political consciousness and real successes in doing your job.

9. Establish a strict organizational discipline in a wholehearted movement of the whole Party, whole state, and whole army under the Party's sole leadership.

10. Inherit and fulfill the great deed of the Juche revolution, the great deed of the *Songun* revolution, started by the Great Leader respected comrade Kim Il Sung, and guided by the Great respected comrades Kim Il Sung and Kim Jong Il, which continues from generation to generation.[6]

down for breakfast on the heated floor, as is customary in Korea, Mansky shows the family being made to run through their lines several times, in an effort to sound as natural as possible, before the final take is approved.

"Zin Mi, you must eat a lot of kimchi because it is our national food," her father instructs. "And if you eat kimchi daily, it provides you with half the daily intake of vitamins."

"Yes!" replies Zin Mi. "If I eat kimchi, it also prevents aging and cancer!" Her father praises her knowledge.

Once this scene was completed, the camera shows the family moving the dining table back to the kitchen. It is full of foods that average North Koreans will never see in their daily lives: scrambled eggs, beef sausages, white rice, cooked vegetables, beef broth soup, and sweet rice cakes.

In another staged scene, the camera focuses on Zin Mi's mother, who is standing in line with her co-workers (whom, in reality, she had never met before). The script has an official telling the assembled workers to congratulate Zin Mi's mother because her daughter has joined the Children's Union. Mansky films the handler saying, "Try not to think about the camera. Can you do that?" But the eight women workers and their supervisor look anything but natural. "Everyone smile when the comrade speaks to you!" they're told.

At the end of the movie, Zin Mi is asked for her thoughts about joining the Children's Union. Instinctively, she delves into a self-criticism session: she decries her shortcomings and promises to work harder for the Great Leader, tears flowing down her cheeks. The handlers can be heard saying, "Calm her down. Tell her everything will be all right."

"Try to think of something good," one suggests to her.

"Like what?" Zin Mi replies sadly.

Eventually the handlers ask her to recite a poem, and after wiping away her tears, Zin Mi is back on track:

Founded by Great Leader Kim Il Sung,
Kindled by Great Brilliant Commander Kim Jong Il,
Led by Respected Leader Kim Jong Un,
I joined the glorious Children's Union and swear,
Always and everywhere,
To think and act in the spirit of the Great Generalissimos
And the teachings of Respected Leader Kim Jong Un
In order to become a reliable reservist of the
Revolutionary Juche movement for the building of Communism
Continuing from generation to generation,
I swear!

Mansky later recalled to an interviewer that he had filmed children all over the world, and all of the children had one thing in common: they were curious and always asked him questions. Except Zin Mi. "Throughout the whole shoot, Zin Mi never once looked at herself in the camera, and never once asked a question," Mansky said. "It was like something out of science fiction."[7]

When the movie was released to critical acclaim, North Korea lodged a formal protest with the Russian foreign ministry, and the North Korean propaganda machinery went into damage-containment mode. The Ri family were trotted out and swore that it was Mansky who had made them act out the scenes. They said they followed his orders only because they thought the documentary was being made in order to enhance cultural exchanges.

Most disturbing, perhaps, is Mansky's suspicion that Zin Mi's family didn't actually live together. "I saw that women work and live at factories, children go to school and live at some sort of boarding school . . . and I have never seen a family walking down the street—mother, father, and a child—never. Only our family was walking down the streets together, for filming."[8]

North Korean media subsequently reported that Zin Mi presented a flower to Kim Jong Un to allay suspicions that she might have been harmed. Still, Mansky says the fate of Zin Mi will "always be a weight on my heart."[9]

Defectors' Stories

Some thirty thousand North Korean defectors live in South Korea. Tens of thousands more are in hiding in China and parts of Southeast Asia. All of them risked their lives to escape North Korea. Crossing the shallow Amrok River (in China called the Yalu River) is the main way to escape North Korea. Brokers smuggle escapees into China, and the lucky ones make it to South Korea. Many North Korean women are sold into prostitution when they arrive in China as the price of leaving the country. China cracks down on North Korean refugees, and if they are caught, they're almost always repatriated to North Korea.

An escapee who is forcibly returned to North Korea faces imprisonment and beatings, is sent to a reeducation camp, or, in the worst case, is executed. Because corruption is so rampant, some are released early after their families pay bribes. In fact, those who have hard currency can pretty much bribe their way through most situations.

Despite the information blockade, many North Koreans know something about their prosperous and free cousins in the South. Most North Koreans have surreptitiously watched South Korean TV. North Korean defectors only learned about the reality of everyday life in South Korea once they got to Seoul. In the beginning, many wondered if the buildings, avenues, and cars were all part of a huge movie set.

The harrowing stories of defectors offer unique insights into North Korea. Safe in the South, the defectors no longer have to act like avatars. Their accounts peel away the fabric of lies put out by North Korea.

Many of the defectors have thrived in South Korea; a large

number also feel like second-class citizens. The younger ones adjust most rapidly, since they go to school and learn to speak in the Seoul dialect; older defectors are instantly identified because of their Pyongyang accent.

One of the biggest problems defectors face is adapting to South Korea's super-competitive culture. In South Korea, *pali, pali* (fast, fast) is a fact of daily life. People who order food in a restaurant expect it to arrive in minutes. In the super-connected world that is modern South Korea, everything can be delivered quickly. You want to establish cable service in your home? It's done within hours of your call. You want to get new prescription glasses? Less than an hour.

South Korea's winner-take-all culture and very strong work ethic enabled it to emerge from the ashes of the Korean War to become the world's eleventh-largest economy within the span of two generations. The social price for this has been very high, however. Among the OECD countries, South Korea has the highest suicide rates for teenagers and for men over age sixty-five. Making it to the top in South Korea involves intense competition and requires money and parental sacrifice.

For North Koreans living in the South, just surviving in this environment is hugely challenging. Moreover, they are largely on their own, unlike in the North, where the party is omnipresent. From birth, North Koreans are told what they can and cannot do. All jobs are assigned by the party. University exams? Only those from certain *songbun* (essentially, castes based on a family's political, social, and economic background; see Chapter Two) can take the exams.

Those who had full careers in the North find life in South Korea very difficult. Integrating themselves into South Korea's intensely networked and very competitive organizational culture is nearly impossible. A former North Korean policeman laments his life in South Korea, where he now works as a construction worker. In North Korea, he says, he was feared but also respected.

A very small number of North Korean defectors have opted to return to the North. One of them is Lim Ji-hyun (known as Jeon Hye Sung in North Korea), who, after her initial defection to the South in 2014, gained fame through South Korean reality and talk shows. In July 2017, however, a videotaped interview of Lim appeared on a North Korean government-run propaganda website. "Every single day of my life in the South was a hell," said Lim. "When I was alone in a dark, cold room, I was heartbroken and I wept every day, missing my fatherland and my parents back home."[10] The South Korean government was unsure if she chose to go back or if she returned because the authorities threatened her family.

Another North Korean defector, Kim Ryen Hi, applied for political asylum in the Vietnamese embassy in Seoul in March 2016, asking for Vietnam's help in returning to North Korea. She said that she had come to the South by mistake: on a trip to China in 2011, she claimed, she had met smugglers who told her that she could make money in South Korea and then return to the North.[11]

Defectors' stories are critical in putting together the pieces of the North Korean puzzle. Yet corroborating defectors' testimonies isn't easy. Many tell South Korean officials what they want to hear. Shin Dong-hyuk, the subject of Blaine Harden's best-seller *Escape from Camp 14*, said that he was tortured and that he watched his mother's and brother's execution in a prison camp. He also said that he was born in the camp. In 2015, however, "he admitted he left out some key parts of the story—like the fact that he spent most of his childhood across the Taedong river in Camp 18, a less draconian prison (although in North Korea, that's a matter of degree). But, he says, the torture he described to Harden all happened, just in a different place and at a different time."[12]

What is unmistakable is the thousands of voices that illustrate the brutal and dark side of everyday life in North Korea. Hye-sonseo Lee, who wrote *The Girl with Seven Names*, escaped from

North Korea in 2006 and has been active in helping to direct the world's attention to the plight of North Koreans. "I want to establish a foundation that will help North Koreans not just now but over the longer term," Lee said. "And it's so important for South Koreans to understand the brutal conditions in the North."[13]

In a widely viewed TED Talk in April 2014, Lee recounted how, after her own escape, she helped her family leave North Korea:

> I took a flight back to China and headed toward the North Korean border. Since my family couldn't speak Chinese, I had to guide them somehow through more than 2,000 miles in China, and then into Southeast Asia. The journey by bus took one week, and we were almost caught several times. One time, our bus was stopped and boarded by a Chinese police officer. He took everyone's ID cards, and he started asking them questions. Since my family couldn't understand Chinese, I thought my family was going to be arrested. As the Chinese officer approached my family, I impulsively stood up, and I told him that these are deaf and dumb people that I was chaperoning. He looked at me suspiciously, but luckily, he believed me.[14]

Lee Hark-joon is a South Korean journalist for the *Chosun Ilbo*, South Korea's largest and most influential newspaper. Lee wrote a landmark book on the journey of North Korean refugees, called *Crossing Heaven's Border*. Lee is also the only journalist who has embedded himself with escapees—he joined a group of North Koreans who walked through China and into Laos.

"I was so worried that someone in the group may not be able to make it but I was sure of myself as I had completed my military service," Lee said. "Surprisingly, I was the one who began to fall behind. The North Koreans' passion for life and freedom helped them overcome their age and physical disadvantages. I was holding the group back so I asked them to leave me and go on. For them, being captured could lead to their repatriation to North Korea, but for me, my punishment would just be spending some time in a Chinese prison."[15]

Among the many journalists who have covered North Korea, Anna Fifield of the *Washington Post* stands out. Based in Seoul, Tokyo, and now Beijing, Fifield has spent more than fifteen years covering North Korea and has made seven visits to Pyongyang. Author of *The Great Successor*—an in-depth look at the evolution of Kim Jong Un—Fifield authored an award-winning piece for the *Washington Post* called "Life Under Kim Jong Un" in November 2017. "Increasingly, North Koreans are not fleeing their totalitarian state because they are hungry, as they did during the 15 or so years following the outbreak of a devastating famine in the mid-1990s," wrote Fifield. "Now, they are leaving because they are disillusioned."[16]

One of the great ironies of the political left in South Korea is its near-total denial of North Korea's gross human rights violations. Like prior progressive governments such as those led by presidents Kim Dae-jung and Roh Moo-hyun, the current government of South Korean president Moon Jae-in continues to discourage North Korean defectors from speaking out about North Korea's atrocious human rights record. Extreme leftists in South Korea constantly attack nongovernmental organizations (NGOs) that attempt to shed light on North Korea's brutal regime. At the same time, the South Korean left, including members of the Moon administration, attack any human rights infractions in the South itself.

Kim Seong-min, head of Free North Korea Radio, is a leading defector who has devoted his life to spreading freedom to North Koreans. When asked what he thinks compels Moon to ignore

North Korea's human rights, Kim surmises that it has to do with the South Korean government's efforts to establish peace with North Korea. Moon "is very concerned about North Korea's reactions. In order for him to achieve his goals, I think he believes there's no real need to address contentious issues."[17] But the effect is that the South Korean left has lost its moral compass when it comes to North Korea, cowering under the guise of Korean nationalism.

Thae Yong Ho, who served as deputy ambassador in North Korea's embassy in Britain, defected to South Korea in April 2016 and became the highest-ranking defector since Hwang Jang Yop, who fled North Korea in 1997. Hwang was a leading intellectual in North Korea and served in various high-level positions, including party secretary for international affairs and chairman of the Standing Committee of the Supreme People's Assembly. Thae has recounted his own story in a Korean best-seller, the title of which translates as "Thae Yong Ho's testimony: the secret code of the third-floor secretariat." In one of the most harrowing sections in his book, Thae writes about the truly evil nature of Kim Jong Un, who ordered the execution not only of his own uncle, Jang Song Thaek, but of more than fifteen government and party officials deemed close to Jang. According to Thae, some four hundred government officials and three hundred members of the armed forces were purged at the same time.[18]

In mid-November 2013, two of Jang's closest advisors, Ri Yong Ha and Jang Su Gil, were executed by a fusillade from antiaircraft guns at the Kang Kon Military Academy—the same place where Jang was killed a month later. Ri was the first vice director of the party's administrative bureau in charge of the security forces, while Jang Su Gil was believed to be a high-level official in the Ministry of People's Security (MPS).[19] According to Thae, the executions were witnessed by a number of top officials, including party secretaries and deputy secretaries and government ministers and vice ministers. A bus carrying lower-level officials who were also to witness the execution arrived as well. One of the people who got off that bus was Jang Song Thaek—which astonished many, given Jang's stature under Kim Jong Il and the fact that he was his brother-in-law.[20]

During a press conference in January 2017, Thae Yong Ho said he thought Kim Jong Un's regime wasn't likely to last all that long, since corruption and discontent within the regime itself were hampering its efforts to control information from the outside.[21] The value of Thae Yong Ho's insights into the North Korean system is somewhat limited, since he wasn't in Kim's inner circle, but he did have direct experience with how the regime functioned—or, more often, malfunctioned.

In May 2015, Thae said, he received an encrypted message from a colleague at the North Korean mission in Paris telling him to expect a very important order from the top. Several messages later, he discovered that his mission was to buy tickets for Eric Clapton's concert at Royal Albert Hall for Kim Jong Chul, Kim Jong Un's older brother.

A diehard Clapton fan and an amateur guitarist, Jong Chul had no interest in becoming Great Leader himself; his father, Kim Jong Il, had seen from a young age that Jong Chul wasn't cut out for politics. Jong Chul did, however, show total loyalty to his brother, who in return allowed him to travel the world to satisfy his musical interests.

It was clear early on that Kim Jong Un was destined to follow in his father's path, and had Jung Chul shown even the minutest of political ambitions, there would have been a major power struggle with Jong Un. So Jong Chul played it smart: as long as he was able to live the life of a prince, with all the attendant privileges but none of the political power, he had everything he needed, and more. In some ways, Jong Chul is luckier than his younger brother, who has not only the power but also the burden of ruling North Korea. As despotic as Kim Jong Un is, he is ultimately responsible for what happens in North Korea. No one will dare challenge his authority or tell him he made a mistake. Deep inside, though, Jong Un is aware of both his successes and his failures.

As Thae Yong Ho tells the story, when Kim Jong Chul landed at Heathrow Airport before the Eric Clapton concert, he was met by Thae, and Jong Chul asked to go to a specific record shop. It was late in the day, and Thae told him as politely as he could that the shop was going to be closed by the time they made it into the city. All during the journey into London Jong Chul couldn't let go of the idea, asking Thae, "If it's closed, can't you just knock on the door or call them? If a diplomat made a request, wouldn't the owner come out? You don't even have such connections?"[22]

When they arrived at the hotel, it was well past midnight, but Jong Chul wanted the trousers he was wearing to be dry-cleaned immediately so that he could wear them the next day. Told that the in-house laundry service was closed, he insisted he couldn't wear any other pants, since the pair he was wearing was his favorite. Thae managed to have someone at the embassy find a dry cleaner that opened at 4:00 a.m., and the cleaned pair of trousers was delivered to Jong Chul's hotel room before he woke up.

When Kim Jong Chul was ready to leave London after the concert, clutching the £2,400 electric guitar he had purchased, he told Thae how grateful he was for his help and said Thae should look him up when he returned to Pyongyang. Thae was glad and proud that he had accomplished the mission he had been tasked with and returned home a little giddy, expecting his two sons to share his moment of joy. Instead, they brought him back down to earth with a thump.

"We wondered where you were, Father, but you were escorting Kim Jong Chul," one of his sons said. The son continued, "Average citizens are forbidden to listen to decrepit capitalist songs by order of Kim Jong Un, and students are even expelled if they listen to foreign songs. The Kim family ordered their people to endure the Arduous March [the North Korean famine in the mid-1990s], but they do whatever they want to do. Does it make sense to you that he spent thousands of dollars a day to be engrossed in decadent Western music?"[23]

Hearing his sons admonish him was a kick in the gut. "My children couldn't hide their anger," writes Thae. "While my generation looked up to the Kim family as gods, a new generation was being formed that held totally different views. I suddenly felt ashamed that I had aided Kim Jong Chul. It really wasn't something to be proud of. It was as if a slave was serving his master."[24]

Soldiers who defect to the South usually traverse the dangerous no-man's-land across the mine-filled DMZ. A few have made it to South Korea by flying MiG fighters across the border. On November 13, 2017, however, a North Korean soldier named Oh Chung Sung, who was assigned to a unit near the Joint Security Area (the one place in the DMZ where North and South Korean forces as well as some U.S. troops are virtually face-to-face), drove his North Korean jeep right along the Military Demarcation Line separating the two Koreas. He stopped near the South Korean guard post some fifty meters from Freedom House— South Korea's meeting point for inter-Korean contacts—and ran like a madman across the invisible line while being shot at by North Korean troops. South Korean soldiers eventually pulled the injured Oh to safety and helicoptered him to a South Korean hospital. South Korea's most well-known emergency surgeon, Dr. Lee Jong-guk, later revealed that the soldier not only suffered from bullet wounds but also had pneumonia and "an enormous number" of parasitic worms in his intestines, some up to twenty-eight centimeters long.[25]

A year after his defection, Oh sat down with a journalist from *Sankei Shimbun* in Tokyo to talk about his perspective (the entire interview was reprinted by *New Daily* in Korean). "About

80 percent of my generation are apathetic toward politics and the leadership and I believe they don't feel loyal to the regime," he said.[26] "The ration system or the state's ability to provide welfare is totally bankrupt, so if you don't have power or money, you die in North Korea."[27] He emphasized that everyone in North Korea looks out for themselves, and security officers or those who wield influence are paid bribes by citizens to look the other way. Oh added that he didn't regret his defection. But the most likely scenario was that his immediate family—including his father, who was a brigadier general in the KPA—would have been executed by the regime or, in the best case, sent to one of North Korea's penal colonies.

Overseas Slave Workers

The urge to escape North Korea can be triggered by several things: hunger, the search for freedom and money, the need to run away from a crime. The first two reasons have been by far the most common, though ever since the great famine of the mid-1990s subsided, most defectors aren't fleeing North Korea because of hunger. Instead, they choose to defect for freedom—and money.

International sanctions haven't really stifled the North Korean economy. Its resilience to foreign pressure stems from decades of coping with economic hardship, lax enforcement of sanctions (especially by China and under the Moon government in South Korea), and, above all, novel ways of making hard currency.

One model the regime has chosen involves siphoning off hundreds of millions of dollars from overseas North Korean laborers. Exact figures are hard to come by, but by one calculation, North Korea "is able to make up to $2.3 billion in hard currency a year by sending some 100,000 or more workers abroad, according to estimates. Up to 80 per cent of them go to China and Russia, where they are employed in what the UN has called 'slave-like conditions' and give up to 90 per cent of their wages to Kim Jong Un's regime."[28] Some North Korean laborers work in Eastern Europe and northern Africa. Kim Seung Chul worked at timber farms in Siberia, toiling thirteen hours each day, and for a month's work received $20.[29] Other estimates of the amount the regime makes annually from these workers range from $200 million to $2 billion.[30]

"The workers wake up each morning on metal bunk beds in fluorescent-lit Chinese dormitories, North Koreans outsourced by their government to process seafood that ends up in American stores and homes," wrote Tim Sullivan for the Associated Press. "This means Americans buying salmon for dinner at Walmart or ALDI may inadvertently have subsidized the North Korean government as it builds its nuclear weapons program."[31]

Part of the reason North Korean workers are attractive to Chinese firms is lower labor costs. Sullivan interviewed one Chinese sales manager for a seafood processor who said that in his factory North Korean workers were paid roughly the same as Chinese workers, between $300 to $385 per month. But, noted Sullivan, "others say North Koreans are routinely paid about $300 a month compared to up to $540 for Chinese."[32] The North Korean workers see very little of the money they make—the North Korean government takes away 70 to 90 percent of their earnings.

UN Security Council Resolution 2375, adopted on September 11, 2017, after North Korea's hydrogen bomb test, explicitly notes that "all Member States shall not provide work authorizations for DPRK nationals in their jurisdictions in connection with admission to their territories unless the Committee determines on a case-by-case basis in advance that employment of DPRK nationals in a member state's jurisdiction is required for the delivery of humanitarian assistance, denuclearization or any other purpose consistent with the objectives of resolutions . . . or in connection with any contract or other transaction where its performance was prevented by reason of the measures imposed by this resolution or previous resolutions."[33]

Despite the resolution, North Koreans continue to find their way to China, which happens only because the Chinese government decides to look the other way. A Sino–North Korean agreement stipulates that a North Korean worker can stay in China for only thirty days, but North Korea "issues passes valid for periods of from six months to a year, and China does not argue over this extended period of validity."[34]

Yulia Kravchenko, a Russian housewife in Vladivostok, said that "North Korean workers are fast, cheap and very reliable, much better than Russian workers. They do nothing but work from morning until late at night."[35] A Vladivostok company promotes North Korean workers by saying, "Surprisingly, these people are hard-working and orderly. They will not take long rests from work, go on frequent cigarette breaks or shirk their duties."[36]

Undercover reporting by the BBC revealed North Koreans working in Polish shipyards without any breaks. "You have to eat trash, you have to give up being a human being," said one of the North Korean workers. A North Korean foreman working for a Polish company remarked that "when there are deadlines, we work without breaks. Not like the Polish, they work eight hours a day and then go home. We don't, we work as long as we have to."[37] The BBC reporter secretly recorded one Polish manager saying that he continued to use North Korean laborers even though he "complained that it was getting harder to get permits for them."[38]

The Gulags of North Korea

If Kim Jong Un wanted to take just one step to reassure the world that he was serious about economic reforms and truly making life better for the masses, all he would have to do is raze his gulags. Yet the moment he does, it'll open a can of worms, because the gulags are the most potent symbols of immense oppression. While the circumstances are different, if Kim Jong Un opted to close all gulags, it would be equivalent to Stalin shuttering all Soviet gulags.

In February 2014, the UN Human Rights Council released an extraordinarily chilling report on North Korea's unparalleled violations of basic human rights, in particular in its gulags. "Gross human rights violations in the Democratic People's Republic of Korea involving detention, executions and disappearances are characterized by a high degree of centralized coordination between different parts of the extensive security apparatus," notes the report. "The use of torture is an established feature of the interrogation process in the Democratic People's Republic of Korea, especially in cases involving political crimes. Starvation and other inhumane conditions of detention are deliberately imposed on suspects to increase the pressure on them to confess and to incriminate other persons."[39]

A U.S. State Department report on human trafficking pointed to the forcible return of North Korean escapees to China by Chinese authorities, with horrible consequences: "These individuals, including potential trafficking victims, were sent to interrogation centers, where they were subjected to forced labor, torture, forced abortions, and sexual abuse by prison guards, and potentially sent on to prison camps." It adds that, according to reports, "infants born to forcibly repatriated victims while in prison were killed."[40]

Known as *kwanliso*, North Korea's "political camps resemble the horrors of camps that totalitarian States established during the twentieth century . . . [and] between 80,000 to 120,000 political prisoners are currently detained in four large political prison camps."[41] They are also known as total control zones, since their prisoners are completely separated from society and are essentially enslaved.

The conclusion of the UN Report of the Commission of Inquiry on Human Rights in the Democratic People's Republic of Korea is simple but powerful:

> The commission carried out its inquiry with a view to ensuring full accountability, in particular where these violations may amount to crimes against humanity. The commission is neither a judicial body nor a prosecutor. It cannot make final determinations of individual criminal responsibility. It can, however, determine whether its findings constitute reasonable grounds establishing that crimes against humanity have been committed so as to merit a criminal investigation by a competent national or international organ of justice. According to that standard, *the commission finds that the body of testimony and other information it received establishes that crimes against humanity have been committed in the Democratic People's Republic of Korea,* pursuant to policies established at the highest level of the State. These crimes against humanity entail extermination, murder, enslavement, torture, imprisonment, rape, forced abortions and other sexual violence, persecution on political, religious, racial and gender grounds, the forcible transfer of populations, the enforced disappearance of persons and the inhumane act of knowingly causing prolonged starvation. The commission further finds that crimes against humanity are ongoing in the Democratic People's Republic of Korea because the policies, institutions and patterns of impunity that lie at their heart remain in place.[42]

Kwanliso, however, aren't the only type of harsh prisons and gulags. NGO reports have identified six different types of prisons: *kyohwaso* (reeducation camps), *kyoyangso* (labor-reform centers), *jipkyulso* (collection centers for low-level criminals), *rodong danryeondae* (labor-training centers), and *kuryujang* (interrogation facilities).[43] The *kwanliso* are the type most well known in the West, but the *kyohwaso* are equally brutal and inhumane. The *kwanliso* are run by the Ministry of State Security (MSS), whereas the *kyohwaso* are run by the Ministry of People's Security (MPS). The MSS (known as the *bowibu*) is the secret police, a North Korean version of the former Soviet Union's KGB or the SS under the Nazis. The MPS, or *anjeonbu*, is North Korea's police agency, though it has much broader powers than the typical national police force.

The *kwanliso* are used to "preemptively purge, punish, and remove" political and social elements deemed as threats to the ruling party and the Kim dynasty.[44] The *kyohwaso* house a general population, although in terms of how inmates are treated, they are as bad as the *kwanliso*. Former prisoners who escaped to South Korea commonly cite "grossly inadequate food rations, arduous and dangerous labor, absence of medical treatment, high rates of deaths in detention with offensive and culturally improper burial of the dead, and widespread and wrongful imprisonment."[45]

In April 2017, the International Bar Association published a major finding on crimes against humanity perpetrated by the Kim family. It noted that political prison camps were established in the 1950s by Kim Il Sung "to eliminate the 'seed' of three generations of class enemies," and hundreds of thousands of people have been sent to them over the past six decades, "with up to three generations of families detained together and forced into slave labor, mostly to work in mines, logging, and agriculture."[46]

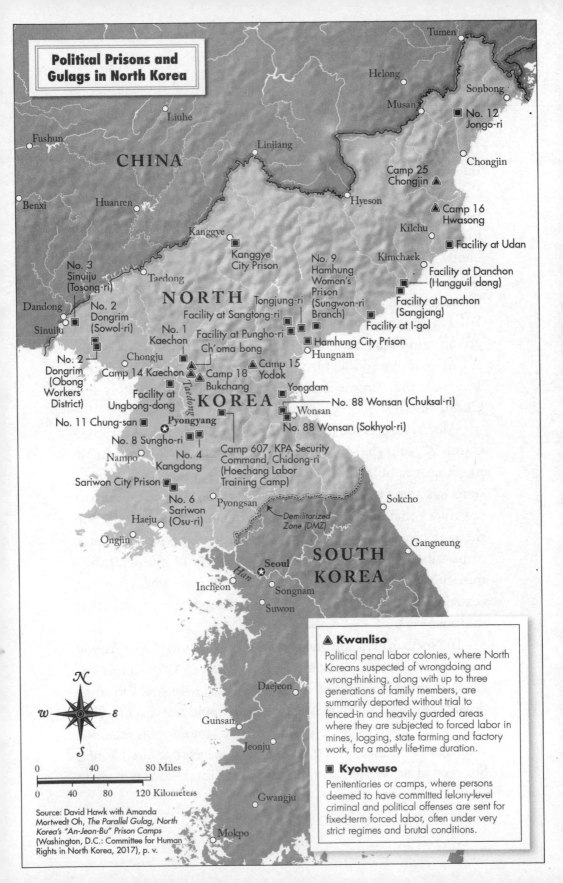

Political Prisons and Gulags in North Korea

CHINA

Tumen
Helong
Sonbong
Musan
No. 12 Jongo-ri
Liuhe
Linjiang
Chongjin
Camp 25 Chongjin
Fushun
Hyeson
Camp 16 Hwasong
Benxi
Huanren
Kilchu
Facility at Udan
Kanggye
Kimchaek
Facility at Danchon (Hangguil dong)
Dandong
No. 3 Sinuiju (Tosong-ri)
Taedong
NORTH
Kanggye City Prison
No. 9 Hamhung Women's Prison (Sungwon-ri Branch)
Facility at Danchon (Sangjang)
Tongjung-ri
No. 2 Dongrim (Sowol-ri)
Facility at Sangtong-ri
Facility at I-gol
Sinuiju
No. 1 Kaechon
Facility at Pungho-ri
Hamhung City Prison
No. 2 Dongrim (Obong Workers' District)
Ch'oma bong
Hamhung
Hungnam
Chongju
Camp 14 Kaechon
Camp 18
Camp 15 Yodok
Facility at Ungbong-dong
Bukchang
KOREA
Yongdam
No. 88 Wonsan (Chuksal-ri)
No. 11 Chung-san
Wonsan
Pyongyang
No. 88 Wonsan (Sokhyol-ri)
No. 8 Sungho-ri
Nampo
No. 4 Kangdong
Camp 607, KPA Security Command, Chidong-ri (Hoechang Labor Training Camp)
Sariwon City Prison
Sokcho
No. 6 Sariwon (Osu-ri)
Pyongsan
Haeju
Demilitarized Zone (DMZ)
Ongjin
Gangneung
SOUTH KOREA
Seoul
Incheon
Songnam
Han
Suwon
Daejeon
Gunsan
Jeonju
Gwangju
Mokpo

▲ Kwanliso

Political penal labor colonies, where North Koreans suspected of wrongdoing and wrong-thinking, along with up to three generations of family members, are summarily deported without trial to fenced-in and heavily guarded areas where they are subjected to forced labor in mines, logging, state farming and factory work, for a mostly life-time duration.

■ Kyohwaso

Penitentiaries or camps, where persons deemed to have committed felony-level criminal and political offenses are sent for fixed-term forced labor, often under very strict regimes and brutal conditions.

0   40   80 Miles
0   40   80   120 Kilometers

Source: David Hawk with Amanda Mortwedt Oh, *The Parallel Gulag, North Korea's "An-Jeon-Bu" Prison Camps* (Washington, D.C.: Committee for Human Rights in North Korea, 2017), p. v.

The unspeakable brutality highlighted in all these reports is confirmed by numerous testimonies from former inmates lucky enough to have been released or, in rare cases, to have escaped. Lee Eun Shil recounted the terrible conditions she had to live in: "People died after about six months. I'm not sure whether the cause was torture, but it was also incredibly unsanitary. Since you don't have water, you collect your urine and use it as water to soften your hardened stool by rubbing and pressing with your hands."[47]

According to the International Bar Association's report, there are four political prisons in North Korea today: Camps 14, 15, 16, and 25. The UN commission noted that a new prison camp may have been built in 2007. The most infamous is Camp 15, in Yodok. Camp 14 is near Kaechon City, Camp 16 is near the Pungye-ri nuclear test site, and Camp 25 is near Chongjin City.

Ahn Myong Chol, the guard who worked in the now-closed Camp 22, said that it was common practice to kill an inmate to set an example and that "there were as many as 20 executions in a given year."[48] The International Bar Association report concludes that, based on its independent assessment, "we find that sufficient evidence exists to conclude that Kim Jong-un is responsible for the crimes against humanity of murder, extermination, enslavement, forcible transfer, imprisonment, torture, sexual violence, persecution, enforced disappearance and other inhumane acts."[49]

In North Korea, anyone can be sent to a gulag. Kim Young Sun was imprisoned in Camp 15 from 1970 to 1979 simply because she was a friend of Sung Hye Rim, who was forced to divorce her husband so that Kim Jong Il could be with her. Kim didn't want anyone who knew Hye Rim to speak of his relationship with her. "There's no time to talk or see anyone else," Young Sun said of her existence in the camp. "It's just hell. You must do hard labor until nightfall. . . . There's no hope. You get up at 3 a.m. and go off to work. Loggers often fall, break their bones, or get crushed by falling trees. People eat poisonous grass, roots, and mushrooms because they're starving, and they eventually die."[50]

One of the most heinous aspects of North Korea's gulags is, as the UN report detailed, that up to three generations of family members can be incarcerated for crimes none of them committed. For example, if a man is incarcerated for political reasons, his children are incarcerated, too; a child unlucky enough to be born inside a camp to a confined parent is automatically considered a criminal. The children are told they're in prison because of what their father did, and so they grow up despising him. When the children are finally adults and can think on their own, they come to realize that their father didn't actually commit a crime. By then, of course, it's too late—he may well be dead, whether from forced labor, disease, accident, or constant beatings. Certainly the psychological burden of being ostracized by his family was another example of mental torture.[51]

Ri Young Guk spent time in Camp 15. "If they say you're slacking, they beat you on your back and your legs with twenty branches that are tied together," said Ri. "Students died from such beatings. There are days when the so-called teachers actually smile, but when they have bad days, you wonder if it's your time to die. Teachers considered us animals and expressed their pleasure or anger in any way they pleased."[52]

According to Ahn, the former prison guard, about two thousand guards are used in each prison camp, including guards from the MSS. "In Camp 22, they imprisoned fifty thousand people. There are two military units on standby to put down possible uprisings, and there are six guard posts in the outer perimeter."[53]

Escapees from these camps have recounted horrible experiences, both their own and ones they witnessed. A pregnant woman may be forced to abort her child by placing a board across her stomach; two inmates seesaw back and forth on the board until either she dies or the unborn child dies. Prisoners are allowed thirty minutes each week to get some sun; those who are caught eating grass during this time, however, are killed by guards who smash their heads with rifle butts. When one of the dogs that are raised by the guards inside the camp kills and eats a young child, the guards applaud the unit for making the dogs aggressive.[54]

No other country in the world has put into place a network of gulags and political prison camps like North Korea, but the camps are largely unknown to foreigners. Instead, Western media fawn over Kim Jong Un's highly choreographed forays into the outside world, and they write articles about the *jangmadang*, the former black markets that over time were transformed into de facto marketplaces throughout North Korea. The North Korean economy is indeed changing. But that in no way alters the fact that North Korea remains a totalitarian state. As the Committee for Human Rights in North Korea asserted in a 2018 report,

> North Korea's political environment operates in an ideological framework supported by a system of political terror so regulated and rigid that organized resistance is nearly impossible under current circumstances. This social control system will continue to impede any meaningful improvement in human rights and prevent the general populace from having any influence on the regime's decision-making process.[55]

Those lucky enough to escape from North Korea's gulags are like the very few who managed to escape from Nazi death camps. It's impossible to come up with an accurate figure for how many people have perished in North Korea's gulags, but defectors have stated that the survival rate is very low. An average prisoner wakes up at 5 a.m. and works until 11 p.m. Thomas Buergenthal, a survivor of Auschwitz and a jurist who served on the International Court of Justice, commented, "I believe that the conditions in the [North] Korean prison camps are as terrible, or even worse, than those I saw and experienced in my youth in these Nazi camps and in my long professional career in the human rights field."[56] The fact that a survivor of one of the most atrocious death camps in human history has deemed the North Korean camps as bad as or worse than Nazi concentration camps begins to convey some sense of the severity of North Korea's human rights abuses.

The Power of Money and Donju

Is it possible for gulags to coexist with de facto markets? If the state economy is no longer able to provide for its people, the answer is yes. With the collapse of the state economy during the great famine of the mid-1990s, when more than a million North Koreans died from starvation or related consequences, North Koreans had little choice but to fend for themselves. As the ration system collapsed, free markets, or *jangmadang*, sprang up throughout North Korea to sell food, goods, and information, and as previously noted, Kim Jong Un had no choice but to legalize them.

The *jangmadang* system today is arguably as powerful as the state economy. And it has led to the emergence of an entirely new class of nouveau riches, called *donju*, or money masters, over the past two decades. According to MBC News in Seoul, there are about ten thousand *donju* with a net worth of at least $100,000, and around two thousand have at least $1 million. And a hundred *donju* are believed to be worth $10 million or more.[57]

What is unique about the *jangmadang* and *donju* is that both are creatures of a failed state economy. Because Kim Jong Un can't satisfy the demands of Pyongyang's elites solely from state coffers, he has grudgingly accepted the existence of the *jangmadang* and *donju*. How long he is going to continue to tolerate them is unknown, although it seems clear that he currently sees them as a way of incentivizing a new cadre of supporters. The *donju* live in North Korea's "parallel universe"—what Anna Fifield has called "Pyonghattan" (a mash-up of "Pyongyang" and "Manhattan").[58]

But allowing the *donju* to prosper is a Faustian bargain. Kim Jong Un wants to retain all of the tyrannical tools at his disposal while using *jangmadang* to provide the masses with what he can't give them: basic living standards. Much more alarming for the Kim family is that North Koreans no longer fear Jong Un as much as they feared his father or grandfather.

Kim Jong Un will never give up his gulags because they are the superglue that keeps his dictatorship in power. The problem is, he can't afford to snuff out *jangmadang* either. And the power of money—highlighted by the swagger of the *donju*—is as strong as the power of fear. When money overtakes fear as the principal currency of coercion, the Kim dynasty's iron grip on power will weaken. That the regime continues to allow *jangmadang* and turns a blind eye to the *donju* creates the risk that a North Korean fifth column will develop. Indeed, a survey of eighty-seven defectors who came over to South Korea in the period from 2017 to 2018 indicated that 60.9 percent of them had sold goods at *jangmadang*.[59]

The Arduous March of the mid- to late 1990s, in which as many as 1.5 million died because of famine and its effects, not only resulted in the collapse of the state rationing system but also led to the virtual meltdown of state banks. The disastrous currency reform of 2009 was the nail in the coffin. The *donju* began to proliferate when factories and state-run companies no longer received backing from the state. The *donju* acted as virtual banks, offering services that included loan sharking, money transfer, and currency exchange. Very rapidly, they established pawnshops, moved into apartment construction, began to offer venture capital, created networks for human trafficking, and engaged in illicit trade. Today, Travis Jeppesen, a frequent visitor to North Korea and author of *See You Again in Pyongyang*, estimates that there are four hundred sanctioned markets or *jangmadang* in North Korea that represent some sixty thousand vendors.[60]

Enormous money continues to be made from Sino–North Korean trade, and the *donju* are indispensable to its functioning. A defector recalled that "it is a well-known secret among border traders that some entrepreneurs eat $1,000 meals at restaurants in China or Russia with local associates."[61]

Jeppesen writes, "My experiences in North Korea have taught me that the *donju* are the closest thing North Korea has to a dissident class. They are savvy and worldly and certainly don't conform to the outside world's image of the brainwashed Kim Jong Un fanatic; they don't buy into the state's propaganda."[62] The *donju* flaunt their wealth: "These new dreamers of North Korea don't have revolution on their minds. Their dreams are wrapped up in business, deals, the attainment and sustenance of personal wealth."[63] Jeppesen also points to a fundamental flaw in North Korea. "[The *donju*'s] existence reveals the inevitable flaw that Kim Il Sung and his cohorts failed to discern when they were designing what to them seemed like their own unique form of socialism: the failure to do away with a class system."[64]

In the end, however, the influence and limitations of the *donju* can perhaps be best illustrated by a verse from the classic hit song "Hotel California" by the Eagles: "You can check out anytime you like, but you can never leave." Ironically, the *donju* are the least likely to support all-out economic reform in North Korea, since that would leave them without special privileges. Their love-hate relationship with the state, and more specifically with Kim Jong Un, is based on the fact that they can't survive without Kim, but neither can they really take off with him.

The *donju* are the new elites of North Korea. They are cornering the market for three critical North Korean exports: coal, fisheries, and clothing. The showcase Ryomyong Street in Pyongyang, with its high-rise apartments, took just thirteen months to complete in April 2017 thanks to investments by the *donju*.[65] But the *donju* are a double-edged sword for Kim. Even though they pay off party, military, and government officials so that they can continue to survive and prosper, their growing power comes at the expense of the Kim family's iron grip.

North Korea's Millennials: The Children of Jangmadang

One might logically wonder why North Koreans continue to put up with the Kim family and its police state. Kim Yoo Sung, who escaped from Giljoo county, Hamkyungbuk-do, in 2005, describes why it's virtually impossible for an Arab Spring or a "people power" revolution to occur in North Korea.

> Foreigners wonder why there is no anti-government movement to topple the dictatorship. Sometimes, they think it's because we North Koreans are too stupid to carry out such an uprising. But ordinary North Koreans are simply too afraid to become part of an anti-government movement, because they know the truth: they cannot bring about change themselves.... If people went out into the streets and said something negative about Kim Jong Un or the government's policies, they would be executed the moment they opened their mouths.[66]

There are many aspects of life in North Korea that the outside world will never know until the two Koreas are unified or the Kim dynasty collapses. North Korea, however, is no longer an enigma. Enough information has seeped out over the years for observers to see that Kim Jong Un is in a very perilous place.

Yes, he is in total control of the party, the armed forces, and security apparatuses, and he is more confident of his power than ever before. Like all dictators, he has learned the game of instilling fear in his people. This is especially true for the elites that are closest to him. At the same time, he knows how to appease them with material goods, foreign travel, and posh vacation homes, and also by allowing his underlings to fill their own coffers. The police state shows no signs of weakening anytime in the near future. North Korea will continue to be a totalitarian state.

The Arduous March, however, irreversibly broke the social contract that had existed during the Kim Il Sung era. Ingrained collectivism is the glue that holds North Korean society together, but it's not nearly as strong as before.

All North Korean babies are sent to state-run nurseries when they are just three months old. From this point on they are brought up in collectives. In nursery school, toddlers learn songs praising Kim Il Sung, Kim Jong Il, and of course the Supreme Leader. In kindergarten, children learn to march to martial music. When they enter elementary school, all students must join the Youth League. A report put out by the South Korean government notes, "The Youth League receives the biggest attention since that's when political indoctrination begins in earnest and since coming to power, Kim Jong Un has officially stressed the need to strengthen the activities of the Youth League."[67] This is where the *songbun* you were born into really begins to determine your collective life—whether you'll become a party member or join a workers' or farmers' union. The regime makes a gargantuan effort to control society through the party's tentacles, which reach every square inch of North Korea. Surveillance is nonstop. Officials can come into any household. Between twenty and forty households form an *inminban*, or people's group, that monitors those within it. According to Amnesty International, this system locks in surveillance.

> Each *inminban* shares the duty of monitoring its members, providing ideological education, and serving as a conduit for various mobilization campaigns. Every North Korean national is required to belong to an *inminban*. The group meets once or twice a week, attended by representatives of each household, who often tend to be women who do not work outside the home. Group leaders watch closely the behaviour and personal relations of residents under their supervision, and have the authority to visit homes at any time, day or night.[68]

While total control remains intact, the system is cracking from within. When a North Korean who defected in 2013 is asked by Anna Fifield what her first impression of Kim Jong Un was, she answers: "I was in my second year at the university when this person was introduced to us as our new leader. I thought it was a joke. Among my closest friends, we were calling him a piece of s——. Everyone thinks this, but you can only say it to your closest friends or to your parents if you know that they agree."[69] The same person recounted what she thought was the superglue that held the system together. "The secret to North Korea's survival is the reign of terror. Why do you think North Korea has public executions? Why do you think they block all communications? Why do you think North Koreans leave, knowing that they will never see their families again? It shows how bad things are. All our rights as people have been stripped away."[70]

Another defector, Kim Jae Young, recalls the first time she saw a South Korean TV drama: "I was in high school. . . . and I was very surprised. I could feel for the first time that South

Koreans were living much better than us. It was shocking to see that young South Koreans of about the same age as me were living a completely different lifestyle."[71] Many North Koreans believe that their poverty is a result of international sanctions, not because of the corruption of the regime. And Jae Young never even thought of criticizing the leadership, since the Kims were thought to be gods.

After she escaped, she found out that North Korea was poor, and that she was not alone in that realization. "With the increasing levels of information coming into North Korea through foreign videos and radio, people are starting to realize that North Korea is much poorer than the outside world," she says.[72]

The single biggest transformation in North Korean society since the great famine has been the spread of the *jangmadang*, as noted earlier in this chapter. Jieun Baek writes in the *New York Times*, "Today an estimated two-thirds of the population depends on the hundreds of street markets for food and other goods, including foreign media. A nascent market economy has taken root."[73]

Other changes are creating fissures within North Korea as well. One of the most striking statistics that Baek writes about is that as many as two thousand phone calls are made illegally between the two Koreas every day.[74] Cell phones that can connect with Chinese cellular networks are popular. But people know to keep most calls to just a minute or two. That way, North Korea's constant surveillance won't be able to trace the signals back to them.

People's minds don't change overnight, especially in a thick bubble like North Korea. Over time, though, as more information makes its way into society like a slow-moving stream, it begins to trigger doubt. These doubts turn into very basic questions, like: Are South Koreans really poorer than North Koreans?

Baek writes about Kim Ha Young, who says she was taught that South Koreans run around the streets naked. "South Koreans don't go to school because they can't pay tuition, and they die on the streets because they can't pay for hospitals," says Ha Young, "but as I watched Korean movies and shows, I thought to myself, 'What kind of bullshit are the textbooks talking about?' I quickly realized that South Korea was more developed than North Korea."[75]

Liberty in North Korea, an NGO devoted to helping North Korean defectors, made an eye-opening documentary in 2017 called *The Jangmadang Generation*. In this powerful film, young North Koreans recount stories of dead bodies piling up in the streets during the great famine. They tell of imprisonment and torture, and of forced adulation of the Kim family. But the documentary also allows them to give voice to their aspirations.

No doubt many of them are like Min Kang, a self-made businessman who now lives in the South and whose dream is to run an inter-Korean travel agency when the country becomes unified.[76] At a young age Kang was separated from his mother and learned to beg and to steal. Eventually, as more and more people around him became underground traders, he too became one. He made enough money to make a dash for China, where he lived for three years before coming to South Korea.

His message is a simple but critical reminder that North Koreans are people. "This is absolutely basic. But this is so basic that people [here] don't think enough about it," says Kang. "North Koreans have their own thoughts. If you look into their eyes, they will see you and you will see them, you feel something inside."

Twenty-five-year-old Kim Danbi recalls that "in the winter, I'd put goods in a water bucket and take it to the river [the Amrok] and slide it across the ice. A Chinese trader would grab it and slide the money over to me." This is how she began to learn about survival.

Joo Yang left North Korea in 2010. She recounts how, "at the height of the famine, many young girls, aged 16 and 17, were sold into forced marriages in China. When you woke up, another girl from the neighborhood had disappeared." She adds, "If I didn't do anything, I was going to starve, so we started trading. If you had rice, you made some rice cakes and sold them. If you had corn, you made corn flour noodles and sold them. So little by little, that's how people started doing private business. I knew I had to make money, so I started thinking about business from the age of 14." Today she's a student at the prestigious Korea University.

Geum Ju left North Korea in 2008 and emphasizes that "since the government became poor, they couldn't take care of us. We lost faith in the government and we knew we had to shape our own futures. That's how I grew up."

In one of the most poignant parts of the documentary, Geum Ju's mother, Hyun Soo, explains why the *jangmadang* generation is, in her mind, fundamentally different from her own. "There was no food and we couldn't provide books or pencils, so the children learned how to do business and they didn't care much for the social controls," Hyun Soo explains. "[So] they didn't pay attention to rules. Our survival came first. The young generation woke up to this reality early on. They grew up seeing and experiencing all of the negative aspects of society, so they grew up to be bold and audacious."

"We're different from our parents. We had to figure out everything ourselves," says Kang Nara. "The year I turned six, the Arduous March famine began, a lot of people died of starvation and cold, government officials at each level were siphoning off food for themselves, so citizens got less and less. In the end, there was almost nothing. No rations."

The *jangmadang* generation won't trigger a bottom-up revolution and cripple the Kim dynasty. They are the first generation, however, to question the rationale for why they live in a police state when the world is passing them by. All revolutions begin with a single doubt. Brought up during the great famine, this group of North Koreans know how much the state has failed them and continues to fail them.

WILL THE REAL KIM JONG UN
PLEASE STAND UP?

Let There Be Light

A twenty-three-year-old woman who has been blind for many years is one of the hundreds of North Korean cataract patients operated on by a Nepalese doctor named Sanuk Ruit. She, like the other patients with bandages covering their eyes, is seated in a large hall.[1]

The young woman is the first patient to have her bandages removed. As undercover National Geographic cameras record the moment, she holds her father's hands in anticipation as an assistant peels off her bandages. Dr. Ruit asks her to open her eyes.

"Can you see?" her father asks.

"Yes, I can see very well, Father!" she shouts, and hugs him.

Any normal father would have hugged her back and thanked the medical team for restoring her eyesight.

This father, however, lives in North Korea. He faces the camera and says, "It's all because of the Great General!"

Then the father turns back to his daughter and says in a trembling voice, "We must make a deep bow to our Great General for this! Thank you, Great General!"

Father and daughter stand in front of two large portraits of North Korea's twin gods, Kim Il Sung and Kim Jong Il, and bow their heads 90 degrees.

"We want to show our deepest gratitude to our Father, the Great General! We are most grateful to our Dear Leader!"

As they bow, the audience erupts in cheers to show their "spontaneous and ever-lasting" love for the Great Leader (Kim Il Sung) and the Dear Leader (Kim Jong Il, referred to also as the Great General).

"Manse! Manse!" Ten thousand years! Ten thousand years!

"Long live the Great Leader!"

The next patient is a thirty-five-year-old woman who works in a salt mine. When her bandages are removed and she is asked whether she can see, she shouts, "I can see! Great Leader, I will work harder at the salt mines. I will get more salt to bring you greater happiness!" In a very traditional Korean way, she prostrates herself in front of the portraits. As she begins to rise, tears flow down her cheeks.

An elderly woman who had been blind in her right eye walks over to the portraits after her bandages are removed. Overwhelmed with emotion, she bows her head and says, "Thank you very much! Thank you very much!"

In a land where cataract operations are a rarity, since the medical system for the masses is totally broken, North Koreans know in a heartbeat whom to thank for the return of their eyesight. And no, it's not Dr. Ruit and his team. Here in North Korea, you're supposedly living in an earthly paradise, as North Koreans always tell foreigners. Everything is provided by the enormous generosity of the Kim family. Two dead leaders are revered as gods, and the third to assume the throne is a living god.

The Royal Family, Aristocrats, and the Masses

No other country on the planet resembles the Democratic People's Republic of Korea. It remains one of the most impoverished countries in Asia but, as previously noted, it has a growing nuclear arsenal—presently between thirty and sixty nuclear warheads, with annual production of three to five more. One U.S. government estimate suggests that North Korea has enough nuclear material—weapons-grade plutonium and enriched uranium—to build as many as twelve warheads annually.[2]

North Korea is the most militarized country in the world. All able-bodied men and women are expected to serve ten years and five to seven years, respectively, in the armed forces, although some students are allowed to finish their undergraduate studies and then serve only about five years in the military. Out of a population of 25 million, 1.2 million serve in the Korean People's Army. Millions more serve in reserves, home guards, and youth brigades. A constant siege mentality permeates the country: accelerated labor campaigns are common, and strike force units specialize in rapid construction. Approximately 20–25 percent of the country's GDP is devoted to defense, including WMD. All goods and services, in theory, are made to promote the goals of the state.

North Korea is also one of the largest criminal syndicates in the world: churning out counterfeit notes (such as fake U.S. $100 bills that are nearly indistinguishable from the real thing); manufacturing and trading illicit drugs; running alcohol- and tobacco-smuggling rings; sending out slave laborers to Russia, China, and parts of the Middle East; and, increasingly, undertaking bank heists through computer hacking.

Figure 1: Kim Dynasty Family Tree

* Kim Jong Il had two official wives—Hong Il Chon and Kim Yong Suk and three unofficial wives—Sung Hye Rim, Ko Yong Hui, and Kim Ok.

Line of succession
Broader Kim Dynasty

Kim Il Sung (1912–1994)

Kim Jong Suk (1917–1949)

Kim Song Ae (1924–2014)

Kim Jong Il (1942–2011)

Kim Kyong Hui (1946–)

Jang Song Thaek (1946–2013) — Executed (2013)

Kim Kyung Jin (1952–)

Kim Pyong Il (1954–)

Kim Young Il (1955–2000)

Exiled as ambassador since early 1970's

Jang Kun Song (1977–2006) — Suicide (2006)

Hong Il Chon (1942–)

Sung Hye Rim (1937–2002)

Kim Yong Suk (1947–)

Ko Yong Hui (1953–2004)

Kim Ok (1964–)

Kim Jong Nam (1971–2015) — Assassinated (2015)

Kim Sol Song (1973–)

Kim Chun Song (1975–)

Kim Jong Chul (1981–)

Kim Jong Un (1983–)

Ri Sol Ju (1989–)

Kim Yo Jong (1987–)

Kim Han Sol (1994–)

Kim Sol Hee (1999–)

Son (2010?)

Daughter (2013?)

Son or Daughter?

?

Source: *Yonhap News*, July 2016 and February 2018.

North Korea is the world's only nominally hybrid communist state run by a family dynasty (see Figure 1). Initially founded on the basis of Marxism-Leninism but replaced by the ideologies of Kim Il Sung and his son Kim Jong Il and run by the same family since inception. The Kim dynasty began in 1945 when the Soviet Union tapped Kim Il Sung to lead northern Korea, which became a separate state in 1948. The mythology surrounding the Kim dynasty is too extensive to cover in its entirety here, except to emphasize that virtually every aspect of that mythology is based on lies and exaggerations.

No system of checks and balances exists in North Korea. Supreme power lies in the hands of only one person: Kim Jong Un. All others, including his wife, sister, brothers, and family elders, derive their privilege from their homage to Kim Jong Un. In order to maintain absolute power, the Kim family has resorted to brutal measures and an unparalleled police state. Every North Korean is beholden to the laws and regulations of the state except for the members of the Paektu bloodline—the direct descendants of the Kim dynasty that began with Kim Il Sung in 1948. The Kim family has ruled North Korea uninterrupted and with an iron fist since 1948. Although direct descendants of state-recognized revolutionaries and national heroes receive various favors, nothing compares to the aura surrounding the Paektu family tree. Political legitimacy stems from the Paektu bloodline.

Although Kim Jong Un is Kim Jong Il's third son, his mother, Ko Yong Hui, was born in Osaka, Japan, to a Japanese mother and a Korean father. She moved with her family to North Korea when she was young. It's ironic that the Supreme Leader's mother was a Korean resident in Japan, given North Korea's portrayal of the Japanese in the most negative terms.

Not only is the Kim family above the law, they live lavish lives totally separate from the masses. At the height of the great North Korean famine in the 1990s, Kim Jong Il asked his Japanese chef, Kenji Fujimoto, to fly to Tokyo via Beijing to buy his favorite sushi fish.

According to Fujimoto, Ko Yong Hui once recounted a story from when she was dating Kim Jong Il. "The two of them [Kim Jong Il and Ko Yong Hui] were riding in Kim's Mercedes-Benz and listened to South Korean songs all night long," writes Fujimoto, "and she [Ko Yung Hui] sang that song to us [Fujimoto]—'Geuttae geusaram' [The Person at That Time]—which was a major hit in South Korea."[3] The king and queen can listen to South Korean songs, but the masses can be sent to prison or re-education camps if they do. Nor can ordinary people watch South Korean TV or movies—though many do, via illegally imported DVDs or thumb drives.

Kim Il Sung's first wife, Kim Jong Suk, died when she was only thirty-two years old. Their son, Kim Jong Il, was brought up by his stepmother, who bore three children, including Kim Pyong Il, who was the spitting image of Kim Il Sung. Kim Jong Il made sure, however, that Pyong Il would never assume the throne; beginning in the early 1970s, he was effectively exiled to various capitals in Eastern Europe as North Korea's ambassador.

The son who did succeed Kim Il Sung, Kim Jong Il (also known as the Dear Leader), had four wives, although he was only officially married twice. Kim Jong Il's first wife was Hong Il Chon, whom he married in 1966, and not much is known of her. He married Kim Yong Suk in 1975 and had a daughter, Sol Song, with her. He fell in love with a famous actress, Sung Hye Rim, who, as mentioned in Chapter One, was already married, but he forced her to divorce her husband. She bore him his oldest son, Kim Jong Nam. With Ko Yong Hui, Kim Jong Il had three more children: Kim Jong Chul, Kim Jong Un, and Kim Yo Jong.

North Korea allegedly is a totally classless society, but every single North Korean is classified from birth according to their parents' backgrounds and political fealty, a system known as *songbun*.[4] It is the most politically determined caste system ever created.

Songbun is divided into two major categories: birth *songbun*, or family ancestry, and social *songbun*, or job category. Birth *songbun* automatically categorizes people into one of five classes: (1) special class, (2) core class, (3) normal class, (4) wavering class, and (5) enemy class. These classes are divided further into fifty-one subcategories. Birth *songbun* determines every facet of a North Korean's life.[5] Those with ancestors born in South Korea or Japan are considered to be particularly untrustworthy, even enemies of the state. But these considerations don't apply to the Kim family.

The special class is composed of the inner circle of the Kim dynasty, such as descendants of the guerrillas who fought with Kim Il Sung during the colonial era, those who served Kim Jong Il and their descendants, and Kim Jong Un's closest circle. They are the super-elites of North Korea's power hierarchy.

The core class comprises those who fought the Japanese during the colonial period and their descendants, Korean War veterans and their families, and "heroes" who have proved their loyalty and allegiance to the state.

The normal class is the largest of the five groups. It comprises workers, farmers, and intellectuals whose loyalty is generally accepted but not guaranteed.

Following them is the wavering class, or those who are under more intrusive surveillance. This class includes Korean-Japanese who were repatriated in the 1960s and early 1970s; criminals and their relatives, who by association are considered disloyal; and any other individual the Korean Workers' Party (KWP) or the Kim family believes to be untrustworthy.

Finally, the enemy class includes descendants of landowners, rich farmers, capitalists, or pro-Japanese sympathizers; members of anti-party factions (one of the main reasons for conducting intermittent purges within the party); defectors and their families;

released political prisoners or those who were sent to reeducation camps; and those accused of spying or potential spies. In short, just about anyone can be categorized as an enemy of the state.

These categories are, in part, intended to abet North Korea's messianic mission to purify and liberate the rest of the Korean Peninsula (i.e., South Korea) from decades of capitalism, residues of colonial rule, a society flowing with material goods, and a people who have lost their true Korean identity. South Koreans are deemed to be ethnically impure since they have tainted *uri minjok*, or "our race," and hence must be cleansed and rectified.

Only the elites can live in Pyongyang. Here reside the leaders of the party, the KPA, the government ministries, security organizations, and major state-run companies, among others. According to their pecking order, they get daily, weekly, or monthly rations, such as rice or other staples, cooking oil, meat, and fish.

The super-elites live in opulent homes outfitted with the latest South Korean or Japanese electronic goods. They have access to special vacation resorts. They shop in hard-currency stores. Their children attend the best schools (including top universities such as Kim Il Sung University, Pyongyang University of Foreign Studies, and Kim Chaek University of Technology), receive private lessons in key subjects, and get choice assignments in the military. They receive privileged healthcare, including treatment in Paris, Beijing, Singapore, or Geneva if needed.

The Beloved Father and a Mafia Regime

The Kim dynasty consists of five concentric circles that reinforce one another and keep the Kim family in power (see Figure 2). At the core is its third king, Kim Jong Un. Every aspect of North Korean life is devoted to sustaining and strengthening the Kim dynasty. All else remains secondary. Surrounding this nucleus are

Figure 2: North Korea's Five Concentric Circles

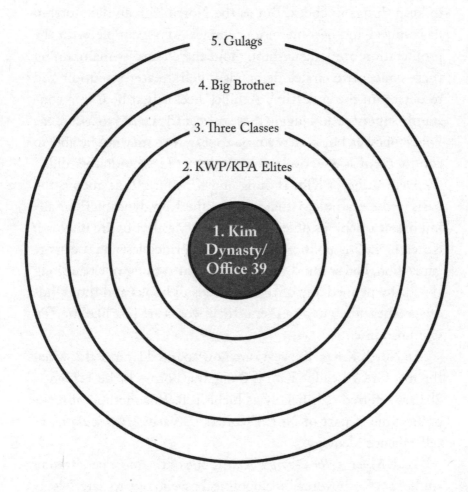

5. Gulags

4. Big Brother

3. Three Classes

2. KWP/KPA Elites

1. Kim Dynasty/ Office 39

four interconnected rings: the party and military elites; the three main classes, including interclass suspicions, within and between them; 24/7 surveillance on all North Koreans; and a massive detention and prison system including gulags. They reinforce and counterbalance each other so that ultimately only Kim is needed to keep things in check. But as the North Korean dictatorship has evolved and become more complex—for example, with the proliferation of markets throughout the country—maintaining these concentric circles demands much greater attention and resources. In the end, Kim's Achilles' heel is that he has to constantly supervise and juggle these concentric circles to assure his hold on power, but as new forces appear, Kim may not be able to control them as effectively as his father or his grandfather did.

Deification of Kim Il Sung and Kim Jong Il as gods is the basis of the mythology that sustains the Kim dynasty. Their all-important teachings officially guide every aspect of life in North Korea, including political ideology, core principles, and social organization. Never mind that neither Kim Il Sung nor Kim Jong Il actually penned any of the hundreds of books and thousands of speeches attributed to them. Their words are just like the Ten Commandments.

In North Korea, the years are now counted from 1912, when the first Great Leader, Kim Il Sung, was born—Juche 1. Hence, 2019 is referred to officially as Juche 108. This method of reckoning time is part of North Korea's pervasive *Juche sasang*, or self-reliance ideology.

B. R. Myers's *The Cleanest Race* is one of the most penetrating studies of North Korea's sociopolitical psychology to date. Myers examines how North Korea's propaganda machinery built a mythology of the Korean race based on three pillars: constant struggles against foreign invaders, exploitation by the ruling classes, and salvation by the Kim family. The Kims must battle insidious contamination by foreign ideologies and customs, foremost among them being residues of Japanese colonialism, American imperialism, and contamination of the Korean race by the South Koreans.

According to Myers, the foundation of North Korea's fixation with racial purity can be traced to Japanese colonialism, when Koreans were taught that they were an extension of Japan's "uniquely pure and virtuous" Yamamoto race (although in practice the Japanese rulers looked down on Koreans as much lower than themselves). But the net result was the notion of a "super-race"—Koreans living in North Korea—that longed for salvation. And who is their savior?

"North Korea regards the country's history as a long foreshadowing to Kim Il Sung," writes Myers, "much as Christians see everything before the birth of Jesus as a *Vorgeschichte* or prehistory."[6] The KWP is an all-encompassing mother that looks after its children under the tutelage of Kim Il Sung and his direct descendants.

In April 2012, five months after the death of Kim Jong Il, North Korea's constitution was revised to immortalize the recently deceased leader as the "Eternal Chairman of the National Defense Commission" (Kim Il Sung was already referred to as the "Eternal President"). In tandem with Kim Jong Un's rise, the party newspaper *Rodong Sinmun* emphasized after the May 2016 Seventh Party Congress that "the propagation of Kim Il Sung–ism and Kim Jong Il–ism is our party's supreme doctrine" and "eternal leadership ideology."[7]

Yet ideology alone isn't enough to sustain the Kim dynasty. Central to the well-being of the Kim family are the super-elites of North Korea (the top 1 percent of the party, military, bureaucracies, and state-run enterprises) and then, one rung down, the elites (who make up about the top 5 percent).

None of the top levels—Kim and his family, the super-elites, or the elites—can survive without some type of support from

Office 39, which is essential to providing critical incentives to Kim's core group of supporters. Office 39 is Kim Jong Un's personal bank, where all hard-currency earnings are funneled and redistributed based on Kim's instructions. It is the most important financial nerve system within the Kim dynasty.

Kim must ensure the loyalty of the super-elites and the elites with tangible goods and incentives. But at the same time, their loyalty is constantly tested: every house, office, and telephone of every member of these groups is surveilled 24/7. Big Brother has been perfected in North Korea. China is hard at work on a digitized monitoring system for its 1.4 billion citizens, but North Korea has a time-tested analog system, although the regime is putting into place a digital surveillance mechanism as a result of the expansion of digital technologies, such as more advanced mobile phones and very limited access to the internet. In North Korea, everyone needs a pass to travel from one city to another. No one can change jobs, switch residences, or get married without state approval. And, as we've seen, North Korea has its gulag system, where as many as 300,000 citizens are imprisoned under the most inhumane conditions—and where many perish.

North Korea's five concentric circles are controlled by an omnipresent party that is based on Leninist power structures but run like a well-oiled fascist machine. Ironically, North Korea proclaims itself to be socialism's paradise, but it rejected Marxism-Leninism and communism beginning in the early 1970s. Kim Il Sung Thought and Kim Jong Il Thought are the guiding ideologies of the North Korean state. It is communist only by dint of its Soviet heritage.

What holds these five circles together is North Korea's growing nuclear weapons arsenal, since it acts as a shield against "dangerous" external enemies. The primary justification for the regime's draconian political system is to defend itself against powerful adversaries such as the United States and its minions, like South Korea and Japan. Because Kim Jong Il first tested nuclear weapons and Kim Jong Un completed North Korea's nuclear arsenal, the state is now impregnable. State propaganda constantly reminds North Koreans that only through the genius leadership of Kim is the DPRK able to fend off enemies and pursue its own unique brand of a powerful socialist state.

Moreover, no other single development since the Korean War—not North Korea's 1.2 million conventional troops, not the long-range artilleries deployed around the 38th parallel, not even its cache of biochemical weapons—has given North Korea as much strategic leverage as nuclear weapons.

Now that North Korea is a successful nuclear power, Kim can afford to take calculated risks, such as taking steps toward inter-Korean détente and even normalization of ties with the United States. He will never give up nuclear weapons, but he will declare his intention of doing so with symbolic gestures such as alluding to dismantling the Yongbyon nuclear facility and the Tongchang-ri missile test site.

A Different Kind of Leader

South Korean president Moon Jae-in believes firmly that Kim is ready to dismantle his nuclear weapons and long-range ballistic missiles so long as the United States meets him halfway. Many proponents of engagement have been arguing—some since the mid-1980s—that North Korea is on the cusp of major economic reforms, like those undertaken in China. Kim Jong Un, they assert, is ready to open up North Korea.

The centrally planned economy began to crumble beginning in the late 1970s and reached its deathbed with the breakup of the USSR and the downfall of communist regimes in Eastern Europe in 1990–1991. Today, it couldn't function without a huge black market that has, over time, morphed into the ubiquitous *jangmadang*. When the North Korean economy began to collapse in earnest soon after Kim Jong Il formally assumed power in 1994, he refused to divert critical resources to the civilian economic sector. Instead, he was hell-bent on expediting North Korea's clandestine nuclear weapons program and beefing up his ballistic missile arsenal. As stopgap measures to alleviate hunger, Kim grudgingly accepted pockets of black markets where people could access goods and services the state no longer provided. However, Kim Jong Il felt that the proliferation of *jangmadang* was fraught with dangers and cracked down on these markets by forcibly closing them and implementing anti-corruption drives to highlight the scourge of unintended capitalism.

"If we stop buying the shaky argument that North Korea is socialist, and begin seeing it as a country with an ultranationalist ideology and a repressive authoritarian state," argues Rüdiger Frank, a prominent North Korea watcher, "then even cases like South Korea under Park Chung-hee or Singapore under Lee Kuan Yew look somewhat familiar."[8] He goes on to say that "authoritarian economic miracles like Singapore, China, or South Korea under Park Chung-hee show that if he plays his hand well, Kim Jong Un can have his cake and eat it, too—reform the economy while keeping his monopolistic grip on power."[9] This is at the very heart of the argument that Kim Jong Un can transform North Korea into the next Asian tiger.

Frank is correct only to the extent that China and Vietnam adopted economic reforms without giving up one-party rule. It's crucial to remember, however, that none of the Asian tigers— South Korea, Taiwan, Singapore, and Hong Kong—were totalitarian states when they began their accelerated economic development. Indeed, Deng Xiaoping was able to implement reforms only after Mao Zedong died in 1976 and the so-called Gang of Four was purged. Vietnam's *doi moi*, or reform policy, was possible because communist Vietnam has never been ruled by a family dynasty fueled by paranoid hypernationalism.

The critical question is whether Kim Jong Un will be a completely different type of leader compared to his grandfather and father and adopt structural economic reforms by doing away with the very foundations of his political legitimacy.

According to Park Young-ja, head of North Korean studies at the Korea Institute for National Unification, "Kim Jong Un is preparing to be in power for the next forty-plus years" and wants to show his people that the DPRK "can become a major economic powerhouse" by 2030.[10] He also covets genuine international legitimacy more than his predecessors did, not content merely with the outrageous personality cult that permeates all levels of North Korean society. He wants to be seen in the eyes of world leaders as a serious, thoughtful, and decisive figure—a leader who will transform North Korea.

"I can do business with Mr. Gorbachev!" proclaimed Margaret Thatcher on the doorstep of 10 Downing Street after she met Mikhail Gorbachev right before he became secretary general of the Communist Party of the Soviet Union. This is what Kim Jong Un wants to hear from Xi Jinping, Donald Trump, Vladimir Putin, Shinzo Abe, and most of all Moon Jae-in. Yet he is trapped in the very system that created him—a brutal dictatorship in the guise of a family dynasty.

Kim wants to become the Deng Xiaoping—arguably the most consequential world leader of the twentieth century—of North Korea, but without giving up any control of the levers of power. Nor does he want to give up the omnipresent personality cult of the Kim dynasty, symbolized by the Kim Il Sung and Kim Jong Il badges that all North Korean adults must wear. He wants to keep the most perverse and pervasive caste system in the world, one that categorizes every single North Korean according to political background and fealty. He wants to keep the police-state apparatus, which is essential to maintaining the Kim dynasty. While corruption is rampant in North Korea, the tentacles of the state are far-reaching, repressive, and brutally efficient when they have to be. Above all, he wants to keep his nuclear weapons. Weakening, much less eradicating, any of these pillars will undo the foundations of the system that supports him.

Yet increasingly Kim is being viewed as a reformer who has already come out of the closet. In 2013 he announced the so-called *byungjin noseon*, or "parallel lines"—a policy that stressed the twin goals of economic development and becoming a nuclear power. In April 2018, Kim dropped *byungjin noseon* and declared that henceforth the DPRK would focus like a laser on economic development, since North Korea had successfully become a nuclear power. As Rüdiger Frank concludes:

> In the very distant future, this could help him to fulfill the vision that his grandfather Kim Il Sung harbored when he was Kim Jong Un's age: national unification under North Korean leadership, driven by a superior military force and unhindered by an inferior economy. It would be a mistake to forget that this is the ultimate goal behind every North Korean policy.[11]

The prevailing assumption in the Moon administration's approach to inter-Korean relations is that, given the enormous economic gap between the two Koreas, South Korea is the richer older brother who looks after his much poorer, angrier, and lost younger brother. Nothing could be further from the truth, because Kim Jong Un is betting on the long game: none of the living autocratic or democratic leaders with a stake on the Korean Peninsula is going to be in power twenty to thirty years from now. South Koreans, for example, elect a new leader every five years in an increasingly polarized political environment. But Kim is only thirty-eight and is planning to still be around decades from now. So time, according to Kim, is on his side.

No country with nuclear weapons has given them up under duress. Intermittent progress in nuclear negotiations between U.S. president Donald Trump and Kim Jong Un is entirely feasible. But totally denuclearizing North Korea through negotiations is a pipe dream.

Kim Jong Un's grand strategy lies in convincing the United States that he's willing to dismantle his nuclear weapons and ICBMs over the longer term while simultaneously locking in inter-Korean détente to ensure a steady increase in South Korean investments and a political "disarmament" in South Korea. Because the left in South Korea shares North Korea's penchant for hypernationalism, it is possible that so long as the progressives retain power, denuclearization will be pushed sideways with just enough lip service to satisfy the United States. It's a risky game, but one that Moon is willing to play with Kim, creating a de facto united front against the United States.

The success of Kim's grand strategy hinges on whether Trump buys a deal that papers over highly technical verification requirements to announce a diplomatic victory. If Trump is convinced that he can announce a diplomatic breakthrough with North Korea, details are peripheral. As a leader who doesn't pay attention to his own intelligence agencies but relies on his gut and pro-Trump comments on Fox News, Trump has preemptively taken credit for "massive foreign policy achievements" such as his meetings with Kim Jong Un.

"You know, deals are deals, okay? Whether it's a real estate or a retail deal, it doesn't matter," said Trump to Lesley Stahl on *60 Minutes*, in connection with his approach to North Korea.[12] When asked by Stahl about the repression, assassinations, and gulags in North Korea, Trump replied, "Sure. I know all of these things. I mean—I'm not a baby. I know these things." But he stressed that "I get along with him [Kim Jong Un] really well. I have a good energy with him. I have a good chemistry with him. Look at the terrible threats that were made. No more threats. No more threats."[13]

For a leader who otherwise has little empathy, it's startling how much Trump connects with repressive leaders: Vladimir Putin, Saudi crown prince Mohammed bin Salman, and Kim Jong Un. So long as he bonds with them on a personal level, that's all that really matters to him. As far as Trump is concerned, a nuclear deal is just like a real estate deal, and he is always the "Great Negotiator."

Personal ties between heads of state can be essential, but just because Trump likes Kim, it doesn't erase the fact that the North Korean leader runs a vicious police state, nor does it justify the enormous price the North Korean people continue to pay under the Kim dynasty. No one chooses to live in a brutal dictatorship or a totalitarian state. Even if Trump has "bonded" with Kim—he's actually said he's in love with him—it in no way changes the fact that North Korea remains a rogue state with the worst human rights record in the world.

The Arduous March

The biggest cost that the vast majority of North Koreans continue to bear is living in one of the most repressive countries in the world. Since the mid-1990s, but especially during the early 2000s, the number of North Korean escapees to South Korea increased sharply. Today, some thirty thousand have resettled in South Korea while tens of thousands continue to live in hiding in China. Under Kim Jong Un's rule, the numbers of North Korean defectors have decreased sharply due to harsher crackdowns. The spike in North Korean escapees peaked in 2005 and has subsided as the food situation gradually stabilized. Most of the escapees since early 2012, right after Kim assumed power, chose to leave North Korea because of the stifling dictatorship.

Masaji Ishikawa's father was a Korean living in Japan, and his mother was Japanese. Ishikawa was born in Japan, but in 1960, when he was a boy, his family moved to North Korea as part of a massive repatriation effort. In 1996, during the height of the great famine, he escaped, leaving behind his wife and children. In his account of the escape, Ishikawa writes that as he stood on the bank of the river dividing North Korea and China, he thought about the thousands of North Koreans like him, and wondered if he would survive the escape. "What difference does it make?" he thought. "If I remain in North Korea, I'll die of starvation. It's as simple as that. At least this way there's a chance—a chance I'll make it, that I will be able to rescue my family or at least help them somehow."[14] But after Ishikawa fled, his wife died of starvation, and he has had no contact with his children since 1998.

"I often think about what would have become of me if I'd stayed in North Korea," writes Ishikawa. "I would probably have starved too. But at least I'd have died in someone's arms with my family gathered around me. We'd have said our goodbyes. What chance of that now?"[15]

During the Kim Jong Il era, the biggest challenge facing North Korea was coping with, and recovering from, the great famine of 1995–1998. The general consensus is that 1 million to as many as 3 million people died, although estimates vary.[16] The North Korean government, for example, maintains that some 235,000 died in the famine. An academic study published in *Population and Development Review* in June 2001 estimated that total deaths from the famine between 1995 and 1998 were between 600,000 and 1 million.[17] But Andrew S. Natsios, former administrator of the U.S. Agency for International Development and author of *The Great North Korean Famine*, believes that between 2.5 million and 3.5 million deaths occurred.[18] A fully accurate accounting of the total deaths from the famine is impossible, given the unreliability and unavailability of North Korean data. But whatever the final number, Stephan Haggard and Marcus Noland write:

> North Korea's food problems pose a distinctive set of challenges for the international community. In many humanitarian crises, the international community faces failed states or conflict settings that make it difficult to provide assistance. In North Korea, by contrast, the international community faces a "hard" state that has repeatedly shown a willingness to allow its population to suffer extreme deprivation. . . . North Korea's tragedy has many roots, but a famine of this magnitude could only have occurred in a system in which the political leadership was insulated from events on the ground and lacking in accountability to its people. The failure of the North Korean government to guarantee adequate supplies of food to its population is inextricably linked to the government's denial of a battery of rights to its citizens: to confront public officials with their shortcomings; to publicize information that allows government officials to know the extent of distress; and to organize collectively in the face of injustice and deprivation.[19]

Fifteen percent of North Korea's farmland was destroyed by flooding in 1995, and the government blames the floods for the humanitarian disaster.[20] But Natsios points out that North Korea's food distribution system was already broken when the famine occurred, and he believes structural causes are largely responsible for the catastrophe. Many deaths could have been avoided if Kim Jong Il had allowed massive and direct food assistance, but it was only in 1996–1997, when the worst part of the famine was nearly over, that foreign food aid was at last permitted to trickle in. "All famines take place in a political context," says Natsios, "and there has been no famine in a democracy. In a democracy, people take action long before that point. Famines take place under centralized governments precisely because information can be hidden."[21]

Politically, North Korea began to accentuate the all-pervasive ideology of *Juche*, or self-reliance ideology, in the early 1970s, with the intention of highlighting its independence from the great powers. It was this ideology that gradually morphed into Kim Il Sung–ism and later Kim Jong Il–ism. Economically, the focus was on *jaryeok gaengsaeng*, a self-reliant economy. So when harvests began to dwindle, Kim Jong Il's response was triage: the first priority was to feed the party, government, and military elites living in Pyongyang. The state was no longer responsible for feeding the masses, who were forced to fend for themselves. Rations for farmers were cut, journalist Jordan Weissmann writes, and, "faced with the unappealing prospect of going hungry, farmers began hiding their grain. In 1996, the World Food Program found that half the country's corn crop had gone missing."[22] When foreign food aid eventually began to flow into North Korea, "much of it was stolen by well-connected elites, who re-sold the aid at marked-up prices. Farmers started doing the same thing with their own crops. As a result, food prices soared, and the poorest continued to starve."[23] Even as the vast majority of the population suffered enormously during the Arduous March, none of the top elites or the Kim family reduced their huge appetites for luxury goods. Kim Jong Il and his family continued to live like billionaires.

As the famine expanded, the minister of agriculture became aware that massive numbers of deaths were taking place. Too afraid to report it up the chain of command, he asked Hwang

Jang Yop, the party's secretary for international affairs and the primary author of the *Juche* ideology, to pass on the bad news to Kim Jong Il. Hwang agreed.

As a routine meeting was nearing its end, Hwang told the Dear Leader about the mounting famine and extreme food shortages. Kim Jong Il was outraged that Hwang had even mentioned it. He slammed his hands on the table and stormed out. That was the last time Hwang or anyone else at that level spoke to Kim about the famine.[24] Kim Jong Il didn't want any responsibility for killing up to 1.5 million North Koreans. The economy, he always argued, was the purview of the premier and his cabinet. Kim himself would focus only on military and political issues. This is how the Dear Leader, the father of all North Koreans, deflected the most basic requirement of leadership: feeding his own people.

From 1994, when he officially succeeded Kim Il Sung, until his death in 2011, Kim Jong Il visited China seven times. As China prodded him to adopt economic reforms, Kim toyed with the idea from time to time. In 2001 Kim visited the Pudong district of Shanghai and remarked, "Shanghai has been totally transformed!"[25] North Korean watchers were sure that this was a signal that the Dear Leader was open to real economic reforms. Chinese premier Zhu Rongzhi, who accompanied Kim on his Shanghai tour, cautiously asked him about the possibility of implementing reforms in North Korea, but the Dear Leader didn't reply.

When Kim revisited Beijing five years later, he was "unable to sleep" because of the shocking speed and breadth of China's economic transformation, according to Chinese press reports.[26] Kim's trip was followed up by Jang Song Thaek—his pro-reformist brother-in-law, widely regarded as the main conduit with China. Even though Jang urged Kim to follow China's path, Kim Jong Il didn't want to.

The abject failure of Kim Jong Il's economic policies had

political and structural causes, such as aftershocks from the downfall of the Soviet Union and the accompanying loss of subsidized energy and other assistance. As economist Nicholas Eberstadt argued back in 2011, that didn't necessarily have to lead to failure:

> The counterexample of Vietnam—another socialist Asian economy heavily dependent on Soviet subsidies in the late 1980s—proves as much. According to the World Bank, Vietnam's per capita income rose by over 150 percent between 1990 and 2007, and its nominal per capita exports (in US dollars) rose by a factor of over 7 times during those same years, whereas North Korea's nominal per capita exports slumped by over 25 percent between 1990 and 2007.[27]

Eberstadt also emphasized two other critical factors that resulted in the collapse of the North Korean economy under Kim Jong Il. First, there was "planning without plans" or "planning without facts." Second, the policy of "military first," or *songun jeongchi*, resulted in a "monstrous military burden."[28] In short, North Korea was drafting economic strategies without the requisite resources and realistic data.

North Korea spends around 20–25 percent of its GDP on its military, according to the U.S. State Department.[29] (Officially, the North Korean government reported that it earmarked 15.9 percent of its 2017 budget for the military, although observers deem this figure to be too low.[30]) While accurate figures are unavailable given the paucity and unreliability of North Korean data, the 20–25 percent figure means that approximately $7–10 billion was spent on defense in 2017, given that the DPRK's GDP was estimated to be $40 billion in that year.[31]

The South Korean government estimates that North Korea

has so far spent a total of between $1.1 billion and $3.2 billion on its nuclear and other WMD programs (although here too, accurate figures are nearly impossible to discern). Recall, also, that this is a country that isn't even able to feed its people and is nearly totally dependent on China for oil and food aid. The upshot is that Kim Jong Il's enduring economic legacy is simple and dark. Kim had no intentions of emulating China's reforms no matter what he said about the PRC's remarkable economic transformation. For Kim Jong Il, the most vital goal was ensuring the survival of the Kim dynasty and his military-first policy. Nothing else mattered. Nothing at all.

The Little Comrade General

Getting glimpses, even fleeting ones, into the Kim dynasty other than state propaganda is very rare. Recently, Kim Jong Un's unprecedented meetings with Moon and Trump—which would have been unthinkable in his father's time, even though Kim Jong Il did participate in summits with former South Korean presidents Kim Dae-jung and Roh Moo-hyun—have shed light on his personality. The Dear Leader was very cautious, much more of a hermit. Kim Jong Un is also a hermit but a more strategic one.

Born on January 8, 1983, Kim Jong Un from the beginning had a very strong personality, with a penchant for winning. He had an older half-brother, Kim Jong Nam, who by tradition as the first son would have been the first choice to succeed Kim Jong Il. Kim Jong Nam's chances of becoming king evaporated in May 2001 when he was caught with a bagful of hundred-dollar bills at Narita Airport in Tokyo. Traveling under a forged passport from the Dominican Republic, Kim Jong Nam was planning to visit Tokyo Disneyland with his four-year-old son, Sol Song, his wife, and their child's nanny. Kim Jong Il was livid, both at his oldest son's sheer stupidity and also for showing the world that the Kim family wasn't entirely made of premium revolutionary stock. Becoming the laughingstock of the world wasn't the worst part; what really angered Kim Jong Il was that the incident happened in Japan, Korea's old colonial master and, after the United States, the most hated country in North Korea.

As noted previously, one of the rare firsthand accounts of the Kim family comes from Kenji Fujimoto, who lived in North Korea on and off for a decade beginning in the mid-1980s. Fujimoto ultimately escaped North Korea and made his way back to Japan, where he wrote best-sellers about his time with the Kim family—and where he feared being assassinated by North Korean agents. Years later he returned to North Korea and, with tears flowing down his cheeks, apologized to Kim Jong Un for his transgressions and begged forgiveness. Because Fujimoto had been the Supreme Leader's playmate as a child, Kim Jong Un forgave him, and he now runs a highly successful Japanese restaurant in Pyongyang. Still, Fujimoto's ultimate fate depends on the whims of Kim Jong Un.

During his years as a companion to Kim Jong Il's sons, Fujimoto played basketball with Kim Jong Un and his older brother Kim Jong Chul. According to Fujimoto, Kim Jong Il once said of Jong Chul, "He doesn't cut it. He's like a girl."[32] Fujimoto never once saw the third brother, Jong Nam, in any of the palaces in Pyongyang or in the countryside.

There is a photo of a young Kim Jong Un dressed in full military regalia. As befitting a prince—and the future crown prince—he was addressed as "Little Comrade General" by those around him. He deeply resented being called "little" and insisted that he was his brother's equal.

On January 8, 1992, officials and family members gathered for the celebration of Kim Jong Un's ninth birthday. During the festivities, the famous Bocheonbo Orchestra, at Kim Jong Il's direction, played a song written especially for Kim Jong Un, called "Footstep." This song was the earliest known homage to Kim Jong Un, although songs were written for Kim Jong Il's other children as well.

> *Thump, thump, thump, footsteps coming*
> *Our general's footsteps,*
> *Spreading the energy, flowing from February*
> *Onward, thump, thump, thump*
> *Step by step, the stronger you walk*
> *The whole nation's mountains and rivers welcome them*
> *Thump, thump, thump.*[33]

Even in his early teens, Kim's urge to win was very strong. After a basketball game, Kim praised those who played well while criticizing others, sometimes harshly. Once he asked Fujimoto if he hadn't been too hard on a player, and Fujimoto replied, "You have to get angry when you have to. Otherwise, how will their techniques improve?" Kim was mightily pleased.

"That's right, Fujimoto!" said Kim with a big smile on his face.[34]

Kim, like his sister and brother, was schooled in Switzerland. Between 1998 and 2000 he was a student at Liebefeld-Steinhölzli school in Koeniz, south of Bern, where he was known by the alias "Pak Un." Students at the time remembered him as a fun classmate; one recalled that "he had a sense of humor and got on well with everyone, even those pupils who came from countries who were enemies of North Korea."[35] His former teacher Michel Riesen told NBC's *Today* that he was a "good student but not an extraordinary one."[36] Fujimoto recalls that Kim Jong Un returned frequently to North Korea while studying in Switzerland, and spent only five months out of each year at school.

When Kim Jong Un succeeded his father in 2011, speculations abounded on whether his Swiss experience could be a harbinger of a more reform-oriented North Korea. It's impossible to gauge how his studies in Switzerland affected Kim, but it would be misleading to read too much into his foreign experiences. Indeed, the most important education he received was after he returned to North Korea and began to be seriously groomed for the succession.

Becoming Deng Xiaoping?

Louis XIV's famous dictum "L'état c'est moi," the personification of the principle of divine right, runs even deeper in North Korea. For Kim Jong Un is not just the rightful inheritor of the throne: he is heir to two gods.

Both Kim Il Sung and Kim Jong Il are embalmed like Lenin. Two of the most auspicious holidays in North Korea are Kim Il Sung's birthday, April 15, known as Taeyang Jeol, or the Day of the Sun, and Kim Jong Il's birthday, February 16, celebrated as Gwangmyeong Jeol, or the Day of the Shining Star. Kim Jong Un was born on January 8, 1983, but so far, his birthday has not been turned into a major national holiday.

Much more relevant is whether Kim Jong Un is going to undo the legacies of his father and his grandfather. Will he embark on pathbreaking economic reforms by emulating China's "socialism with Chinese characteristics"—a fig leaf for adopting market economic principles? Is he going to startle the world and his people by ultimately giving up his precious nuclear weapons and ballistic missiles? Most importantly, is he willing to give his people enough freedom to basically do what they want to do so long as they stay loyal to the regime? Can Kim Jong Un undo his gulags and still survive?

The Moon government earnestly believes that Kim is a reformist. Moon himself believes that Kim has already done a major U-turn.

"I profoundly respect the determination and actions by Chairman Kim," Moon said in Pyongyang during a joint press conference with Kim in September 2018, and added, "Chairman Kim has clearly shown the way to denuclearization of the Korean Peninsula, and we have agreed on the vision of freeing the Peninsula from nuclear weapons, nuclear threat and war."[37] This was about three months after Kim and Trump had met for the first time, and Moon urged everyone to redouble their efforts to schedule a second Kim-Trump summit so that "denuclearization and the peace process on the Korean Peninsula make significant headway."[38] Moon also emphasized that "a new order is about to take shape on the Korean Peninsula. This new order on the Peninsula will lead to a new order in Northeast Asia."[39] Moon's comments reflected three themes that were emphasized by the South Korean government in 2018 about events on the Korean Peninsula: peace is at hand; North Korea is committed to denuclearization; and a bright new era is dawning for the Korean people.

There is little doubt that Kim Jong Un is stylistically very different from his father. He is more urbane and nuanced, and understands the enormous value of branding and image-making. So the fundamental question remains: Is Kim Jong Un North Korea's Mikhail Gorbachev or Deng Xiaoping?

Kim will never seek to emulate Gorbachev, since Gorbachev's reforms led not only to his downfall but also to the collapse of the Soviet Union (something Russian president Vladimir Putin called the biggest historical mistake of the twentieth century). The more appropriate model is Deng Xiaoping's market-style reforms (which began with the establishment of special economic zones) or Vietnam's adoption of similar reforms.

Moon is very eager to host Kim in Seoul to demonstrate that the Korean peace train is well on track. His affinity for Kim, however, has not only blinded him to reality, it has also led to the mushrooming of pro–Kim Jong Un groups in South Korea. Die-hard leftists and North Korean sympathizers in South Korea put up billboards heralding the Supreme Leader's prospective visit to Seoul. South Korea's public TV channel hosted a program highlighting why Kim Jong Un was such an incredibly different young leader.

When Moon visited Kim in Pyongyang, Kim dangled the possibility of making a landmark visit to Seoul by the end of 2018. Kim didn't show up, but according to South Korea's Blue House, he sent a personal letter to Moon in the last days of 2018 conveying his disappointment at having been unable to visit Seoul that year. In the letter, Kim told Moon that he would try hard to make it to Seoul in 2019.

Kim also met with U.S. secretary of state Mike Pompeo four times in 2018, in addition to his meeting with Trump in June of that year. Trump was very eager for a second summit, which was held in Hanoi, Vietnam, in February 2019. Trump chose to walk away rather than agree to a bad deal, and the Hanoi meeting illustrated once again the perils of two self-obsessed leaders convinced that they alone could change the other's mindset.

Domestically, Kim has built ski resorts, amusement parks, and high-end restaurants, but they're primarily for propaganda purposes. During his many inspection tours, Kim talks about producing quality consumer goods for the masses. He has refurbished Pyongyang with new apartments and a North Korean version of Silicon Valley.

Kim is brutal and smart, and he genuinely wants to transform North Korea into an economic powerhouse; he believes he can do so without loosening his grip on power or giving up his nuclear weapons. Although he is caricatured abroad as an overweight dictator with a crazy haircut, that focus is not only wrong but woefully simplistic. At the same time, magnifying Kim's alleged reformist tendencies and the abiding belief that he will give up his nuclear weapons in order to devote his undivided attention to economic development is also a mistake.

"He is seeking the kind of rapid economic development growth seen in China," argues Lee Jeong-seok, a former South Korean minister of unification and a key national security advisor during the Roh Moo-hyun government. "We have looked only on the nuclear side of Kim Jong Un's rule, trying hard not to look at the other side. He is ready to bargain away nuclear weapons for the sake of economic development. If he were content with just feeding his people three meals a day, he would not give up his nuclear weapons."[40] Such statements are typical of South Korean experts who are convinced of Kim's underlying reformist inclinations.

After Kim's third meeting with Xi Jinping on June 20, 2018, a week after Kim's summit with Trump, the progressive *Hankyoreh Sinmun* reported that Kim was on the verge of instituting economic reforms through the twin pillars of modernization of farming and railway construction. Reporting on Kim's visit to Beijing's traffic control center and a key infrastructure investment corporation, the newspaper noted that these visits "illustrated the North Korean leadership's very high interest in railways and infrastructure modernization, which are critical to economic development."[41]

As this was all happening in South Korea in 2018, in North Korean in April a video was shown to lower-level North Korean officials in state-run companies to highlight just how much heartache the Supreme Leader was feeling when economic goals weren't met. In the video, a person purported to be Kim Jong

Un stands on a seashore and stares at the horizon. Tears flow down his cheeks. The narrator says, "[The Supreme Leader] is crying because he is feeling heavy in his chest because of the lack and unevenness of reforms in order to build a strong nation!" Wrote the newspaper *Chosun Ilbo*, "It is significant that the video was shown to officials in the countryside and managers in state-run firms rather than central party members whose loyalties are high." The paper speculated that the party wanted to instill guilt in the minds of these managers by showing the tears of Kim Jong Un, who is treated as a deity in North Korea.[42]

Mike Hay is a Western lawyer who practiced in North Korea for twelve years. Unlike other foreigners who stay for limited periods, Hay was deeply involved in a variety of business enterprises in Pyongyang. Speaking of his colleagues, Hay recalled that "they were excellent English speakers, all graduates of Kim Il Sung University College of Law, with considerable experience of interacting with foreign entities and companies."[43] One way he survived and prospered was to never talk about political subjects or the leadership and to always abide by local customs. Hay pulled out of North Korea as international sanctions mounted and foreign clients dried up; he joined a law firm in Seoul. He remains adamant, however, that given the chance, North Korea can prosper.

"The DPRK does not give a rat's ass about sanctions, and the current state of play seems to bear that up. The economic development—the construction, the gorgeous restaurants, the emerging middle class, the money available—is all working with sanctions."[44] It's virgin territory for foreign firms if, and when, the North opens up to the world, he says. "They have the stuff [minerals] in the ground but don't have the equipment to get it out of the ground: there is the opportunity awaiting foreign investors."[45]

Hay says that there is every reason to believe that North Korea could be radically transformed economically under the right circumstances. But Kim Jong Un faces an existential dilemma: if the state is to prosper, he needs to open up the country, but the moment that opening reaches the point of no return, his dynasty will be imperiled. Many argue that China and Vietnam undertook reforms while maintaining their communist systems. That is a fair statement. Both Hanoi and Beijing, however, weren't run by a cold-blooded family dynasty that is corrupt to the core and demands total obeisance from its people.

Kim Jong Un's Catch-22

Since his rise to power in December 2011, Kim has stressed "worldwide trends," an approach very different from his father's emphasis on *Juche* ideology. Kim, of course, maintains the importance of Kim Il Sung Thought and Kim Jong Il Thought to justify his legitimacy and the Kim dynasty's rule. But within the confines of the North Korean system, Kim is remarkably pragmatic.

In 2002, Kim Jong Il announced the so-called July 1 Economic Management Improvement Measures, which partially recognized market economic functions. He did so because as the state's central planning continued to fail, small markets proliferated and the black market increased exponentially in size. By giving collective farms and other working units some autonomy and officially opening state-sanctioned comprehensive markets, the state believed it would still be able to exert control over them. As these policies began to bear fruit, however, the boundary between the planned economy and the informal economy blurred far too rapidly for Kim Jong Il's tastes.

> People began to open businesses outside of the sanctioned comprehensive markets, such as ad hoc, alleyway, and mobile shops, and there was a boom in individual

economic activities. Specifically, wide-ranging service businesses began to flourish, such as karaoke bars, PC game rooms, private lodgings, movers, bathhouses, restaurants, repair shops, and bike and motorcycle deliveries. Some factories and enterprises entered into the fray to make greater margins or to entice investments from the *donju* so that they could afford to pay a percentage of the profits to the state.[46]

As the informal economic sector continued to grow, the regime realized that it might overtake the command economy, so the July 1 Measures were formally discarded in the second half of 2005.

On November 30, 2009, North Korea announced currency reforms and introduced new banknotes, but this triggered massive pushback from North Koreans, who stood to lose 80 percent of the net value of existing notes. In a highly unusual move, the regime withdrew this policy after two months. Subsequently, the party secretary in charge of the economy, who only followed Kim Jong Il's orders, was made the fall guy and executed. Kim Jong Il had wanted to showcase currency reform to bolster Kim Jong Un's image, but it backfired completely. The policy was supposed to introduce the masses to Kim Jong Un's leadership skills, since he had only been groomed to succeed Kim Jong Il for a short period, starting in earnest after Kim's stroke in 2008. Not only was the general population against the measure, so were the elites. And Kim Jong Il could ill afford to anger the elites whose support would be essential in elevating his number-three son to the throne.

This fiasco was yet another reminder that the planned economy didn't function. For Kim Jong Un, it meant that without the help of the *donju*, his dreams of enacting economic reforms weren't likely to succeed. So he had to look the other way and allow them to continue their quasi-informal activities.

Originally functioning as loan sharks and black-market currency swappers, the *donju* began to act as key financial middlemen. Given the absence of lending institutions, the *donju* have expanded to provide loans and money transfers, financial transactions, collateral-based financing, and angel investors for new enterprises.[47]

Since April 2018, when Kim announced that North Korea would focus exclusively on economic development, he has stressed the importance of finding a unique North Korean model for economic development and expanding it nationwide. Farmers are allowed to keep more of their harvests; factories have more leeway to make their own decisions on quality control, prices, and wages; and a greater number of direct business-to-business interactions among small enterprises are authorized.

Economic change was unavoidable. With the downfall of the Soviet Union and Eastern Europe, North Korea began experimenting with very limited economic reforms. It set up special economic zones (SEZs) and opened the Mount Kumgang tourist region through an investment made by the Hyundai group and the Kaesong Industrial Complex as a symbol of inter-Korean economic cooperation. In practice, however, none of the SEZs first set up by Kim Jong Il or, later, by Kim Jong Un have taken off. Kim Jong Il was unwilling to make a political decision since he was afraid of the socioeconomic consequences. Under Kim Jong Un, ongoing international sanctions and an inability to shift key resources in a shrinking economy have stymied SEZs.

Under Kim Jong Il, piecemeal efforts at opening the economy were like "mosquito net" reforms, designed to filter out undesirable elements such as foreign capital, technology, and ideas, since he had no interest in reforming the broken North Korean economy.[48] Kim Jong Un believes that he can eat his cake and have it too. That is, he acts as if he's going to give up his nuclear weapons while locking South Korea into a web of irreversible inter-Korean projects, exploiting the opportunities tendered by a softening of South Korea's national security resolve, and enacting a series of controlled economic reforms, all while keeping in place the system that sustains his dynasty—the world's most Orwellian police state, a caste system that affects every single North Korean, a 1.2 million–strong military, and the gulags that imprison hundreds of thousands of North Koreans in inhumane conditions.

What he wants and thinks he can achieve is rapid economic growth while retaining the privileges, power, and influence he currently enjoys. Can his huge criminal syndicate be transformed into more legitimate businesses? It is possible in bits and pieces. But structural reforms are extremely risky, since the framework of control has already been weakened by the infiltration of hard currency to all levels of North Korean society and decades of numbing indoctrination that no one really believes anymore; additional reforms would only further weaken the framework.

How much freedom is Kim willing to give to the masses? To what extent will he allow relatively free information flows? There are some 5 million to 6 million cell phones being used in North Korea today, which means that about 25 percent of the population has them. Of course, they can't make international calls, and there's no internet connection for the masses. In 2010, 1,024 internet addresses were put under the control of Star Joint Venture, a Pyongyang-based company owned partly by Thailand's Loxley Pacific.[49] According to Recorded Future, an internet threat intelligence company, a few North Koreans (the top "0.1 percent") have access to the internet. North Koreans gain access through their nine top-level .kp domains, China Netcom, and a Russian satellite company.[50]

A recent assessment by Recorded Future noted that "North Korea's ruling elite are technologically savvy, use a full range of older and cutting-edge computers, phones, and devices, use the internet as a tool for sanctions circumvention, and recently shifted to embrace Chinese social networking services over Western ones."[51] This report also mentioned that North Korean senior leaders with internet access had much greater operational security awareness than they did in 2017 and that several countries were likely to be hosting North Korean workers involved in the information economy, including China, India, Bangladesh, Nepal, Mozambique, Kenya, Thailand, and Indonesia.[52]

North Korea operates an intranet through which people have access to officially sanctioned services and apps but ordinary citizens are denied internet connections. Even though Kim Jong Un knows that he can't really modernize his country without opening up to the internet, he also realizes that enabling the masses to freely connect with the outside world would open a floodgate he wouldn't be able to control. If average North Koreans accessed the internet like the citizens of China and Vietnam do, the entire edifice of lies they've been told all their lives, such as the "heavenly genius" of the Kim family, will come tumbling down. And even Kim Jong Un won't be able to massacre 25 million North Koreans.

The apparatus of Kim's police state remains unchallenged, but the level of corruption at all levels of the government, the military, and the party long ago passed the point of no return. What passed for centrally planned economic policies or, more recently, five-year plans can't keep pace with the hundreds of *jangmadang* that serve as the main conduit for the exchange of goods and services. The rise of small markets and the thirst for hard currency have replaced Kim Il Sung Thought and Kim Jong Il Thought as the lubricant for the Kim dynasty's machinery.

According to Gareth Leather and Krystal Tan of Capital Economics, "While North Korea's natural resources, geographical location and low labor costs mean its economy has plenty of potential, Kim Jong Un's hopes of North Korea emulating the economic achievements of Vietnam are slim."[53]

Seoul's KBS News has reported, based on a Chinese source, that Kim Jong Un recently set up an office within the party called the Reform and Opening Leaders Department and asked the Chinese Communist Party for support. While this report has not been independently verified, it said that "North Korea is believed to be recruiting personnel for the department, and Pak Tae Song, deputy chairman of the Korean Workers' Party, who visited China in May 2018 to observe China's scientific and technological development, and others are likely to be involved."[54]

Whether Kim Jong Un is going to make an effort to emulate China, or even Vietnam, is an open question. "Reform and opening up could be highly damaging to political stability. International investors will be extremely skeptical of Pyongyang, while the country's solipsistic attitude to the world will make it very difficult [to] create trust and mutually beneficial investment schemes," writes Peter Ward of *NK News*. Consequently, "South Korean government-backed 'cooperation' is likely to form the bulk of any future investment 'boom.'"[55]

Like Saudi crown prince Mohammed bin Salman, who spearheaded his Vision 2030 initiative to transform Saudi Arabia into an economic powerhouse, Kim faces huge structural challenges. But Kim's problems are even more pronounced, because while Crown Prince Salman can be replaced, in Kim Jong Un's North Korea Kim himself is irreplaceable. Short of a coup led by key leaders in the party and the military, he cannot be ousted.

Ultimately, Kim cannot undertake massive economic reforms without allowing the free flow of information, because unfettered economic transactions depend on it. Moreover, the political caste system that enslaves all North Koreans except for the super-elites cannot continue to exist if Kim is serious about systemic economic reforms. Free will is, after all, humanity's most powerful weapon, even if at present it is repressed in North Korea like nowhere else.

What Kim is most afraid of isn't the United States or its South Korean lackeys. It's the specter of a single North Korean who has the courage to say "No more!," like the lone individual who faced down a tank in the middle of Beijing's Tiananmen Square in June 1989.

North Korea *is* changing under Kim Jong Un, but it is changing within the confines of what is for all intents and purposes a movie set, like in *The Truman Show*. If Kim really believes in transforming North Korea, then he must set his sights far beyond his Potemkin village, Pyongyang, and go for broke.

THREE

THE SUPREME LEADER ENTERS THE WORLD

Kim Yo Jong Comes to Seoul

The most famous and powerful woman in North Korea isn't Kim Jong Un's wife, Ri Sol Ju, but Kim Yo Jong—Kim's only sister. As deputy chief of the propaganda and agitation department of the KWP, an alternate member of the Politburo, and a member of the central committee and the Supreme People's Assembly, Yo Jong works at the apex of the North Korean political system. The thirty-one-year-old is powerful not because she holds these influential posts in the party but because she hails from the Paektu bloodline. A granddaughter of North Korea's founder and longtime leader Kim Il Sung (1912–1994), Kim Yo Jong became a superstar the moment her plane landed at South Korea's Incheon International Airport in February 2018, the first member of the ruling family to set foot in South Korea since the Korean War.

Korean and foreign media recorded every moment of her

public appearance. It was hard to imagine that her main job was running information warfare campaigns on behalf of her brother and ensuring his grip on power. No one had seen a member of the Kim family quite like her: elegant, poised, and with a killer smile. As the media focused on her looks, the tailored black overcoat, and the fact that she tilted her head ever so slightly upward, Yo Jong became a symbol of a new North Korean leadership.

Kim Yo Jong understands how dangerous it is to walk the halls of power. Her aunt Kim Kyong Hui, who was Yo Jong's grandfather's doting daughter and Yo Jong's father's beloved sister, married Jang Song Thaek. Just two years after Kim Jong Un became Supreme Leader, he ordered Jang's execution. By killing his uncle, Kim Jong Un solidified his hold on power. It was a powerful reminder that no one stands in the way of the Supreme Leader. Having watched all of this in real time, Kim Yo Jong understands that her power flows from her brother's largesse.

Kim Yo Jong was acutely aware of her mission: to charm South Korea (and the rest of the world) in order to pave the way for Kim Jong Un's meeting with South Korean president Moon Jae-in. The ultimate goals: relief from international sanctions on North Korea and recognition of Kim Jong Un as a dynamic and a reform-minded leader—something like a very young Deng Xiaoping.

Reinventing the Supreme Leader

The Supreme Leader was ready to make his move. His charge to his sister was simple but powerful: *Tell Moon I want to meet him because I really want to focus on economic growth. I am willing to give up my nuclear arsenal and negotiate face-to-face with Donald Trump.* This was the first sortie in an unprecedented campaign of what the Soviets used to call *maskirovka*, or a camouflage, deception, and disinformation operation.

The days of saber-rattling were over, at least for the moment.

Kim Jong Un needed to completely rebrand his image on the world stage. Otherwise, harsher UN sanctions would really begin to erode North Korea's hard-currency earnings. Without dollars or euros, Kim couldn't sustain his regime. Although the ideology of *Juche* was still pervasive in North Korea, the reality was totally different.

North Korea depends on China for 90 percent of its fuel and food. Never mind that Kim spends huge amounts of money on his nuclear weapons and missile programs—nearly $100 million on missile tests alone between 2011 and 2017, according to South Korean estimates.[1] Overall, the estimated $1.3 billion spent on missile programs in North Korea since 2011, when Kim came to power, could buy 4.6 million tons of corn—enough to feed North Korea for four to five years.

By late 2017 and early 2018, UN sanctions were beginning to bite. Resolution 1718 had been passed in 2006 after North Korea detonated its first atomic bomb, and sanctions hardened as Pyongyang conducted successive tests. In September 2017, the UN passed Resolution 2375 after North Korea conducted a hydrogen bomb test. And while each of Kim's generals knew they could be demoted, purged, sent to a reeducation camp, imprisoned in a gulag, or even executed by antiaircraft guns, Kim couldn't help wondering if the stresses from the sanctions could lead party elites to begin to doubt his leadership. What would happen if twenty, thirty, or a hundred worried colonels and generals began to plot his ouster? Kim Jong Un needed a new strategy, and he calculated that the Winter Olympic Games would be the perfect launchpad for his reinvention of himself.

Kim was often caricatured in the West as a "boy general" with little experience, someone who spent time caressing his nuclear warheads. He was known mostly for executing his uncle, who had been instrumental in his ascendance; for assassinating his older half-brother in broad daylight in a Kuala Lumpur airport;

and for ordering the death of his minister of defense because the man was caught dozing off in a meeting.

Those who said Kim wouldn't be able to hold on to power were wrong. He is savvy and fully understands how and when to manipulate the levers of power. Unlike his father and grandfather, Kim is unafraid to rock the boat. Just how far he can rock it without capsizing it is the great unknown.

The killings of his uncle and his older brother had shocked the North Korean elites, as no previous North Korean leader had ever killed a close relative. Yet this brutal show of force had an unintended benefit beyond striking fear into the elites: according to veteran North Korea watchers in South Korea's intelligence community, the masses welcomed Kim's purge because those targeted had been symbols of their oppression.[2]

Assured of his own power within North Korea, and having successfully countered the United States with the development of advanced nuclear weapons and the demonstration of ICBM capabilities, Kim Jong Un now felt it was time to turn the page.

The Princess of Pyeongchang

The only person Kim Jong Un can trust entirely is his younger sister, Kim Yo Jong. Although North Korea experts differ in their speculations about what would happen if Kim Jong Un suddenly died, it is entirely possible, even probable, that Kim Yo Jong would replace him. Unless the North Korean military decides to eliminate Kim and his entire clan—nearly unthinkable, although not impossible—Yo Jong is the only one in the Kim dynasty who can assume the mantle. Detractors say that the military and party leadership would never accept a woman as their Great Leader, but in the pantheon of North Korean politics, the Kim family has a virtually untouchable aura.

Kim Yo Jong's own personal aura was certainly burnished by

her performance at the Olympic opening ceremony in February 2018. Although she was accompanied by a coterie of North Korean officials, the South Korean press had zero interest in covering any other members of the North Korean delegation.[3] Though at times Yo Jong was photographed looking stern and supremely confident, befitting her status, more commonly she was pictured with a warm smile and an open demeanor, and that was what made her a movie star—so much so that many South Korean men said that if they could, they'd marry her in a heartbeat.

When the opening ceremony began and the VIPs were being seated, President and Mrs. Moon stood to greet Kim Yo Jong and Kim Yong Nam, the then nominal head of state. Conscious that the world was recording her every movement, Kim Yo Jong was deferential to the president, bowing ever so slightly as she shook Moon's hand.

"Mr. President, it's a real pleasure to meet you," she said.

"It's very nice to meet you. Thank you for coming to the opening ceremony," replied Moon.

Then she shook hands with South Korea's First Lady.

The cameras caught these moments, but they also captured U.S. vice president Mike Pence, seated one row above Kim. Pence and his wife looked tense, surely thinking about how they would react if Kim Yo Jong suddenly turned to them and said hello. But she did not acknowledge them. And Pence didn't acknowledge her either.

Kim Yo Jong would meet with President Moon a total of four times during her three-day stay in South Korea. At a luncheon at the Blue House the day after the Olympic opening ceremony, she delivered an official letter from her brother and conveyed his invitation to Moon to visit Pyongyang. Moon smiled and said, "Let's work together toward creating the right environment," but he seemed positively inclined. The "Olympic thaw" had begun, and Kim Yo Jong was leading it.

From Little Rocket Man to My New Best Friend

On June 12, 2018, seven and a half years after he succeeded his father as Supreme Leader of North Korea, Kim Jong Un walked onto a stage in Singapore and extended his hand to U.S. president Donald J. Trump. Neither seemed to mind that just six months earlier, the two had been trading increasingly vicious denouncements. After the summit, Trump hailed his meeting with Kim as a "total success" and announced that he had bonded with the North Korean leader.

From the summer of 2017 until early 2018, however, the world media had been abuzz with daily breaking news on the growing threat of war on the Korean Peninsula. Americans were genuinely frightened by a North Korea that could fire a nuclear-tipped ICBM. No state had ever threatened the United States the way North Korea had. North Korean propagandists posted crude videos on YouTube of mushroom clouds engulfing the White House and of the Capitol blown to pieces. It was as if some installment of the *Die Hard* movie series was playing out in the real world.

On August 8, 2017, a gruff Trump said that any attack launched by North Korea would be met with "fire and fury like the world has never seen."[4] Pyongyang reacted swiftly with its own threat to create "an envelope of fire" around Guam, and added, "It is a daydream for the U.S. to think that its mainland is an invulnerable Heavenly Kingdom."[5]

When Trump's first secretary of state, Rex Tillerson, opined that the administration was willing to talk with Kim Jong Un, Trump famously tweeted, "I told Rex Tillerson, our wonderful Secretary of State, that he is wasting his time to negotiate with Little Rocket Man [Kim Jong Un] . . . Save your energy Rex, we'll do what has to be done."[6]

Everyone wondered what the plan was behind Trump's North Korea strategy. The U.S. foreign policy bureaucracy was being blindsided right and left by the president's tweets. In Trump's maiden speech before the United Nations General Assembly on September 20, 2017, the American president announced that while America was very powerful and patient, "if it is forced to defend itself or its allies, we have no choice but to totally destroy North Korea."[7] No U.S. president had ever uttered such threats before, not even at the height of the Cold War.

Not to be outdone, Kim shot back that "the entire United States is within range of our nuclear weapons; a nuclear button is always on my desk. This is reality, not a threat."[8]

Trump, who couldn't resist having the last word, subsequently tweeted, "Will someone from his depleted and food starved regime please inform him that I too have a Nuclear Button, but it is a much bigger & more powerful one than his, and my Button works!"[9]

The Olympic Thaw

So, what happened? How, after all these threats from both sides, did Trump and Kim wind up meeting in Singapore?

For Kim, a summit with a sitting U.S. president would provide a legitimacy that he sorely lacked on the international stage. For Trump, it was an opportunity to demonstrate his foreign policy bona fides and his negotiating skills against a determined and skilled adversary. The "Great Negotiator" was about to meet with the "Great Leader."

Trump wanted to show his detractors that, unlike any previous occupant of the Oval Office, he would be able to convince Kim Jong Un to dismantle his nuclear weapons. It was Trumpian to the core: follow your instincts, even if your advisors tell you otherwise.

The first hint of a thaw had come with Kim Jong Un's New Year's speech in January 2018. These annual speeches are generally much like the long, turgid, self-congratulatory speeches

Soviet leaders used to make during the Cold War; even so, intelligence analysts in Seoul, Tokyo, and Washington spend a lot of time assessing these speeches in an effort to gather insights into Pyongyang's strategy for the coming year.

But in January 2018, Kim Jong Un delivered a very different message. He appeared in a light gray suit and a matching tie rather than his usual Mao suit. Unlike his earlier speeches, when he had looked ill at ease as he read his lines, now Kim appeared to own the podium. And as he began his speech, he bowed and wished his countrymen a happy New Year. This was unprecedented—neither his father nor his grandfather had ever bowed in such circumstances. After all, they were living deities; how could gods bow before mere mortals?

In the speech he attacked the United States and South Korea, as expected, but simultaneously reached out to Seoul. "A very special achievement that was accomplished last year by our party, our country, and our people was the historical completion of our nation's nuclear weapons capabilities," he said.[10] He announced that he was certain the United States would never be able to attack the fatherland because North Korea now had a range of weapons to deter it, including nuclear ones.

Kim listed North Korea's usual spectacular achievements in all fields despite the burden of international sanctions, and he castigated South Korea for playing along with the rest of the international community. Yet he also stressed the importance of celebrating the two major events coming up in the new year: the seventieth anniversary of the founding of North Korea and the hosting of the Winter Olympic Games in South Korea.

If I were to comment on the opening of the Winter Olympic Games in the near future in South Korea, this is a good opportunity to display our brethren's status, and we sincerely wish that the games will be successful. In this light, we stand ready to send a delegation and discuss necessary steps; to this end, the officials of the North and the South could meet rapidly.[11]

It was a carefully crafted speech that highlighted the "peaceful" intentions of North Korea as a "responsible nuclear power." So long as enemy forces didn't impinge upon the nation's independence and sovereignty, Kim remarked, "we will not use nuclear weapons nor threaten any state with nuclear weapons."[12]

Within three hours, a spokesman for the South Korean Ministry of Unification welcomed Kim's desire to send a delegation to the Winter Olympic Games. South Korea was ready, said the spokesman, to discuss all related measures as soon as possible.

The Olympics would be a perfect stage to kick off Kim's peace initiative, since he was 100 percent certain that Moon would be a willing partner. While South Korea had spent billions of dollars preparing for the games, all Kim had to do was to send his sister with a high-powered delegation. Of course, athletes would go. But since only two North Korean athletes had prequalified, the highlight of the Pyeongchang Games wouldn't be the snowboarding and skiing competitions; it would be Kim Yo Jong.

The seed for inter-Korean détente had been planted soon after Moon Jae-in became president in May 2017. He promised during the campaign that he would continue the "sunshine policy," or policy of active engagement, begun by previous progressive governments. Moon's choice for director of the National Intelligence Service was Suh Hoon, who had served former president Roh Moo-hyun as deputy director for operations and played a key role in setting up the second inter-Korean summit in October 2007.

As head of the NIS, Suh began communicating with his counterpart in Pyongyang through discreet channels even as

North Korea tested missiles and carried out its sixth and most powerful nuclear test on September 3, 2017 (Pyongyang claimed it was a hydrogen bomb). The contacts with the North Korean Reconnaissance General Bureau—Pyongyang's main intelligence agency—that Suh had cultivated as deputy director a decade back began to pay dividends.

As far as Pyongyang was concerned, they couldn't have hoped for a better team in Seoul to work with. After ten years of conservative leaders in Seoul, someone was now going to pick up the phone when Pyongyang called.

In his first speech as head of South Korea, in July 2017, Moon outlined his vision for a completely different approach to inter-Korean ties. Moon pledged that as his government pursued denuclearization, it would also provide a security guarantee to the North Korean regime. Reminiscent of one of Ronald Reagan's favorite phrases in describing U.S.-Soviet relations, Moon said that "it takes two to tango. This is only possible when North Korea fully stops its nuclear provocations and comes out to the forum of bilateral and multilateral dialogue on denuclearization."[13]

Moon explicitly asked the North to consider taking advantage of the Winter Olympic Games scheduled for February 2018 in Pyeongchang, South Korea, just a hundred kilometers from the DMZ.

> I am ready to meet with Chairman Kim Jong Un of North Korea at any time at any place, if the conditions are met and if it will provide an opportunity to transform the tension and confrontation on the Korean Peninsula. We can place on the dialogue table all issues of interest between the South and the North, including the nuclear issue and the peace treaty, and discuss peace on the Korean Peninsula and inter-Korean cooperation.[14]

The South Korean leader was sending a very clear message to Kim Jong Un: *Meet me halfway. Let's break the patterns we've established as the world's last Cold War frontier. Give the Americans what they want—a denuclearized North Korea—and we both get what we want:* Koreans *taking charge of our nation's fate,* Koreans *united against the great powers,* Koreans *who can reunify the fatherland. It's our turn,* Moon was telling Kim; *make it happen.*

Moon Landing in Pyongyang

At a pace that no one expected, President Moon would end up holding three meetings with Kim in 2018: in April, May, and September. For the September meeting, Moon made his first trip to Pyongyang. Kim Jong Un choreographed every single moment of the three-day South-North lovefest.

Standing on the tarmac of Sunan Airport, Kim Jong Un and his wife, Ri Sol Ju, awaited Moon's arrival. As South Korea's 747 Air Force One opened its door, President Moon and his wife waved to the hundreds of North Koreans handpicked to welcome them. North Korea's ceremonial guards gave Moon a twenty-one-gun salute. As he walked down the long red carpet, Moon shook hands with some of the welcoming crowd. At the end of the row of carefully chosen North Koreans shouting their welcome, President Moon bowed his head 45 degrees—a sign of deep respect in Korean culture. North Korean television repeatedly showed this particular clip to demonstrate that Moon was paying homage to the Supreme Leader and his people.

Smiling, Kim and Moon shook hands and hugged each other three times. The two leaders set off from the airport in different cars, but as they approached the center of Pyongyang, the two leaders' vehicles formed a motorcade. Tens of thousands of Pyongyang citizens lined the streets shouting and cheering as the two leaders passed.

The following day, Kim and Moon announced the Pyong-yang Declaration, which highlighted a new military cooperation agreement. And on September 20, 2018, in a stadium filled with 150,000 North Koreans, Moon gave a speech—a first for a South Korean leader. Accentuating Korean nationalism and the oneness of Koreans, Moon declared, "Our people are outstanding. Our people are resilient. Our people love peace. And our people must live together."[15]

"During my stay in Pyongyang, I have witnessed the city's remarkable progress," Moon went on. "Deep in my heart, I have recognized what kind of country Chairman Kim and his compatriots in the North want to build."[16]

After more meetings, luncheons, and a state dinner, Moon and Kim took a cable car to the top of Mount Paektu, at the northeastern tip of the Korean Peninsula. Mount Paektu is known in North Korea as the birthplace of Kim's father, Kim Jong Il—a total fiction—but it has a wider significance across the peninsula as the birthplace of the mythical figure Dangun, who founded Korea five thousand years ago. There TV crews filmed Moon and Kim holding hands.

Crisscrossing the DMZ

As noted earlier, Moon's September visit to North Korea was the third of three meetings between the two Korean leaders that year. The first one had taken place on April 27 in Panmunjom. At precisely 9:00 a.m. on that day, Kim Jong Un walked down the stairs of Panmungak, the official building on the northern side of the dividing line between the two Koreas. President Moon stood waiting on the southern side of the concrete strip that cuts across the demilitarized zone, hundreds of TV cameras recording every moment. Smiling and extremely conscious of how he would be portrayed by the South Korean and world media, Kim

Jong Un walked toward Moon, and the two shook hands across the slightly elevated concrete barrier that divides the two Koreas.

As Moon caught Kim's hand he said, "It's a real pleasure to meet you, Chairman Kim! Welcome!"

"It has taken such a long time to cross such a short distance!" Kim replied.

"How long will it take for me to visit the North?" Moon asked.

"Come across now!" Kim answered. Then, holding hands, the two crossed onto the North Korean side of the 38th parallel. As Kim crossed back into the South Korean zone, the men hugged each other, smiling as if they'd won the lottery.

The pageantry was complete. Traditional and contemporary South Korean military honor guards welcomed the two leaders as they walked down the red carpet toward the Peace House for their first meeting. Kim suggested that they take a group picture with their respective delegations.

The first meeting between the principals included Moon's intelligence chief, Suh Hoon, and chief of staff, Im Jong-seok. On Kim's left was his sister, Kim Yo Jong, whom the TV cameras captured taking notes. President Moon remarked what a star she had been during the opening ceremony of the Winter Olympic Games, and Kim Yo Jong smiled and blushed. Kim Jong Un told Moon that "I won't interrupt your early morning sleep anymore [by testing weapons]" and also that "I am willing to go to the Blue House at any time" if invited. Moon, of course, told him he would be most welcome.[17]

Why did Kim meet with Moon in April 2018? Three key motivations spurred Kim to extend his hand to Moon: (1) to send a clear message to Donald Trump that he was a worthy negotiating partner; (2) to demonstrate to the United States that North Korea didn't want an outbreak of war on the Korean Peninsula; and (3) to show the world and his own people how confident he was in the world arena, demonstrating the difference between his reign and his father's.[18]

But most of all, it seemed as if Moon's, Kim's, Trump's, and even Xi's interests were all in alignment for the first time. Each looked at the summit through his own prism and concluded that the benefits far outweighed the risks.

Through the Panmunjom Declaration, Moon and Kim announced that the Korean War was over and that a new era of peace was dawning on the peninsula. The communiqué covered the gamut of improvements in inter-Korean ties, from reuniting separated families to denuclearization. The declaration was highly symbolic, though details were limited. On the nuclear issue, both leaders agreed that:

> South and North Korea confirmed the common goal of realizing, through complete denuclearization, a nuclear-free Korean Peninsula. South and North Korea shared the view that the measures being initiated by North Korea are very meaningful and crucial for the denuclearization of the Korean Peninsula and agreed to carry out their respective roles and responsibilities in this regard. South and North Korea agreed to actively seek the support and cooperation of the international community for the denuclearization of the Korean Peninsula.[19]

Moon and Kim also announced that they were going to turn the DMZ into a peace zone and that the Northern Limitation Line, the maritime boundary between the two Koreas, was going to be transformed into "a maritime peace zone in order to prevent accidental military clashes and guarantee safe fishing activities."[20]

The Blue House then surprised the world by announcing that a second summit would be held on May 26, 2018, at Panmungak on the North Korean side of the DMZ. The main reason for the second meeting was to ensure that the first-ever meeting of one of the Kims with a U.S. president would come off in June 2018 as planned.

Before, during, and after the April and May meetings, debate continued on whether Kim could possibly be serious about denuclearization in exchange for security guarantees. Still, those in favor of sustained dialogue with the North contended that symbolism matters. As one North Korean watcher said, "[Kim] has already created powerful, novel symbols of both his nation's and South Korea's yearning for peace. The recent Moon-Kim summit in Panmunjom powerfully showed values dear to their cultures: respect, filial piety, harmony and order."[21]

The Singapore Sling

The South Koreans' concerns about possible problems with the Kim-Trump summit were not unwarranted: on May 24, a little under three weeks before Trump was scheduled to shake hands with Kim, he abruptly canceled the meeting after the North Korean press labeled Vice President Pence a "political dummy" and threatened a "nuclear showdown."[22] But, ever the reality TV showman, Trump announced on June 1 that the summit was on again. Trump was keen on meeting Kim for numerous reasons, but one of the most important was to amplify his made-for-television branding as the "Great Negotiator."

Trump has always believed that he has the Midas touch. During an interview on *Meet the Press* with Tim Russert on October 24, 1999, Russert asked Trump what he would do about the burgeoning North Korean nuclear threat if he was president. Trump replied,

> First I'd negotiate and be sure I could get the best deal possible. . . . These people in three or four years are going to have nuclear weapons. . . . The biggest problem

this world has is nuclear proliferation. And we have a country out there in North Korea which is sort of whacko, which is not a bunch of dummies and they are developing nuclear weapons. . . . If that negotiation doesn't work then better solve the problem now [with a preemptive attack] than solve it later. . . . You want to do it in five years when they have warheads all over the place, every one of them pointed to New York City, to Washington . . . is that when you want to do it? . . . You'd better do it now. And if they think you're serious . . . they'll negotiate and it'll never come to that.[23]

Leaving aside Trump's rhetoric and his self-proclaimed negotiating prowess, the "maximum pressure" strategy did seem to have paid some dividends. Barry Pavel of the Atlantic Council gave credit to the Trump administration for implementing "an unprecedented and relentless pressure campaign that undoubtedly played a role in changing the North Korean leader's approach."[24]

After a closed, one-on-one session with Kim Jong Un and a broader meeting with their respective delegations, Trump declared that his meeting with Kim had been "over the top." In a joint statement signed by both leaders, it was noted that "President Trump committed to provide security guarantees to the DPRK, and Chairman Kim Jong Un reaffirmed his firm and unwavering commitment to complete denuclearization of the Korean Peninsula."[25] In remarks to the press corps, Trump said that "the meeting worked out for both of us far better than any of us expected" and that he felt he had a "special bond" with Kim Jong Un. Trump was asked about the brutal nature of the North Korean regime, which he had castigated on numerous occasions, but he demurred and said, "It's a rough situation, but it's rough in a lot of places." Trump's fondness for authoritarian rulers is well known—his constant admiration for how strong Vladimir Putin is at home is merely one example. So when he was asked how he could trust a brutal dictator who runs a police state, Trump avoided a direct answer, replying, "I'm given what I'm given." He added, "His country loves him. His people, you see the fervor. They have a great fervor."[26]

Although Trump insisted that there had been no discussion about pulling U.S. forces from South Korea, he emphasized, "We're not gonna play the [U.S.–South Korean] war games. You know, I wanted to stop the war games, I thought they were very provocative. But I also think they're very expensive. We're running the country properly, I think they're very, very expensive."[27] During an earlier press conference, Trump had been asked a similar question, and at that time he answered,

> We have done exercises working with South Korea for a long time. We call them war games. I call them war games. They are tremendously expensive. The amount of money we spend on that is incredible. South Korea contributes, but not 100 percent, which is a subject that we have to talk to them about also. That has to do with the military expense and also the trade. We actually have a new deal with South Korea. . . . Under the circumstances we are negotiating a comprehensive and complete deal. It is inappropriate to have war games. Number one, we save money. A lot. Number two, it is really something they very much appreciated.[28]

Not once, however, did Trump mention the fact that North Korea had *not agreed* to stop its own military exercises. Nor did Trump mention what Kim gave up in return for the U.S. pledge to cease the joint exercises with South Korea. Moreover, for a U.S. president to state on the record that the joint military exercises were "provocative" to the North was unprecedented. After all, American troops were stationed in South Korea as a critical symbol of America's commitment to South Korean defense. Joint exercises with the Republic of Korea's (ROK) armed forces—the very capable and most Americanized of any allied forces who fought with the United States during the Korean and Vietnam wars—were essential to maintaining interoperability.

After their forty-five-minute one-on-one meeting, Trump and Kim took a short walk together. A second round of talks was held with key staff members, including Secretary of State Mike Pompeo, Chief of Staff John Kelly, and National Security Advisor John Bolton on the U.S. side. While Kim Yo Jong was in Singapore for the duration of the summit, she didn't attend the extended meeting. The North Korean delegation included Kim Yong Chol, head of the Unification Front of the KWP and former director of the Reconnaissance General Bureau; Ri Su Yong, vice chairman of the Central Committee of the KWP; and Minister of Foreign Affairs Ri Yong Ho.

The summit ended with a four-point joint statement but no agreement on a denuclearization road map. "Having acknowledged that the U.S.–DPRK summit—the first in history—was an epochal event of great significance in overcoming decades of tensions and hostilities between the two countries," the statement said, "President Trump and Chairman Kim Jong Un commit to implement the stipulations in this joint statement fully and expeditiously."[29]

In a subsequent interview with George Stephanopoulos of ABC News, Trump was asked how he could trust Kim to actually denuclearize as he promised. Trump replied, "Yeah, he's de-nuking, I mean he's de-nuking the whole place. It's going to start very quickly. I think he's going to start now."[30]

Trump was very sure of his achievements. In January 2019, Trump tweeted, "No more Rockets or M's [missiles] being fired over Japan or anywhere else and, most importantly, no Nuclear Testing. This is more than has ever been accomplished with

North Korea and the Fake News knows it."[31] And while the first Singapore summit no doubt was meaningful simply because it took place, any road toward actual denuclearization will be infinitely more complex and riddled with hurdles. For Kim Jong Un, the promise of denuclearization was used only as bait to get Moon and Trump on board the Pyongyang peace train. For North Korea, denuclearization must be symmetrical, with the withdrawal of the U.S. nuclear umbrella over South Korea—not unilateral disarmament, as demanded by the United States.

In the end, Kim got a measure of respect from the international community, and however small or fleeting it was, it counted as a victory, since international respect was the one commodity no previous North Korean leader had ever had. He also bought time to string along South Korea, leading it deeper into the peace initiative and diluting international sanctions. As one observer noted,

> The summit definitely bolstered Kim's image in the international arena, and while many other countries and international organizations will want to see the details of the plan for denuclearization, many governments and businesses are looking to North Korea for signs of change and opening—which could lead to pressure for sanctions relief. China will certainly be interested in taking an active role. And South Korea will continue to work hard to dial up investment and development plans, as well as other forms of humanitarian and cultural engagements.[32]

Kim came out of the Singapore summit the winner in terms of luring South Korea and the United States into a denuclearization rabbit hole. The value to him of his newfound image as a "responsible and a reasonable leader" was incalculable. As Kim celebrated his diplomatic coup on the way back to Pyongyang on a Chinese airplane—his personal Soviet-made jet was too unreliable for a long flight—it certainly was clear to him that making it work with Trump was going to hinge on pushing denuclearization as far into the future as possible. He had no intentions of giving up those nuclear weapons.

After the Singapore and Pyongyang summits, Kim could congratulate himself on having achieved two of his major goals. The first was watering down the ROK's military preparedness, which he accomplished when Trump agreed to forgo the joint military exercises with South Korea. The second was giving Moon a major boost in domestic politics, and that paid off for North Korea: in late August 2018, the South Korean defense ministry announced that it was considering excising references to North Korea as an "enemy state" in future defense white papers.[33]

The Hanoi Walkaway

As soon as Trump returned to Washington, D.C., after the Singapore summit, he tweeted that the North Korean nuclear threat was over. "Just landed—a long trip, but everybody can now feel much safer than the day I took office," Trump said, and he proclaimed that "there is no longer a Nuclear Threat from North Korea. Meeting with Kim Jong Un was an interesting and very positive experience. North Korea has great potential for the future!"[34]

But saying that the North Korean nuclear threat was over was simply not true. North Korea's work on its nuclear weapons had continued before the Singapore summit, and it continued afterward. In January 2019, Dan Coats, the director of national intelligence, stated in congressional testimony, "We currently assess that North Korea seeks to retain its WMD capabilities and is unlikely to completely give up its nuclear weapons and production capabilities because its leaders ultimately view nuclear weapons as critical to regime survival."[35]

Secretary of State Mike Pompeo bent over backward to explain Trump's remarks. In February 2019, he claimed in an interview with CNN that Trump hadn't really said that there was no longer a North Korean threat. Instead, Pompeo explained, "what he [Trump] said was the efforts that had been made in Singapore, this commitment that Chairman Kim made, have substantially taken down the risk to the American people. We're aiming to achieve that."[36]

Eight months after the Singapore summit, the White House announced that a second summit was going to be held in Hanoi, Vietnam. While various administration officials attempted to temper expectations about what could be achieved at the February 27–28 summit, it was clear that after the Singapore meeting had ended with no tangible agreement, Trump was eager to demonstrate his negotiation skills.

For Kim, the Hanoi summit was another opportunity to appear as a respected world leader. To maximize publicity, and for security reasons, Kim traveled on his personal train—a sixty-hour journey. As Christopher Green of the International Crisis Group remarked, "This is legacy politics. . . . North Korea will want to play up Kim's succession to the role of his grandfather, who successfully built up North Korea's international legitimacy after the establishment of the state."[37]

South Korea's Moon was banking on a major breakthrough in Hanoi. Having invested nearly all of his political capital on inter-Korean détente, Moon, even more than Trump, was pushing for tangible progress.

U.S. Special Representative for North Korea Steve Biegun was involved in intense discussions with his North Korean counterparts prior to the Hanoi meeting. In January 2019, North Korea's top negotiator, Kim Yong Chol, visited Trump at the White House. In a series of remarks intended to set the tone for the Hanoi summit, Trump said that the United States had been on the brink of war with North Korea when Obama was in office but that he had turned it around. In February 2019, Trump said that when he met Barack Obama on the day of his inauguration, he was under the impression that Obama "would've gone to war with North Korea. I think he was ready to go to war. In fact he told me that he was so close to starting a big war with North Korea."[38] Senior aides under Obama sharply disagreed with Trump's assertions. Former deputy national security advisor Ben Rhodes said, "We were not on the brink of war with North Korea in 2016," and former CIA director John Brennan stated, "President Obama was never on the verge of starting any war with North Korea, large or small."[39]

Trump's incessant need for the limelight was on full display when he asked Japanese prime minister Shinzo Abe to nominate him for the Nobel Peace Prize because of his dialogue with North Korea. Trump showed his "beautiful copy" of the nomination letter given to him in mid-February by Abe—without revealing that Abe had prepared the letter after a request from the Trump administration.[40]

For their second summit, Kim and Trump broke the ice with a one-on-one meeting on February 27, followed by a private dinner. After his thirty-minute meeting with Kim, Trump couldn't resist showing off and said, "Boy, if you could have heard that dialogue, what you would pay for that dialogue. It was good. A lot of things are going to be solved, I hope. And I think it will lead to, really, a wonderful situation long-term."[41]

A full-dress meeting was held the next day, and expectations were running high. The White House scheduled a signing ceremony in the afternoon, to follow formal discussions, and the South Korean Blue House announced that President Moon was planning to watch the signing ceremony as it was broadcast worldwide.

Then the ground caved in.

Trump announced that he was walking away from the Hanoi summit. North Korea wanted sanctions relief and was prepared to partially dismantle the Yongbyon nuclear facility; Trump wanted a North Korean promise to destroy all nuclear weapons as well as other weapons of mass destruction. Trump noted, "They wanted the sanctions lifted in their entirety, and we couldn't do that. They were willing to denuke a large portion of the areas that we wanted, but we couldn't give up all of the sanctions for that."[42] Secretary of State Pompeo put the best spin he could on it, saying, "The President and Chairman Kim both felt good that they had made that progress but couldn't quite get along the line any further to make a deal that would have been bigger at this point."[43]

At a press conference after the negotiations collapsed, Trump alluded to the fact that Kim had been told that the United States knew of the existence of a second North Korean uranium enrichment plant, beyond what North Korea had revealed to the Americans: "And we brought many, many points up that I think they were surprised that we knew."[44]

At another point in the press conference, Trump was put on the defensive when he was asked whether he thought Kim Jong Un was responsible for the death of Otto Warmbier, an American college student who had been jailed and tortured in North Korea, then returned to the United States in a vegetative state; he died shortly afterward.

"I did speak about it, and don't believe that he [Kim Jong Un] would've allowed that to happen. . . . I really don't believe that he was—I don't believe he knew about it. . . . He tells me that he didn't know about it, and I will take him at his word."[45]

After the press conference, Warmbier's parents spoke out. "Kim and his evil regime are responsible for the death of our son Otto," they said in a statement. "Kim and his evil regime are responsible for unimaginable cruelty and inhumanity. No excuses or lavish praise can change that."[46] Speaker of the House Nancy Pelosi stated that "there's something wrong with Putin, Kim Jong Un—in my view, thugs—that the president chooses to believe."[47]

Despite the lack of any agreement, U.S. national security advisor John Bolton asserted in an interview after the summit that Hanoi was not a failure: "I consider it a success defined as the president protecting and advancing American national interest." When Bolton was pressed about an earlier remark he had made to the effect that North Korea could be denuclearized in a year, he replied, "There is no expiration date. As I say, the president is fully prepared to keep negotiating at lower levels or to speak to Kim Jong Un again when it's appropriate."[48]

Bolton was asked if he thought Kim Jong Un was going to deliver on his promises to dismantle his nuclear weapons. His reply was very cautious: "I think he is the authoritative ruler of that country and if he were to make the strategic decision to denuclearize, we think it would happen."[49]

In a rare move, North Korean foreign minister Ri Yong Ho, in a middle-of-the-night news conference, contradicted what Trump had said earlier about Kim insisting on the total lifting of sanctions in return for partial denuclearization. "What we proposed was not the removal of all sanctions but the partial removal," said Ri. In return for partial sanctions relief, he said, North Korea was prepared to "permanently and completely dismantle all the nuclear material production facilities in the Yongbyon area, including plutonium and uranium, in the presence of U.S. experts."[50]

In an effort to bolster Kim's standing domestically and internationally after the failure of the Hanoi summit, veteran North Korean diplomat Choe Son Hui intimated that Kim's patience was running thin: "Chairman Kim got the feeling that he didn't understand the way Americans calculate. I have a feeling that Chairman Kim may have lost the will" to continue to negotiate.[51] She also said that North Korea would "never yield" to American pressure. Will North Korea ultimately give up its nuclear weapons? North Korean expert Andrei Lankov doubts that Kim will keep his word.

> [Denuclearization is for] a distant future, when U.S. forces are completely withdrawn not necessarily from only the Korean Peninsula, but maybe from the entire East Asia, maybe from the Pacific and what about Hawaii, or what about surrender of U.S. nukes and Russian nukes and Chinese nukes? When that happens, the North Korean government will probably be happy to surrender its nukes as well.[52]

The message Kim wants to send to the Americans is that North Korea will never take steps toward denuclearization unless and until there is rapid movement on building a peace regime on the Korean Peninsula. Kim needs sanctions relief, and even though he has been able to get backing from China and Russia and from a South Korean government that is all too eager to pursue massive investments into the North, the UN remains a roadblock.

As for Trump, it had never been clear how he would have been able to put his master plan into action even if there had been some agreement. After all, North Korea has reneged on every agreement it has made with the United States since the early 1990s. Even so, with a South Korean president eager for lasting détente and a U.S. president in search of a major foreign policy achievement (especially after Trump pulled out of the Iranian nuclear agreement and reimposed sanctions on Tehran), by agreeing to these meetings Kim Jong Un was able to gain something he hadn't had before: time. Time to water down international sanctions. Time to increase multipronged pressures on South Korea, such as convincing it to look the other way when North Korean ships violated UN sanctions. Time to provide the world with evidence of a handful of obviously decommissioned nuclear weapons and ballistic missiles to demonstrate that North Korea *was* dismantling its nuclear program and missile sites. Most of all, Kim needed time to lock in Chinese and Russian support and to make sure Moon was going to be with him until 2022, when Moon's five-year term comes to an end.

Even if Moon continues to emphasize the all-important U.S.-ROK alliance, Kim knows that Moon's eagerness to establish inter-Korean cooperation during the remaining years of his term means that the Blue House will continue to pursue South-North dialogue. Should North Korea conduct another nuclear weapon or ICBM test, Kim now knows that so long as a leftist president sits in the Blue House, he has nothing to worry about. Besides, Xi Jinping and Vladimir Putin both want Kim Jong Un to remain in power as long as possible. So long as Xi and Putin know that Kim's only patrons are China and, to a much lesser extent, Russia, he isn't likely to deviate from Chinese and Russian interests, especially if Kim remains in power for two to three decades.

The U.S.–North Korea nuclear saga has been ongoing since the early 1990s, and both Trump and Kim have a vested interest in reaching what would be a historic agreement. For Trump, it would be the culmination of his quest for a decisive foreign policy victory. For Kim, a carefully crafted accord in which North Korea promises to give up certain nuclear capabilities in exchange for sanctions relief and moving toward normalization of relations will solidify his diplomatic reputation.

As Trump prepares for a high-stakes presidential contest in November 2020 and Moon tries his hardest not to derail the peace train as he heads into a crucial April 2020 National Assembly election, time is on Kim's side. No one today believes that North Korea's nuclear capacity can be rolled back by military force without triggering a second Korean War. In this respect, the side that blinked isn't Kim Jong Un, but Trump and Moon.

FOUR

A NEW KING RISES

Long Live the King

Wearing a black Korean national dress, Ri Chun Hee, the most famous anchor in North Korea, appeared on Korean Central TV at noon on December 19, 2011, to announce the death of Kim Jong Il. The Dear Leader had died two days earlier, on December 17, but it took the regime forty-eight hours to announce his death.

Choreographed to perfection, like almost every other public aspect of North Korea, Ri's performance was nearly flawless. "It is with unfathomable grief that we announce the passing of our Great Leader Comrade Kim Jong Il," Ri said solemnly, "who died of a sudden illness on December 17 at 8:30 p.m. in the year Juche 100 [2011] during an inspection tour."[1] But because all North Korean anchors speak as if they were preprogrammed, everything about her was unnatural, even her well-practiced grief. This was the second time Ri had announced the death of a living deity.

The first time had been on July 8, 1994, when she announced the passing of the Great Leader, Kim Il Sung.

On December 29, 2011, at 1:57 p.m., Ri anchored the live broadcast of the Dear Leader's funeral procession. His hearse began its slow journey on a preplanned route through Pyongyang so that the masses could pay their last respects. The people lined up as they had back in 1994. As the crowds spied the stretch Lincoln Continental approaching from afar—the very same vehicle that had carried Kim Il Sung's coffin on the roof years before—people screamed with anguish, beat their chests in disbelief, and cried tears that streamed down their faces, just like in 1994. It was déjà vu. Except it was snowing this time, with the flurries getting progressively stronger.

In the world's most Orwellian state, how one acted during a state funeral was critical to physical and political survival. When Kim Il Sung died of a massive heart attack in July 1994, North Koreans had never known any other leader. There was genuine sorrow. But the people also knew that if they didn't fall on their knees, scream their lungs out, and beat their chest with their fists, someone would notice and report them. Big Brother watched over North Koreans constantly, in search of citizens who didn't cry as genuinely as they should or who didn't express their sorrow as deeply as they should.

No one, especially officials, could let their guard down. Kim Jong Un reportedly ordered the execution of former KPA vice minister Kim Chol by mortar fire after he was charged with drinking alcohol during the official one-hundred-day mourning period following the Dear Leader's death.[2] Even in death, the Dear Leader kept his grip on the people.

While the masses wailed and mourned for Kim Jong Il as they had for Kim Il Sung, something was a bit off this time. One couldn't really put a finger on it. Even though North Koreans seemed to be grieving over their fallen king, the emotions didn't seem quite as genuine as when the founding father died. Perhaps it was because Kim Jong Il hadn't batted an eye when so many North Koreans starved to death in the great famine of the mid- to late 1990s. Perhaps it was because the people knew instinctively that he had never cared for them. Perhaps they were just tired of acting like puppets their entire lives.

As the cameras rolled, thousands of officials from the party, the armed forces, the government, and all people's voluntary or- ganizations stood in perfectly aligned units in Musudan Square and bowed their heads in unison as Kim Jong Il's coffin passed. Eight men walked alongside the hearse, four on each side, ac- cording to their rank in the funeral committee. In the former Soviet Union, the identities of the funeral committee members offered a glimpse into the emerging power structure. In North Korea, however, even if you were high up in the funeral commit- tee, your future was hardly guaranteed.

Kim Jong Un led the procession on the right side of the vehi- cle, looking somber. Right behind him was his uncle, Jang Song Thaek, the second most powerful person in North Korea. Jang had promised Kim Jong Il that he would do everything in his power to ensure Kim Jong Un's successful coronation. Jang also served as the deputy chairman of the Central Military Com- mission, the most important organ of the North Korean state under the Dear Leader. Following Jang were party secretary Kim Ki Nam; the chairman of the Supreme People's Assembly, Choe Tae Bok; the chief of the General Staff, Ri Yong Ho; the minister of the People's Armed Forces, Kim Yong Choon; the first deputy political commissar of the KPA, Kang Jung Gak, and the first vice minister of the Ministry of State Security, U Tong Chuk. Dubbed by the South Korean press as the "Gang of Seven," all but one would be either executed or purged by December 2013.[3]

As the Dear Leader's embalmed body lay in state, top officials

filed by to pay their last respects. When he walked by his father's corpse, Kim Jong Un stood at attention for a brief moment,
bowed his head, and shed tears. His sister, Kim Yo Jong, was
sobbing in the back. Behind the veneer of mourning, however,
Kim's utmost priority was ensuring that he was *actually* going to
succeed his father. Critically, he needed the backing of the armed
forces and support from his uncle Jang.

The North Korean propaganda machinery was already working overtime to legitimize Kim Jong Un's rise to the throne. All
over North Korea, pledges of loyalty to the new leader were announced. Throughout the period when Kim Jong Il lay in state,
Korean Central TV broadcast daily feeds showing the thousands
of citizens across North Korea who paid their respects under a
huge picture of a smiling Dear Leader.

In Kim Il Sung Square—the Tiananmen Square of
Pyongyang—North Koreans from all walks of life were organized into square columns. Like clockwork, row after row would
march up to a giant portrait of the Dear Leader, bow their heads
in unison, and beat their chests. As the television announcer
characterized it, the people were at the same time expressing
their "spontaneous best wishes" to the new Great Leader, Kim
Jong Un. As a group of men laid flowers under a huge portrait
of Kim Jong Il, the camera zoomed in on one young man; with
tears streaming down his face, he declared solemnly, "I will stay
at the forefront of protecting our respected comrade Kim Jong
Un as his most loyal servant!"[4]

As the funeral progressed, state TV made sure that paying
respects to the fallen king was equated with greeting the people's
new king. In her distinctive voice, Ri Chun Hee proclaimed not
only that all the offspring of "Kim Il Sung mourn the passing
of our General and Dear Leader" but also that "all of our countrymen with burning hearts pledge our loyalty to Comrade Kim
Jong Un."[5]

Kim Jong Un was the new leader, but he had to ask himself if the old guard was really going to support him, an untested twenty-eight-year-old who had been educated partially in a Swiss school. Would the generals and party leaders handpicked by his father allow him to reign? As North Korea's official mourning continued, Kim knew that he was far from being in full command. Who could he really trust?

A Mafia State with Nuclear Weapons

North Korea isn't, strictly speaking, a traditional communist state: in the revised 1972 constitution, Marxism-Leninism was replaced by Kim Il Sung–ism as the official ideology. Closely tied to Kim Il Sung–ism is *Juche sasang*, or self-reliance ideology, a new ideology crafted by one of North Korea's premier intellectuals, Hwang Jang Yop.

When it was first promulgated in the early 1970s, *Juche* was meant to rectify Marxism-Leninism with North Korean characteristics. Rapidly, however, it morphed into a justification of the supreme primacy of Kim Il Sung and of a pervasive, fiction-based personality cult to support him.[6]

In a move that even Hitler's Nazi Germany or Stalin's Soviet Union hadn't tried, the people were told that Kim Il Sung was not only the head of the KWP and North Korea but also the true father of all North Koreans. The personality cult became so overwhelming that every North Korean had to wear their Kim Il Sung and Kim Jong Il badges slightly above their heart to symbolize their total loyalty to the two leaders.

Every North Korean home must display pictures of the Great Leader and the Dear Leader. Every building in North Korea does the same, and it is considered a sacred duty to dust these pictures before the official day begins. Newspapers that have pictures of the Kim family cannot be used to wrap fish or groceries, since any such use would tarnish their images. As a fire was engulfing a building, a man jumped out the window while holding the portraits of the two Kims. He was lauded as a people's hero.

Hwang Jang Yop, who played a major role in the construction of *Juche*, defected to South Korea in 1997. In a book written after his defection, he explains the totally narcissistic nature of the personality cult that reached new heights under Kim Jong Il:

> A "Supreme Commander" means that he is the highest commander, which means that he has the same duty as all of the soldiers of the People's Army to lay down their lives for their nation and fellow countrymen. But the soldiers are told to lay down their lives for Kim Jong Il, who only became the supreme commander because of his lineage. To ask the soldiers to die on his behalf is a profound insult because he considers the state as his personal property. . . . The more that Kim Jong Il demands total and unconditional loyalty from his citizens and soldiers, the more he is exposing himself as a traitor against his country and all of humanity by ignoring every ethical norm. The reason the moral foundations of the armed forces are crumbling is connected with such realities.[7]

When Kim Jong Il took over, Kim Jong Il–ism was added as an official ideology. And when he died in 2011, North Koreans had to officially worship two eternal gods.

Party and government organs and the armed forces reflect Leninist structures, including the principle of democratic centralism: information filters upward, but once a decision is made by the party, everyone must obey. In North Korea, this means submitting to the Kim family. Political commissars play key roles in the KPA to watch over the professional military, just as happened in the former Soviet Union's Red Army or China's People's Liberation Army. But the militarization of the state in North Korea is unlike what is seen in China or even the former USSR; it has no parallel in the modern world. What C. Christine Fair has argued regarding Pakistan could be said of North Korea: it is an army pretending to be a country. While the political systems are very different, the common ingredient between North Korea and Pakistan is the overwhelming influence of the military. This symbiosis led to a unique WMD partnership: Pakistan's transfer of nuclear weapons technology to North Korea in exchange for Pyongyang's transfer of ballistic missile technologies to Islamabad.[8]

Another element contributing to North Korea's unique ideology is the unprecedented level of corruption in a state that is essentially a crime syndicate headed by the Kim family. There are surprisingly apt parallels between the structure of classic Mafia organizations, with each "family" headed by a boss, under whom are several ranks of underbosses, capos, and soldiers.[9] Profits are funneled up from the foot soldiers to the very top. In North Korea, the Kim family and their inner circle siphon off hundreds of millions of dollars annually, often through euphemisms such as "revolutionary funds" or "special contributions" (such as for the birthdays of Kim Il Sung and Kim Jong Il). And only the Supreme Leader has the final say on how hard-currency funds can be used through Office 39, which lies at the heart of the North Korean crime syndicate as the personal piggy bank of the Kim family and conduit for special projects cherished by Kim.

This official slush fund was set up by Kim Il Sung in the 1970s. Over the years it has been involved in illicit drug trafficking, counterfeiting, human trafficking, and more recently computer hacking.[10] In 2016, hackers from this office stole $81 million from the Bangladesh Central Bank; but for a spelling mistake on a funds transfer request, they could have gotten away with as much as $1 billion.[11]

"North Korea procured Russian-produced fuel from Singapore brokers and others since the 1990s," according to Ri Jong Ho, a former senior official in Office 39 who defected to South Korea. The office "is an organisation that manages the supreme leader's coffers and the party's funds to rule the country. It also leads trade activities to earn foreign currency."[12] As one British newspaper reported, "They have no real exports so they manufacture lots of fake drugs and target Western companies."[13] Office 39 operates a number of businesses; one, the KKG taxi fleet in Pyongyang, is run in cooperation with the Queensway Group, based in Hong Kong.[14] According to the European Union, which added Office 39 to its sanctions list after the United States did so in 2010, Office 39 reported directly to Kim Jong Il and, after his death, to Kim Jong Un.

Preparing for the Inevitable

In mid-August 2008, Kim Jong Il suffered a major stroke. The news was kept quiet; no one outside of Kim's immediate family and a few trusted insiders knew about his condition. But because all major decisions had to receive Kim's approval, the government came to a standstill.

It was at this time that So Nam Sik, who was in charge of the Ministry of Railways, and several others were executed for the April 22, 2004, railway explosion at Yongcheon Station that killed 160 people and injured hundreds more. The date was important because it coincided with Kim Jong Il's return to North Korea after visiting China. While the train was purportedly carrying thirty tons of TNT or another extremely flammable material and the most probable cause was an electric spark that triggered the enormous explosion, rumors were rife that it was an assassination attempt on Kim Jong Il, who was said to have passed through the station several hours before the explosion. Still, why were officials executed *four years* after the Yongcheon disaster? The arrests and executions, which had to have been ordered by someone in Kim Jong Il's inner circle, were a reminder to both the power elites and the masses that Big Brother was always watching out for counterrevolutionaries and enemies of the state—and one way of turning attention away from the prolonged absence of Kim Jong Il.

There was a protocol in place in case the Dear Leader was physically unable to carry out his duties, but after his stroke, no one was sure whether he would live or die, and Kim Jong Un had not yet been designated as his father's successor. So during this time Jang Song Thaek played a key role, serving as the main gatekeeper. Still, as powerful as he was, Jang wasn't going to succeed Kim Jong Il. Only a direct blood relative would.

Kim was out of the public's sight for three months while recovering from his stroke. During that time, leading stroke specialists were flown in from Paris and traditional Chinese doctors were consulted. Every possible medical treatment short of transferring him out of North Korea was provided.

After three months, state media published a picture of Kim watching a soccer match to reassure the masses that the Dear Leader was healthy. But only in May 2010, however, did North Korean TV show video footage of him, during his visit to China. In that footage, Kim dragged his left foot in a small arc as he walked—a sign that he hadn't fully recovered from the 2008 stroke.

No state media would dare to remark on the foot-dragging, just as they had never mentioned his stroke or his recovery. However, South Korean and U.S. intelligence knew about his condition; among other things, they had intercepted CT scans being sent to a hospital in Paris.[15] Based on this intelligence and other information, such as that he had had cardiac surgery in 2007 and had been put on dialysis in 2009, the agencies' consensus was that Kim Jong Il would most likely live only about three to five more years. Accurate information on the health of very senior North Korean officials and especially the top leader was a high priority for U.S. and South Korean intelligence. According to a diplomatic source, when a very well-known North Korean general was seeking treatment in Paris for a terminal illness in the 1990s, a CIA officer disguised himself as a French doctor and actually spoke to the general. He was queried on some sensitive issues but didn't respond fully.[16]

After his stroke, Kim was a man in a hurry, because he wanted to put into place a mechanism that would guarantee his succession by Kim Jong Un. The situation had been different when Kim Jong Il was young; he had been groomed to succeed his father, Kim Il Sung, beginning in the early 1970s, when Kim was in his early thirties. By the time the Great Leader died in July 1994, Kim Jong Il had had decades to learn the intricate ropes of the political system and put his men into key positions of influence and authority. But Kim Jong Il's own hand-picked successor, Number Three Son Kim Jong Un, would be lucky if he had three years to learn what he needed to know. Moreover, Kim Jong Il had no absolute guarantee that Kim Jong Un would be able to consolidate power after he died. In his own case, Kim Jong Il had made sure that his half-brother Kim Pyong Il, who greatly resembled Kim Il Sung, would never stand in his way. Kim Pyong Il was put into perpetual exile as ambassador to various East European countries and currently serves as Pyongyang's envoy to the Czech Republic.

Kim Jong Il was assured by Jang Song Thaek that Jang would look after Kim Jong Un throughout his rise to power but would have hardly been surprised that his son ultimately ordered the execution of his uncle—the one person who was perhaps most responsible for Kim Jong Un's political well-being. Kim Jong Il recovered enough to travel to China in May 2010 and May 2011. His last foreign trip was to the Russian Far East to meet with President Dmitry Medvedev in August 2011. But he knew that time was running out. On September 28, 2010, during the Third Party Plenum of the KWP, Kim Jong Un was officially nominated as Kim Jong Il's successor. Two days later North Koreans saw the first picture of their next leader, Kim Jong Un, in the party daily *Rodong Sinmun*.[17]

Pictures, TV programs, movies, documentaries, songs, and plays are some of the tools used by North Korea's propaganda machinery to create and maintain the personality cult of the leader. Official biographies of Kim Jong Il, for example, hailed him as a preternatural military genius, claiming he had led a band of anti-Japanese Korean child fighters when he was all of three years old. And, as previously noted, North Koreans are taught that he was born on Mount Paektu, to propagate the fiction that he was born as a living god. In reality, Kim Jong Il was born near Ussuriiski (or Vyatskoe according to other sources) near Khabarovsk in the Soviet Union. Brought up by a Russian nanny, Kim Jong Il was known as Yura and became fluent in Russian.

As Kim Jong Il's health continued to worsen, he took steps to further solidify Jong Un's position as successor. In North Korea, this meant getting approval from China. During the Joseon Dynasty (1392–1910), Korean kings and crown princes had to receive formal approval from the Chinese emperor. More than eighty years after the end of that dynasty, and despite the ideology of *Juche*, it was galling for Kim Jong Il not just to have to rely so much on China for food supplies, energy, and political cover but also to need Beijing's seal of approval for his son.

The Earlier Changing of the Guard

As he was nearing death, Kim Jong Il certainly would have re-flected on his own rise to power and the copious amount of blood that had been spilled to cement his authority. Prior to becoming officially designated as the Dear Leader in 1980, he became the de facto successor in 1973, when the North Korean press began referring to him obliquely as "Party Center."

To ensure his own power base in the party, Kim Jong Il cre-ated the Organizational Guidance Department to monitor every facet of the party's activities. Through the OGD and, over time, the Ministry of State Security and other critical organs in the party and the intelligence agencies, Kim built an impenetrable power base. All reports headed to Kim Il Sung's desk had to be preap-proved by Kim Jong Il. A Second Guard Command was created in the mid-1970s to safeguard Kim Jong Il's security, but as the years passed it became much more powerful than the First Guard Command, which was in charge of ensuring the safety of Kim Il Sung.

Kim Jong Il's security forces were handpicked, with candi-dates subject to exhaustive background checks—even a candi-date's *eleventh cousins* had to be vetted. If even a single one of those dozens upon dozens of relatives was tainted by a criminal record, was a member of the so-called enemy class, had relatives in South Korea or Japan, or was otherwise deemed unsuitable by the party, then the candidate was crossed off the list.

The Guard Command was not just responsible for safeguard-ing the life of the Kim family. The command took care of every aspect of the two Great Leaders' lives, including the inspection of their food supplies. Twenty women inspectors had to hand-select every single grain of rice destined for the two Kims. If a grain was cracked or otherwise uneven, it was discarded.[18]

On the pretense of reducing the workload of the Great

Leader, Kim Jong Il began transforming his father into a paper tiger. Only good news reached Kim Il Sung. Critical matters of state would be handled only by Kim Jong Il.

No one was keener than Kim Jong Il on keeping tabs on his father's health. It wasn't because Kim was such a loyal son. To the contrary—it was to exploit weaknesses in Kim Il Sung's health to his own political advantage. Of course, an entire hospital was devoted solely to ensuring the health of the Great Leader and the Dear Leader. Building special hospitals for the ruling elite in dictatorships was hardly unique, but only North Korea found men with physiques similar to the Great Leader's to be used as living guinea pigs: the doctors tested various medicines, diets, and other treatments on these men before they used them on the Great Leader or the Dear Leader.

After Kim Il Sung spoke at length during the Sixth Plenary and Twenty-First Session of the Central Committee in December 1993, where he heavily criticized Kim Jong Il's handling of economic affairs, it so happened that on a rare on-site inspection tour to the countryside, the Great Leader noticed an emaciated-looking soldier wearing a tattered uniform. He asked his aides why the soldier—*his* soldier—looked so terrible. None of his aides wanted to tell him the truth, but one finally blurted out that rations to soldiers had had to be curtailed. This was news to Kim Il Sung, who had been reading constant reports of bumper harvests year after year. Finally he realized he was being duped. That's when he took Kim Jong Il to the woodshed, so to speak. Even as power slipped away from Kim Il Sung's hands, the Old Lion wasn't dead. At least not yet.

Kim Il Sung's Last Hoorah

As the first North Korean nuclear crisis reached a tipping point in early 1994 and the Clinton administration was considering military options (which South Korea's president, Kim Young-sam, opposed), North Korea and the United States were playing a dangerous game of chicken. For Kim Il Sung, however, the nuclear crisis provided him with a golden opportunity to regain some of his influence through diplomacy. Unexpectedly, former U.S. president Jimmy Carter proposed a meeting in early August 1994 to attempt to defuse the nuclear crisis. Kim Il Sung accepted without consulting his son.

Kim Jong Il was livid that his father had bypassed him, but he could not prevent the Kim-Carter meeting. More important, when Kim Il Sung accepted President Kim Young-sam's invitation to hold the first inter-Korean summit in Pyongyang on July 25–27, 1994, Kim Jong Il was certain that his prestige would suffer once the Great Leader resumed his position at center stage.

On July 6, 1994, Kim Il Sung visited his villa at Myohyang Mountain to prepare for the historic upcoming talks with South Korean president Kim Young-sam and asked key ministers and party officials to join him. According to the *Chosun Ilbo*, during a morning meeting on the following day, Kim Il Sung pressed his aides on various aspects of the scheduled visit and asked the railways minister how long it would take to add an additional railway line between Kaesong and Pyongyang. The railways minister replied that it wasn't possible; when pressed as to why, he said that unless the workers were fed, they couldn't work. A vice minister told the Great Leader that the state food rationing system had stopped working a long time back.

Furious, Kim Il Sung stormed out of the meeting. After the session was reconvened in the afternoon, Kim Il Sung suffered a seizure and had a serious heart attack that evening. He was airlifted out by helicopter, but owing to a weather delay, the Great Leader had died by the time he landed in Pyongyang.

The Great Purge

How long it would take the twenty-eight-year-old Kim Jong Un to consolidate power after the death of his father was the defining question for North Korea watchers. Contrary to predictions that he wouldn't last, Kim Jong Un strengthened his iron grip with a series of purges and a more open, audacious leadership style. His grandfather and father had been brutal dictators who killed opponents or sent them to gulags, but neither one had killed their closest relatives, as Kim Jong Un did. The murders of his uncle and half-brother were just two examples of Kim Jong Un's determination to leave his mark as soon as possible.

In September 2015 at a meeting of military cadres that filled an entire great hall, Kim Jong Un strode onto the podium with folders under his arm. After he sat down, he went through the folders one by one and called out a number of officers by name and rank. Initially these officers were certain that the Supreme Leader was going to reward them with promotions. When he was done listing the names, however, Kim announced that "these enemies of the state showed total disrespect by dozing off in a crucial meeting"; they were marched out and executed that very day. (Ironically, however, Kim himself appeared to doze off for about five seconds during the Fourth Plenum and Thirteenth Session of the Supreme People's Assembly in June 2016. Of course, no one dared remark upon this. If you're a living god, it doesn't matter what you do.)

By the end of 2016, after five years at the helm, Kim Jong Un had ordered the executions of more than 150 officials and had had several hundred more purged or imprisoned. As he grew more comfortable exercising power, Kim Jong Un became increasingly confident. In a move straight out of the history books, when the new monarch eliminates the old guard loyal to the late king, Kim's most calculated move was arresting his uncle on December 8, 2013.

In a hall filled with officials all dressed in black Mao suits, Jang's name was called out. He rose but never lifted his head, and was whisked out by two security officers. No one looked at Jang; all eyes were focused ahead in total fear. Jang was denounced as a "despicable human scum, who was worse than a dog, perpetrated thrice-cursed acts of treachery in betrayal of such profound trust and warmest paternal love shown by the party and the leader for him. . . . Jang committed such an unpardonable thrice-cursed treason as overtly and covertly standing in the way of settling the issue of succession to the leadership."[19] In Jang's last moments, his two guards forced him to prostrate himself before three judges. A six-page indictment was read. He was sentenced to death and moments later shot with antiaircraft guns that shredded his body.

Kim Jong Un understood that Jang's help had been critical in propelling him to power. But he also knew that Jang himself had built up his own power base in the party, army, and intelligence agencies.

Moreover, Jang and his cronies were siphoning off a significant chunk of hard-currency earnings. If Jang wasn't killed, there was no assurance he wouldn't topple his nephew. According to a former senior South Korean national security official, South Korea's psychological operations also had a hand in Kim Jong Un's wariness and paranoia about Jang's growing political influence. A concerted effort was made to bolster Jang's image and influence in the South Korean press, to the point where he was deemed as influential as Kim Jong Un. Since North Korea monitors the South Korean press very closely, a sustained buildup of Jang's perceived influence would have been reported to Kim Jong Un.[20] In May 2019, according to the *Washington Post*, President Trump told a private group of supporters that Kim told him that after he'd had Jang executed, he "displayed his head for others to see."[21]

Since most accounts of Jang's execution state that he was killed by antiaircraft guns, if what Kim told Trump is true, it would reveal just how evil Kim Jong Un is capable of being.

Another concern for Kim Jong Un was the specter of being overthrown by his half-brother Kim Jong Nam. As already mentioned, though he had originally been designated as his father's successor, Jong Nam had blown his chance by being caught in Tokyo in May 2011 traveling under a Dominican passport. Although he was released after a few days, the damage was done—TV stations and newspapers reported the sensational story across the world. Kim Jong Il was enraged, and Jong Nam with his wife and two children went into exile in Macao and Hong Kong. In February 2017, then NIS director Lee Byung-ho told the National Assembly's intelligence committee that "all members of Kim Jong Nam's family including Kim Han Sol is under the protection of Chinese authorities."[22] According to the NIS, Kim Jong Nam's first wife, Shin Myung Hee, and their son, Geum Sol, live in Beijing, while his second wife, Ri Hye Gyung, and their two children—Han Sol and Sol Hee—live in Macao.[23]

During his exile, Kim Jong Nam gave sporadic interviews to South Korean and foreign media that must have irked Pyongyang. In one TV interview, Jong Nam said that he did not support a third dynastic succession.[24]

Yoji Komi of *Tokyo Shimbun* was the foreign journalist closest to Kim Jong Nam. Komi interviewed Kim several times between 2004 and 2012 and exchanged some 150 emails with him. According to Komi, Jong Nam was very astute in those interviews but never went into detail about North Korean politics or the rule of his younger half-brother in particular. Komi wasn't sure why Jong Nam would say publicly that he was against a third succession, but he thought that perhaps the statement reflected Jong Nam's complex feelings when he had initially been chosen to succeed his father. Kim Jong Nam, Komi said, had suspected that people around Kim Jong Il might have been pushing him to select Jong Un as his successor instead of Jong Nam. When Jong Nam returned to North Korea from time to time, he often talked to Kim Jong Il of the need to implement economic reforms, and the Dear Leader would retort, "Since when did you become so supportive of capitalism?"[25]

As long as Kim Jong Nam was in Chinese territory, he and his family were under the indirect protection of the Chinese authorities. Moreover, North Korea knew that Beijing would react strongly if North Korean agents assassinated members of the Kim family in mainland China or its special administrative regions of Macao and Hong Kong.

At 9:00 a.m. on February 13, 2017, Kim Jong Nam was at the Kuala Lumpur International Airport to take a flight to Macao. In a scene straight out of a Hollywood spy thriller, Kim is caught on a CCTV wearing a light suit and carrying a backpack on his right shoulder. He stops for a moment, looks up, and then walks onward. As he continues through the terminal, a woman in a white long-sleeved T-shirt comes up from behind him, covers his face with her hands, and then walks away.

Seeming shaken, Kim heads to a terminal assistant dressed in red and describes what just happened to him. She escorts him to three police officers, and Kim speaks quickly and uses hand gestures as he holds his passport in his left hand. They take him to the airport's medical center, and Kim sits down in a corner chair, slumped back with his knees apart. Fifteen minutes later, as he was being transferred to a hospital in an ambulance, Kim died of massive organ failure.

Footage from various CCTVs in the airport identified two North Korean–trained agents, twenty-nine-year-old Doan Thi Huong from Vietnam and twenty-five-year-old Siti Aisyah from Indonesia; they were accused of smearing the nerve agent VX on Kim's face. Later on, footage also showed several other North

Korean agents seated in a coffee shop and dispersed throughout the terminal.

Subsequently, it was revealed that Kim Jong Nam had been carrying twelve vials of atropine as a possible antidote, suggesting he was prepared for some type of poisoning.[26] While atropine can be used against exposure to chemical nerve agents, atropine "by itself is not an effective antidote for VX poisoning."[27] In a judicial travesty, while Doan was initially charged with murder and served twenty-seven months in prison, she was released in May 2019. Earlier, in March 2019, Siti was released after an intense appeal from the Indonesian government.[28]

Kim Jong Un now stood at the apex of the North Korean state. He was, finally, the Supreme Leader. The more his inner circle trembled and feared him, the greater Kim's satisfaction. He wasn't the new king just because of his lineage; he now commanded respect. The Kim dynasty finally had a merciless dictator who was also modern, media savvy, and strategic—a young Supreme Leader who was betting that he'd outlive all of his enemies, foreign and domestic.[29]

_____

THE KIM DYNASTY AND PYONGYANG'S POWER ELITES

Who Was General Kim Il Sung?

On October 14, 1945, Pyongyang citizens got their first glimpse of Kim Il Sung, future Great Leader and founder of the DPRK. As he mounted the podium at the Pyongyang Citizens' Welcoming Masses rally, the audience was expecting someone a lot older and more experienced. Instead, a nervous thirty-three-year-old read from a prepared text.

"Imperial Japan, which crushed us for thirty-six years, has been destroyed by the heroic struggles of the Red Army," Kim remarked, and called on all Koreans to "pool our strength to create a new democratic Joseon [Korea]."[1] A contemporary account, despite the rhetoric, provides a very unflattering image of Kim.

They saw a young man of about 30 with a manuscript approaching the microphone. He was about 166 or 167 centimeters in height, of medium weight, and wore a blue suit that was a bit too small for him. His complexion was slightly dark and he had a haircut like a Chinese waiter. His hair at the forehead was about an inch long, reminding one of a lightweight boxing champion. "He is fake!" All of the people gathered upon the athletic field felt an electrifying sense of distrust, disappointment, discontent, and anger.[2]

Unaccustomed to speaking before a large crowd, Kim sounded stilted, and "the people at this point completely lost their respect and hope for General Kim Il Sung."[3] Making matters worse, Kim was preceded by Cho Man-sik, a major nationalist leader who gave a rapturous thirty-minute speech—even dropping his eyeglasses at one point because he was so energized—so the audience was even more disappointed by Kim. When the audience began to vocalize their disenchantment, however, a Red Army soldier fired off an empty round. Only then did the crowd fall into line.

Three years after this inauspicious start, however, Kim Il Sung would become North Korea's leader. Two years after that, in June 1950, he unleashed a fratricidal war. Betting that the Americans, who had withdrawn their military forces from South Korea in 1949, wouldn't come to Seoul's defense, Kim's blitzkrieg worked brilliantly until he was cut off by General Douglas MacArthur. North Korea was saved from total defeat only with the help of the PRC.

No communist country since the formation of the Soviet Union in 1917 has been led by a family-run dynasty, with two exceptions: North Korea and Cuba. Raúl Castro succeeded his brother Fidel after Fidel stepped down as president due to failing health in July 2006. Fidel subsequently resigned from the Communist Party Central Committee in April 2011. None of their children were trained to succeed them.

Importantly, Fidel and Raúl were contemporaries in the Cuban Revolution, which brought down the Batista regime in 1959. As of this writing, the eighty-seven-year-old Raúl remains First Secretary of the Communist Party of Cuba but stepped down as president in April 2018. Although the Castros have dominated Cuban politics since 1959, they never built a grotesque personality cult like exists in North Korea under the Kims.

Nicolae Ceaușescu, who ruled Romania from 1965 to 1989, came close to forming a dynasty when he shared power with his wife, Elena. As the Eastern bloc began to crumble, the people turned on Ceaușescu. He and his wife were arrested, tried by a military tribunal, convicted, and shot in December 1989. In today's North Korea, however, it's impossible to imagine a similar situation in which thousands of citizens call for Kim Jong Un's ouster.

The seeds of the North Korean police state were planted and nurtured by the Soviet Union, but Kim Il Sung outdid his Soviet handlers: he created the world's most ruthless dictatorship and set up a family dynasty that has ruled North Korea for seventy years. This is the story of how the dynasty was founded and how it is sustained.

Planting Moscow's Man in Pyongyang

Kim Il Sung was born in 1912 as Kim Song Ju. His mother, Kang Ban Sok, was active in the Presbyterian church. The family later fled to Manchuria from their hometown not far from Pyongyang due to worsening economic conditions and the oppressive nature of Japanese rule. His father was Kim Hyong Jik, who was educated at Pyongyang's Sunwha and Sungshil schools, founded by American missionaries. American missionary Nelson Bell, whose son-in-law was the famous evangelist Billy Graham, introduced Kim Il Sung's parents to each other.[4] Perhaps owing to this very unique connection (although neither Kim Il Sung nor North Korean sources have ever admitted it), Graham twice visited North Korea and met with Kim Il Sung in 1992 and 1994.[5]

A CIA assessment of Kim Il Sung (prepared in 1949) claimed that while still in high school he murdered a classmate and another person for money, and at the age of eighteen he became a member of the Chinese Communist Youth Group.[6] He first joined the Communist Party of China (CPC) in 1930 and subsequently became a member of the Northeast Anti-Japanese Army under the CPC in 1935.[7] The CIA assessment noted that "in 1938, Kim was made commander of the Second Army of the [Chinese Communist Forces] to fight the Japanese, and in 1942 he was made a high official of the CPC. Kim was known for his brutality even among his Chinese comrades, and by the late fall of 1942 all but five of his followers left him."[8]

As more Russian archival materials have come to light, historians continue to study how Moscow ultimately chose Kim Il Sung as their point man in Pyongyang. For instance, North Korea experts such as Andrei Lankov based in Seoul argue that initial U.S. intelligence estimates that explained Russia's master plan on the Korean Peninsula were somewhat exaggerated.[9] However, according to Soviet reports on communism in Korea in 1945, there is little doubt that Moscow had its eyes on Kim Il Sung and the creation of a pro-Soviet regime from the outset.

In a cable sent to the main political directorate of the Red Army in 1945, Soviet officers noted that "The name of Kim Il Sung is known in broad sections of the Korean people. He is known as a fighter and hero of the Korean people against Japanese imperialism. The Korean people have created many legends about him, and he has indeed become a legendary hero of the Korean people. The Japanese used any means to catch Kim Il Sung and offered a large sum of money for his head." Furthermore, the report stated that "Kim Il Sung is popular among all democratic sections of the population, especially among the peasants. Kim Il Sung is a suitable candidate in a future Korean government. With the creation of a popular democratic front, Kim Il Sung will be a suitable candidate to head it."[10]

Yu Seong-cheol, a Korean War veteran who was an officer in the KPA nursing corps, first met Kim Il Sung in September 1943 not far from Khabarovsk, where Kim's 88th Special Independent Strike Brigade was based. "Comrade, do you speak Korean?" asked Kim Il Sung, and when Yu replied she did, he said, "That's good. Come work for me as my Russian translator."[11] Fluent in Chinese, Kim spoke only passable Russian.

Kim headed a battalion of about two hundred Korean soldiers in the 88th Brigade, which included Soviets, Chinese, and Koreans. The main goal of the 88th Brigade was to infiltrate Japanese-held areas and retrieve intelligence. The Soviets wanted to use the brigade as a bridgehead to help set up communist regimes in China and Korea once the Japanese surrendered. "Unlike today [1991], Kim was physically weak and I never saw him lead a reconnaissance mission," recalled Yu, "but he was regarded as someone with a sharp mind with leadership skills, and that's why he captured the Soviets' attention."[12]

Soviet support for Kim was the reason that several years later he would be able to beat out both the Yenan faction (those who fought with the CPC) and the Soviet faction (Korean communists trained in the Soviet Union) to take control of the new North Korean state in 1948. Yet this basic historical fact has been completely erased from official state history. North Koreans are taught that, much as Moses led the Jews when they were expelled from Egypt, Kim Il Sung liberated North Koreans from Imperial Japan. According to the myth, it was Kim Il Sung's absolute military genius that defeated Japan on the Korean Peninsula; never mind that, in reality, he led only two hundred soldiers toward the end of World War II.

As the history given here shows, the foundations of North Korea's political, economic, and military systems were laid down by the Soviet Union. But recognizing this is anathema to the mythology of the Kim family. In that mythology, only Kim Il Sung emerged to save the Korean people from the yoke of Japanese colonialism—even though the truth is that he played just a very minor role in the anti-Japanese struggle.

As Japan neared defeat in the spring of 1945, Moscow turned its attention to Korea—a small but geopolitically vital piece of real estate. At the time Seoul, rather than Pyongyang, was the epicenter of Korea's communist activity, and it was here that the Korean Communist Party (KCP) was based when Korea was liberated from Japan in August 1945.[13]

When Japan surrendered unconditionally on August 15, the United States' primary preoccupation was ensuring that the Soviets wouldn't have a hand in controlling postwar Japan. The Soviet Union had declared war against Japan on August 8—a week before Japan's surrender—and immediately its troops crossed into northern Korea. Washington became concerned that the Red Army would occupy the entire peninsula.

Despite the wishes of Koreans for immediate independence, the peninsula was divided into Soviet and American zones along the 38th parallel. Two American colonels—Dean Rusk, who later became secretary of state, and Charles Bonesteel, who went on to become commander of the U.S. Forces Korea—were ordered to figure out where to place the American zone of occupation.

As they huddled in an office in the War Department in Washington, they found a copy of *National Geographic* that had a map of Korea. "Working in haste and under great pressure, we had a formidable task: to pick a zone for the American occupation," wrote Rusk. "Neither Tic [Bonesteel] nor I was a Korea expert, but it seemed to us that Seoul, the capital, should be in the American sector."[14] Rusk and Bonesteel were amazed that their superiors "accepted it without too much haggling, and surprisingly, so did the Soviets."[15]

Little did they know that their decision would have longerterm consequences. Rusk subsequently stated that they would have chosen another demarcation line had he been aware of the historical importance of the 38th parallel. In 1896, as RussoJapanese ties worsened over Korea, Japan proposed to divide the peninsula along the 38th parallel into Russian and Japanese spheres of influence, a proposal that Russia rejected.[16] In 1903 the Russians proposed a similar idea, with the dividing line along the 39th parallel, but it was rejected by the Japanese.[17]

General Douglas MacArthur, who headed the Allied forces based in Tokyo, dispatched Lieutenant General John R. Hodge to administer the southern zone, while Colonel General Terentii Fomich Shtykov, under whom Kim had received his political training, became the head of the Soviet occupation zone. "For all practical purposes [Shtykov] was the supreme ruler of North Korea in everything but name," according to Andrei Lankov, and "it was under his tutelage that Kim Il-sung's system was born."[18]

Despite the propaganda that fraternal Soviet soldiers liberated Korea, the reality was that the Red Army pillaged and raped its way to Pyongyang. Once there, the Soviets didn't waste any time in setting up a communist system in northern Korea. Stalin ordered the creation of a "wide-ranging bourgeois democratic regime" in September 1945—as soon as his forces had occupied the region north of the 38th parallel. The Soviets created administrative units in all five provinces in northern Korea, disarmed all resistance groups and fighters, and ordered all "anti-Japanese parties and organizations" to register with the Russian authorities.[19]

Subsequently the Soviet authorities opted to form the Korean Communist Party North Korea Bureau—ostensibly in order to facilitate operations, but in reality Moscow wanted it to be entirely separate from the existing KCP. In December 1945, the KCP

North Korea Bureau elected Kim Il Sung as First Secretary. He immediately lashed out at his opponents. Because it was essential for Kim Il Sung and his Soviet backers to create a new political entity that could rival the indigenous communist party based in Seoul, a comprehensive propaganda campaign was launched to undermine the KCP in Seoul and eliminate all organizational linkages between the existing communist party and the new communist party under Kim Il Sung's leadership. "After organizing the North Korea Bureau, nothing was done from October to December," Kim wrote, and "the third enlarged conference was convened because of the infiltration by undesirable and jealous elements who began operations to dismember the bureau and party leaders who just looked to Seoul for directions."[20] In practical terms, this meant that all of the northern provinces were now under the direct control of the KCP North Korea Bureau and, by extension, Kim Il Sung.

The nascent U.S. Central Intelligence Agency wrote in November 1947 that "Soviet tactics in Korea have clearly demonstrated that the USSR is intent on securing all of Korea as a satellite" and that "details of an alleged Soviet 'Master Plan for Korea' were compromised in mid-1946, and subsequent events tend to confirm the fact that the USSR has been following the essential outline of this 'Plan' with minor divergences necessitated by tactical considerations."[21]

In a March 1948 assessment, the agency warned that the absorption of Korea into the Soviet orbit would have serious consequences, such as "adverse political and psychological impact throughout the already unstable Far East, particularly in China, Japan, and the Philippines; which would increase in direct proportion to the investment made by the US in Korea prior to any surrenders of that country to Soviet domination."[22] A more chilling analysis was made by the CIA in February 1949 on the consequences of U.S. troop withdrawal from South Korea:

Withdrawal of US forces from Korea in the spring of 1949 would probably in time be followed by an invasion, timed to coincide with Communist-led South Korean revolts, by the North Korean People's Army possibly assisted by small battle-trained units from Communist Manchuria. Although it can be presumed that South Korean security forces will eventually develop sufficient strength to resist such an invasion, they will not have achieved that capability by the spring of 1949. It is unlikely that such strength will be achieved before January 1950.[23]

Yet despite such warnings, the United States withdrew its forces from South Korea at the end of 1949. South Korea's own armed forces were no match for North Korea's military, which was trained and armed by the Soviet Union.

In January 1950, six months prior to the outbreak of war on the Korean Peninsula, U.S. secretary of state Dean Acheson remarked in a speech at the National Press Club that the U.S. defense perimeter in the Far East didn't include South Korea. For Kim Il Sung, this seemed to be a green light signaling that the United States wouldn't intervene if the South was attacked. The irony, of course, is that while U.S. intelligence correctly assessed that the communization of the peninsula would have negative consequences for U.S. interests in the Far East, until the outbreak of war in June 1950 the administration of President Truman didn't believe that South Korea was important enough to warrant serious attention.

The Korean War and the Making of a Living God

At 8 p.m. on March 5, 1949, six months after he became North Korea's leader, Kim Il Sung led a North Korean delegation to meet with Stalin. The Soviet leader agreed to most of Kim's requests for economic and technological assistance, though Kim's real objective was to get approval for an invasion of South Korea. But events elsewhere were more pressing—the Berlin blockade was ongoing, tensions with the United States were intensifying, and the Kremlin faced the enormous task of rebuilding the war-torn USSR—so Stalin told Kim to be patient. Although the Soviet Union would be withdrawing its forces from North Korea, Stalin promised to provide military aid—airplanes, automobiles, and other equipment and assistance worth about 200 million rubles (roughly $40 million).[24]

By the end of 1949, however, two developments pushed Stalin to give a thumbs-up to Kim Il Sung's plan to invade the South: the successful testing of the Soviet Union's first atomic bomb in August 1949 and the founding of the People's Republic of China (PRC) in October 1949. If the United States did indeed respond to a North Korean invasion of the South, it would now face the specter of a united communist front.

Kim also sought assistance from China even before the official founding of the PRC. Soviet specialists in northeastern China cabled Moscow in May 1949 to inform their comrades of Mao's meeting with Kim and North Korea's intention to invade the South. "Comrade Mao Zedong said that such aid [military personnel and weapons] would be granted," the report said. Further, Mao told Kim that "we have also trained 200 officers who are undergoing additional training right now and in a month they can be sent to North Korea."[25] By early 1950, Kim Il Sung was ready for war.

Six days before North Korean forces invaded South Korea, the CIA wrote an estimate of the North Korean regime's capabilities. The DPRK, the report noted, was in firm control but also totally dependent upon the Soviet Union for its existence.[26] North Korea was increasing its "program of propaganda, infiltration, sabotage, subversion, and guerrilla operations against southern Korea," but the strength of anti-communist sentiments in the South meant that such actions alone wouldn't succeed in breaking South Korea.[27] An attempt by the communists to control the entire peninsula would likely be deterred by South Korean troops' willingness to resist and the lack of popular support for the communist regime in the South. That said, however, the estimate emphasized that although the northern and southern forces were nearly equal in terms of combat effectiveness, training, and leadership, the northern Koreans possessed a superiority in armor, heavy artillery, and aircraft. Thus, northern Korea's armed forces, even as constituted and supported, had the capability to attain limited objectives in short-term military operations against southern Korea, including the capture of Seoul.[28]

Kim's blitzkrieg strategy saw initial success because the South Korean military didn't have the mechanized forces, long-range artillery, or combat aircraft needed to hold off Kim's onslaught. However, Kim miscalculated on two counts: his belief that the United States wouldn't defend the ROK and his perception that pro-communist forces in South Korea would rise up against the "puppet regime" the moment North Korea attacked.

Nevertheless, in the Kim mythology, it is *impossible* for the Great Leader to have made any mistakes. So the only explanation for the war's disastrous outcome was that Kim *must* have been duped by counterrevolutionaries and American spies. Conveniently for Kim, he could choose to purge whomever he wanted to. Major figures such as Ho Kai—sent by the Soviets to North Korea and the person who controlled all party affairs—were charged and tried by a kangaroo court and executed. Hundreds of military officers and party officials were purged or executed for losing the war.

As the postwar purges began in earnest, Kim was faced with

a startling development in the Soviet Union: de-Stalinization by Nikita Khrushchev beginning in February 1956. "Stalin acted not through persuasion, explanation, and patient cooperation with people," Khrushchev said in a speech, "but by imposing his concepts and demanding absolute submission to his opinion."[29] Using words that no Soviet would have dared utter when Stalin was alive, Khrushchev went on, "Whoever opposed this concept or tried to prove his viewpoint, and the correctness of his position—was doomed to removal from the leading collective and to subsequent moral and physical annihilation."[30]

For Kim Il Sung, this was abject heresy. If the most powerful communist country in the world could bring down the very man who had installed Kim, then how secure could he be? What would his enemies in North Korea think? Wouldn't they be encouraged to oust him?

Another part of Khrushchev's speech said:

> It is clear that here Stalin showed in a whole series of cases his intolerance, his brutality, and his abuse of power. Instead of proving his political correctness and mobilizing the masses, he often chose the path of repression and physical annihilation, not only against actual enemies, but also against individuals who had not committed any crimes against the party and the Soviet Government.[31]

If one changes "Stalin" to "Kim" and "Soviet" to "Korean," these words would be equally applicable to Kim Il Sung's North Korea.

Kim immediately realized that such revisionism must be rooted out in the North *before* it could appear on the surface— much like in the movie *Minority Report*, where someone can be arrested for a "pre-crime." Kim also understood that his legacy could be guaranteed only by building his own brand of communism, independent from Marxism-Leninism, and by grooming his son Kim Jong Il to succeed him.

By 1964, when Kim Jong Il graduated from Kim Il Sung University—with the highest grades ever given to a student, and where professors said they learned pathbreaking lessons from him—the stage was set for two forces to begin converging toward the establishment of the world's first truly Orwellian state. First, Kim Il Sung paved the way for Kim Jong Il to oust his own brother, Kim Yong Ju, who had been seen until then as Kim's successor. Second, in the mid-1960s, Hwang Jang Yop, North Korea's premier political ideologist and head of Kim Il Sung University, began to develop *Juche* as an indigenous form of socialism. In 1972 *Juche* became official political ideology, and very quickly it was turned into an instrument for glorifying the Great Leader.

Hwang later defected to South Korea and wrote critically about *Juche*. "What maintains the North Korean system?" wrote Hwang. "*Juche* has become a tool to enslave the North Korean people . . . and the myth of absolutism surrounding Kim Il Sung and Kim Jong Il is based on the so-called revolutionary history based on a fabrication of lies and exaggerations and the ideological justification for worshipping the two Great Leaders."[32]

"Kim Jong Il believes that the people are his possession," Hwang continued. "Regardless of the crimes a Great Leader commits, it is not thought of as a crime. There isn't a notion of trampling on human rights. Because in North Korea, the most important objective of the people is pledging absolute loyalty in mind and body to the Great Leader."[33]

Each place that Kim Il Sung (and subsequently Kim Jong Il) visited became a sacred site. A park bench where Kim Il Sung once sat is encased in glass. A giant statue of Kim Il Sung with his right arm stretched toward the masses overlooks Pyongyang. A student's desk remains empty save for a fresh flower to memorialize the moment the Great Leader sat in the chair to offer on-the-spot guidance. His birthplace, Mangyongdae, is the mecca of North Korea. All North Koreans are urged to visit the site and pay their respects, as are foreign visitors.

But in March 2011 the impossible happened. A twenty-four-year-old physics major at Kim Il Sung University became sick of his professors and student leaders routinely demanding payoffs. Plus he had to find a way to pay for his tuition. He decided to defect to South Korea but had heard that if he brought across with him an artifact stolen from Mangyongdae, he would become a rich man. While almost everything in Kim's birthplace was a replica or a reconstruction, he found out that one small door had remained unchanged. By paying bribes and exploiting security blind spots, he managed to steal the door.

Caught during a routine inspection two weeks later as he was planning to board a ship transporting coal from Haeju to the Chinese coastal city of Dalian, he was handed over to the Ministry of State Security. He was subsequently executed—and so were three generations of his family.[34] Furthermore, Kim Jong Il was livid that such an outrageous crime hadn't been prevented, and numerous security officials were removed from their posts.

How long North Korea can sustain the mythology of the Kim dynasty remains unclear. No one really believes in it anymore. But North Koreans continue to adhere to it, at least on the surface, partly out of fear. In addition, it's also partly due to the twisted logic of preserving the racial purity of North Koreans through ethnic cleansing, otherwise known as "liberating" the genetically and spiritually "tainted" Koreans in the South.

Big Brother's Keepers

One of the most searing images of North Korea is phalanxes of perfectly aligned goose-stepping soldiers taking part in the world's largest military parades. As the soldiers pass by the Great Hall of the People and the Supreme Leader, all of them turn their heads upward and to the right, acknowledging Kim, at exactly the same time.[35] And while such images convey the impression that the party, the military, and the security forces all function like a well-oiled machine, looks can be deceiving. Because while they are very efficient at certain things—carrying out Kim Jong Un's orders, recruiting the best and the brightest, and maintaining control over the masses—the triad is also corrupt to the core.

Especially during the Kim Jong Il era, intense competition and rivalries between contending centers of power were encouraged, in part to divert the elites' attention away from the disastrous famine that was literally killing hundreds of thousands of North Koreans. One major side effect of this internecine competition was the explosion of corruption at all levels of governance. Because virtually no North Korean officials in the party or the government live on their wages, kickbacks are routine and pervasive. As *jangmadang* and the *donju* gain increasing influence, party and government officials have to compete against each other to get bigger cuts of the kickback pie. Knowing the up-and-coming *donju*, for example, means that critical intelligence is a major asset in preserving your illicit income stream, which feeds competition between officials.

As illicit hard-currency earnings—from actions such as counterfeiting, selling arms, drug trafficking, and sending slave laborers overseas—began to fluctuate in the late 1990s due to tighter international sanctions, Kim Jong Il resorted to squeezing the party and military elites, forcing them to double their hard-currency earnings. In turn, this meant that the class immediately below them was also tasked with achieving specific annual hard-currency quotas that could be funneled up the structure, as was the class below them, and so on down the line.

Anti-corruption campaigns have been launched but with little effect. Kim Jong Il periodically made examples of the greediest officials by demoting them, sending them to reeducation camps or gulags, and even executing some, and Kim Jong Un has followed suit. In the end, however, Kim Jong Un cannot stop the corruption. The Kim dynasty made a Faustian bargain with North Korea's super-elites—much as the Saudi ruling family did with the Wahhabi sect, one of the most fundamentalist branches of Islam. The leadership and the elites keep each other alive through a web of incentives and a sharing of the spoils. Kim Jong Un cannot cut off the arm that feeds him.

Pyongyang's Power Elites

During Kim Jong Il's reign, North Korea's primary aim was *gangseong daeguk*, or a powerful and prosperous country; it became the goal of Kim's military-first policy. The policy was first promulgated in 1998, and throughout the early 2000s the propaganda machinery churned out numerous studies attributed to Kim Jong Il, such as *Military-First Policy* (2000), *The Great Leader Comrade Kim Jong Il's Unique Thoughts on Military-First Revolution* (2002), and *The Glorious Military-First Era* (2005), among many others. Of course, Kim didn't pen a single word himself, but these works were written to justify why the bulk of the country's already dwindling resources had to be shifted into the military sector. The responsibility for carrying out this policy fell to the National Defense Commission (NDC), the most powerful organ in Kim Jong Il's North Korea; Kim served as the commission's First Chairman.

When Kim Jong Il died in 2011, he was posthumously elevated to the position of Eternal Chairman of the NDC. Kim Jong Un assumed the title of First Chairman of the NDC.[36] However, in June 2016 Kim Jong Un opted to create a new highest decision-making body, the State Affairs Commission (SAC). The establishment of the SAC was Kim Jong Un's way of differentiating his rule from his father's. He has consolidated power and put into place his own cadre of loyalists throughout the party, the KPA, the security apparatus, and the cabinet. Unsurprisingly, Kim has opted for a divide-and-rule strategy. For example, Kim initially appointed General Kim Won Hong as head of the Ministry of the Protection of State (still widely referred to in the West by its former name, the Ministry of State Security [MSS]), a post that had been vacant for twenty-five years. In January 2017, the general was demoted to major general and his core lieutenants were executed for high crimes.[37] And while under Kim the SAC replaced the NDC as the most powerful decision-making body in North Korea, and the Presidium of the Politburo is the highest-ranking office in the party, it's difficult to imagine any real give-and-take between Kim Jong Un and members of the Politburo. Still, the party is a unique organization, since it is so pervasive; key party departments, such as organization and guidance, propaganda and agitation, cadres, and general affairs, have much more influence than their titles suggest.

As noted in previous chapters, Office 39, in charge of all hard-currency operations and holdings, is the most important unit in the secretariat, or Kim Jong Un's main office. Here one can see a contrast to China: although China's Xi Jinping has consolidated more power than any other leader since Deng Xiaoping, collective leadership has been merely weakened, not completely discarded. No such collective leadership ever existed in North Korea except during its earliest days (1948–1950), and even then Kim Il Sung was always the most powerful figure.

"All of the critical personnel changes made by Kim Jong Un have been based on absolute loyalty, preservation of *Juche* ideology and Kim Il Sung / Kim Jong Il Thought, and the strengthening and consolidation of his power," according to an assessment made by the Institute for National Security Strategy, a think tank under South Korea's NIS.[38] During Kim Jong Il's era, the military-first policy meant that the KPA received greater attention than the KWP, much to the consternation of party leaders. The National Defense Commission was the highest decision-making body under Kim Jong Il, but, as noted earlier, Kim Jong Un abolished it and replaced it with the SAC. Even before he eliminated the NDC, its power was reduced: during his first year in power, 2011–2012, the NDC had sixteen members, but by 2016, the number had been reduced to eleven.[39]

North Korea's dictatorship is unique both in its longevity and in the absolute concentration of power in the top leader. This doesn't mean that Kim decides everything himself; that would be impossible. Still, no policy or directive can be implemented without his approval. Under Kim, the party has gained the upper hand, and political commissars throughout the KPA relay the party's orders.

Pyongyang's highest elites are those that are in charge or have important roles in the party, security apparatuses, the KPA, government, and state-run import-export companies or those charged with specific hard-currency earnings (see figures 3,4,5). They include the top 5 percent of the core class, ministers or officeholders with ministerial rank, and Kim's inner circle: members of the SAC, the Central Military Commission of the KWP, and the Main Department of Intelligence.

In April 2019, Kim Jong Un undertook the most extensive leadership change since he assumed power. Longtime confidant Choe Ryong Hae was named the nominal head of state, or president of the Presidium of the Supreme People's Assembly (SPA), replacing Kim Yong Nam, who had held that post for over twenty years. Kim also named Kim Jae Ryong as the new prime minister, replacing Pak Pong Ju, who was moved to vice chairman in charge of economics at the central committee of the KWP.[40] Pak Pong Ju is also a member of the standing committee

Figure 3: Party Organs

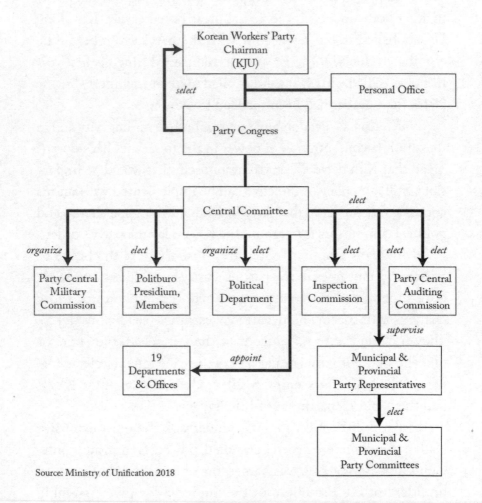

Source: Ministry of Unification 2018

Figure 4: Government Organs

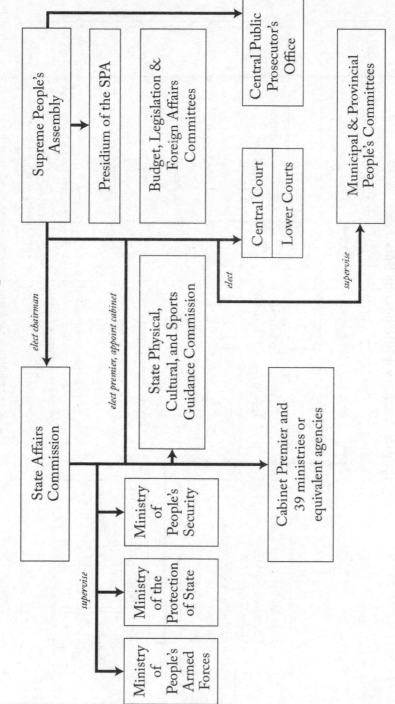

Figure 5: Security & Intelligence Services

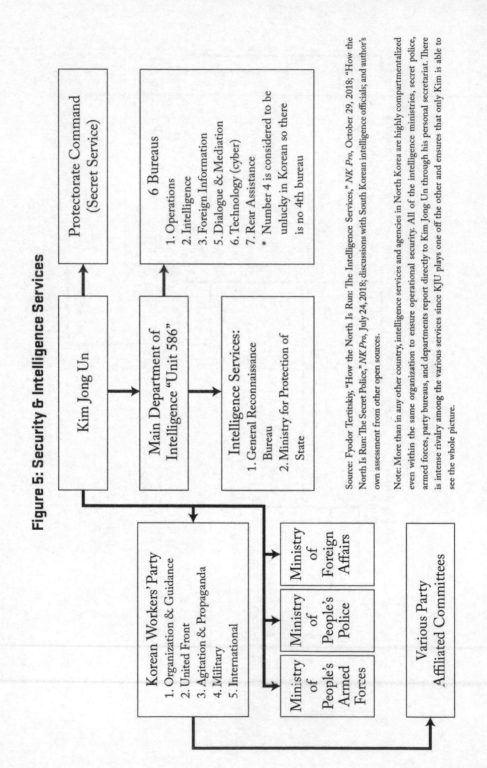

Kim Jong Un

Protectorate Command (Secret Service)

Main Department of Intelligence "Unit 586"

6 Bureaus
1. Operations
2. Intelligence
3. Foreign Information
5. Dialogue & Mediation
6. Technology (cyber)
7. Rear Assistance
* Number 4 is considered to be unlucky in Korean so there is no 4th bureau

Intelligence Services:
1. General Reconnaissance Bureau
2. Ministry for Protection of State

Korean Workers' Party
1. Organization & Guidance
2. United Front
3. Agitation & Propaganda
4. Military
5. International

Ministry of People's Armed Forces

Ministry of People's Police

Ministry of Foreign Affairs

Various Party Affiliated Committees

Source: Fyodor Tertitskiy, "How the North Is Run: The Intelligence Services," *NK Pro*, October 29, 2018; "How the North Is Run: The Secret Police," *NK Pro*, July 24, 2018; discussions with South Korean intelligence officials; and author's own assessment from other open sources.

Note: More than in any other country, intelligence services and agencies in North Korea are highly compartmentalized even within the same organization to ensure operational security. All of the intelligence ministries, secret police, armed forces, party bureaus, and departments report directly to Kim Jong Un through his personal secretariat. There is intense rivalry among the various services since KJU plays one off the other and ensures that only Kim is able to see the whole picture.

of the Politburo and vice chairman of the SAC.[41] These moves suggest that Pak will continue to have a major voice on economic affairs, while Choe will be able to steer the SPA to bolster Kim's position and support Kim as first vice chairman of the SAC.

Also notable were the promotions of several others to the SAC: Vice Foreign Minister Choe Son Hui; Kim Yong Chol, head of the united front of the KWP (in charge of South-North issues); Ri Su Yong, head of international affairs of the KWP; and Ri Yong Ho, foreign minister. Many of the old guard were replaced and key economic policy elites were promoted to the central committee.[42] At the same time, Kim was referred to as the Supreme Commander of the DPRK, Supreme Leader of Our Party and State, and Supreme Leader of the Armed Forces. Previously, Kim was usually referred to as the Supreme Commander of the Korean People's Army, rather than supreme leader of all of North Korea's armed forces. This change signals even greater control over all military and paramilitary forces.[43]

Mindful of the ongoing pressure from international sanctions, Kim reaffirmed the importance of a self-reliant economy and the need for North Korea to continue to pursue a "my way" economic policy. He made a special point on "decisively enhancing the role of the Party organizations in the struggle to vigorously speed up the socialist construction under the banner of self-reliance."[44] Kim today is in full control of the party, the KPA, and the intelligence services and has begun to move loyalists into key positions. The real litmus test, however, lies in whether Kim is going to turn around the economy under onerous international sanctions while continuing to devote resources to WMD development.

The Power Beside the Throne

The one person who remains outside of any power flow chart is Kim Yo Jong. Her formal title is alternate member of the Politburo and deputy director of the Agitation and Propaganda Department of the KWP. Because she is of the Paektu bloodline, Yo Jong carries much more weight than even Kim Jong Un's wife, Ri Sol Ju. By planting Yo Jong in one of the most important party departments, Jong Un is making sure that anyone else who wields significant power, such as Choe Ryong Hae, who heads the SPA and is also vice chairman of the party, can be checked.

As Kim Jong Il's daughter, Yo Jong played a critical behind-the-scenes role in ensuring Jong Un's succession. And, as described elsewhere in this book, she was the star of the opening ceremony of the February 2018 Winter Olympic Games in South Korea, and she never left her brother's side during the April and May 2018 inter-Korean summits. The South Korean and world media made her into an instant global sensation. Her political influence is second only to her brother's, although Kim might pull her back from the limelight if she gets too much attention. While Kim Yo Jong was next to her brother during meetings with South Korean president Moon Jae-in in 2018, and was in Singapore and Hanoi when Kim met with Trump, she was noticeably absent when Kim met with Russian president Vladimir Putin in Vladivostok in April 2019. Although the South Korean press speculated that this was a sign that Yo Jong's influence was ebbing, it was more likely a deliberate move either by Yo Jong herself or by Kim Jong Un to control her much-reported public appearances.

Should anything happen to Kim Jong Un, Yo Jong would be able to succeed him, even though that runs contrary to conventional wisdom because she's a woman, is relatively inexperienced, and has no military credentials. The only scenario in which she wouldn't be able to succeed her brother is if the military launches a coup to take out the Supreme Leader and his entire family. Because of her position, she has learned many lessons about how to manipulate and cement power. She observed the silent but potentially deadly shifts in political loyalties after her father's stroke in 2008. She also watched as her brother implemented bloody purges after he took power.

As previously discussed, during Kim Jong Il's recuperation, day-to-day affairs were handled by Yo Jong's uncle Jang Song Thaek—Kim Jong Il's brother-in-law. Jang's power stemmed from his marriage to Kim Kyong Hui—Kim Jong Il's sister and Kim Il Sung's only daughter. A pro-reform figure who was a key conduit to China, Jang was sent for several reeducation stints to remind him of his place in the power hierarchy. Yet Kim Jong Il always brought him back, since he needed a member of the royal family to carry out his orders.

But Jang's status as a member of the family enabled him to build his own coterie of supporters and his own flow of hard-currency earnings. At the same time, he made enemies, not least because Kim Jong Il used him to keep his underlings at bay. Jang mistakenly believed that being married to royalty actually made him royalty.

"His fate was sealed a long time ago," writes Ra Jong Il, a leading North Korea watcher, former deputy director for foreign intelligence at the NIS, and former national security advisor. "The beginning of the end for [Jang] was simultaneously Kim Jong Il's death and Kim Jong Un's rise. Perhaps it goes back even further, when Kim Kyong Hui was madly chasing after him, or to the period when he married her and was picked by Kim Jong Il and began on the road to power."[45] Jang's fate was also affected by the fact that he was handsome, smart, and suave—all features that attracted people to him. In a system where even a hint of empire building can bring about a fall, Jang played with fire.[46]

As Kim Jong Il pondered his third son's ascendance, he must have wondered: What if Jang killed him in a coup? Was Jong Un ready to stand up to the powerful generals? How was he going to purge the old guard?

Although Kim Jong Il needed Jang's help to ensure that Jong Un took power, he must also have told Jong Un not to trust his uncle. Whether he explicitly told Kim Jong Un to kill his uncle when the time was ripe will never be known, but when absolute power and the legacy of a dynasty were at stake, killing one's uncle was just part of what a Great Leader had to do.

And so as powerful as Kim Yo Jong is, and as much as Jong Un needs her, she can never be totally certain of her and her husband's fate. Kim Yo Jong only needs to look at the misfortunes of her aunt Kim Kyong Hui. Kim Il Sung doted on her, and so Kim Kyong Hui and her husband, Jang, were untouchable as long as he or Kim Jong Il was alive. While their marriage faltered over time and their only child committed suicide, Kim Kyong Hui probably could never have imagined that her husband would be arrested, hauled off like an animal, and killed the same day.

This is the world that Kim Yo Jong inherited and in which she has to survive and thrive. A world where family members can be killed. A world where you really can't trust anyone. A world where you always have to be on your toes.

SIX

WAR MACHINE AND NUCLEAR WEAPONS

Mission Accomplished

In February 2017, six months before a tipping point in North Korea's nuclear program, Kim Jong Un was standing in front of a camouflage-painted ballistic missile while giving orders to a coterie of officials with their omnipresent notebooks and pens.

The center of attention wasn't him, but a polished metal sphere—a miniaturized nuclear warhead. Wearing a beige military overcoat with a fur collar and a Russian-style fur hat, Kim was master of the universe. He was telling the world that he had achieved a remarkable technological feat despite international sanctions and pressures.

Like Pakistan, another impoverished nation run by its armed forces—and which, not coincidentally, is North Korea's most important WMD partner—North Korea is today a significant nuclear power. North Korea is now able to theoretically hit the United States with nuclear-warhead-tipped ICBMs.

At precisely 12:00 p.m. on September 3, 2017, the ground shook with a fury at Pungye-ri, North Korea's nuclear test site, as North Korea conducted its first thermonuclear bomb test. Shortly thereafter, Ri Chun Hee, the ubiquitous North Korean anchor, announced, "The test of a hydrogen bomb designed to be mounted on an ICBM was a perfect success!"[1] Korea Central News Agency (KCNA) released a picture of the Supreme Leader inspecting a peanut-shaped thermonuclear warhead painted white. This time Kim was wearing a black Mao suit, as were all those who surrounded him.

Foreign observers didn't just take Ri's word for it. "When I look at a thing that size, I as a military officer assume that it's a hydrogen bomb," said U.S. Air Force general John E. Hyten, commander of the Strategic Command. "I saw the event. I saw the indications from that event."[2] According to a nuclear specialist, the bomb tested in September 2017 had a yield in excess of 100 kilotons—powerful enough to kill more than 2 million people if it was dropped on Seoul. For comparison purposes, the bombs detonated at Hiroshima and Nagasaki "were less than 0.1 percent as powerful as modern hydrogen bombs."[3]

U.S. secretary of defense James Mattis warned North Korea that "any threat to the United States or its territory, including Guam or our allies, will be met with a massive military response."[4] Yet the reality was that after six North Korean nuclear tests, the United States had few viable options. Talk of a preemptive military strike against North Korea hit a peak after the September 2017 hydrogen bomb test, but everyone knew that any massive U.S. military operation against North Korea's nuclear and ballistic missile sites would most certainly entail North Korean retaliations against the U.S. forces in Korea or South Korea's own military forces. Another problem would involve real-time intelligence on North Korean nuclear assets: obtaining accurate information on North Korea, especially its military, is always problematic, but the intelligence would have to be nearly perfect if a massive military strike was to be carried out effectively. Moreover, the United States and South Korea would have to be ready for all-out war if such a preemptive strike actually took place—a prospect that no South Korean government would agree to.

Trump's famous roller-coaster North Korea policy—from "fire and fury" to "I'm in love with Kim Jong Un"—was on full display after the test. "North Korea is a rogue nation which has become a great threat and embarrassment to China, which is trying to help but with little success," Trump said. "South Korea is finding, as I have told them, that their talk of appeasement with North Korea will not work, they only understand one thing!"[5]

Two months after North Korea tested its hydrogen bomb, the Earth's crust shifted as part of the aftershocks. "When you have a large nuclear test, it moves the earth's crust around the area," a U.S. Geological Survey official said, "and it takes a while for it to fully subside. We've had a few of them since the sixth [North Korean] nuclear test."[6] A seismologist noted that "these aftershocks for a 6.3 magnitude nuclear test are not very surprising . . . the fact that the source of the earthquake is an explosion doesn't change how we expect the energy to redistribute."[7]

Exploding a nuclear weapon that literally shakes the planet is no mean feat for a nation that can hardly feed its people. It was under Kim Jong Il in October 2006 that North Korea tested its first nuclear weapon. A little over a decade later, his son, Kim Jong Un, succeeded in exploding a hydrogen bomb. North Korea achieved what many said could never be done: indigenously developing, testing, and manufacturing nuclear weapons.

Until 2006, when Pyongyang conducted its first nuclear test, major political figures sympathetic to North Korea, such as

former minister of unification Jung Sae-hyun, argued vocifer-
ously that North Korea would *never* develop nuclear weapons.
Even if it did, he asserted, such a weapon would be targeted
against the United States, not South Korea. After Pyongyang
tested its first bomb in 2006, however, Jung and others like him
claimed that North Korea's nuclear weapons were "purely defensive," as a protective measure against a hostile United States. If
Washington provides a firm security guarantee, drops sanctions,
and normalizes ties, they argue, North Korea will give up its
nuclear capabilities.

"North Korea seeks to exchange normalization of relations
between North Korea and the United States," said Jung. Further,
"normalization of ties can be achieved by guaranteeing regime
security, and military threats can be mitigated by signing a peace
treaty."[8]

The South Korean left, which in its own way is just as hy-
pernationalistic as North Korea, maintains that North Korea has
the right to defend itself against the United States, which continues to provide South Korea with a nuclear umbrella. However,
they oppose any scenario in which South Korea develops its own
nuclear armament, since such a move would affect the military
balance between the two Koreas and would inevitably be seen as
a threat by North Korea.

Such naiveté runs strong in South Korea; after all, no outside
power such as the United States or China can *guarantee* regime
security. Yes, the Chinese will continue to provide vital economic
and energy assistance to North Korea. Yes, so long as the left is
in power in South Korea, the Blue House will push for more engagement, assistance, and investments. But ruthless dictators can
survive for a long time. Take Syria: Bashar al-Assad succeeded
his father in 2000 and began a bloody genocide in 2011 when
civil war erupted during the Arab Spring. More than 500,000
Syrians have died, but Assad remains in power. Russia and Iran

sent troops to bolster Assad, and with a haphazard Western (especially American) policy toward Syria, Assad will hold on to power for some time.

So long as China and Russia protect North Korea, Kim Jong Un can survive, perhaps even thrive. In the long run, however, contradictory forces within North Korea cannot but mount. Greater information flows will be met with harsher crackdowns. Twenty-five million avatars can't be controlled like robots. The Kim dynasty's ability to control North Koreans is already weakening. At some point down the road, little pockets of dissent will appear. There will be a backlash against those too; the regime has no compunction about holding public executions and forcing family members and the public to watch them. Fear is the currency of control, but already money is partially cushioning fear.

For Kim Jong Un, the nuclear dream begun by his grandfather and pursued by his father is now virtually complete. The young dictator has shown the world and his people, but most importantly his generals and regional powers, that he is now a major military figure to be reckoned with. It doesn't make any difference if the world continues to mock North Korea, because Kim is laughing all the way to the bank. For Kim, Koreans on both sides of the DMZ can be proud: finally the Korean nation is a nuclear power.

The Foundations of the War Machine

Kim Il Sung's existential lesson from the Korean War—a conflict that he unleashed thinking he could win it within a few months, provided that the Americans didn't intervene—was delivered by superior U.S. airpower, which pummeled his forces. Kim rebuilt the Korean People's Army after the three-year war ended in a draw, but he was determined to strike at the heart of the United States one day.

Even his generals would have laughed at the Great Leader if he had told them he was going to build nuclear weapons. North Korea had no technical expertise with which to jump-start a nuclear weapons program in the 1960s. Yet Kim Il Sung was determined to have the one weapon that would both deter the United States and, if needed, destroy South Korea: nuclear bombs. For the time being, however, he placed emphasis on making North Korea a vast war machine with the KPA at its nucleus.

Like the state itself, the KPA was made possible only with the support of the Soviet Union, although here too North Korea has progressively erased the narrative of the USSR's critical role in giving birth to the KPA. On February 8, 1948, seven months before the founding of North Korea, the KPA held its first parade in Pyongyang. The *Rodong Sinmun* showed a picture of the top North Korean leadership watching the parade under a large picture of Kim Il Sung and a banner that read "Long Live General Kim Il Sung, Our Nation's Leader!" North Korea's propaganda machinery, however, wasn't satisfied that the KPA was established in 1948. In February 1978, the party newspaper proclaimed that actually the army had been founded in 1932 when Kim Il Sung created the Korean People's Revolutionary Army (KPRA).[9] As Fyodor Tertitskiy writes, however, this was a big lie:

> The problem was, of course, that the entire story of the "Korean People's Revolutionary Army" was a complete and utter fabrication. Kim Il Sung was a middle-ranking member of an anti-Japanese partisan movement in Manchukuo, which was led by Chinese fighters. The movement was crushed and Kim fled to the Soviet Union. This is not what they teach in North Korea, as Pyongyang claims not only that the "Korean People's Revolutionary Army" existed but also that it was the force that defeated Imperial Japan.[10]

North Korea celebrates both dates, 1932 and 1948, since Pyongyang argues that the KPRA was the precursor of the KPA. It is essential to the mythology of the Kim dynasty that Kim Il Sung not only fought against Imperialist Japan (which he did, though only in a bit part) but also founded a revolutionary army. And as small as his role might have been, Kim Il Sung is the only member of the Kim dynasty who actually fought in a military campaign. Kim Jong Il and Kim Jong Un never entered military service, as do all other able-bodied North Korean men and women.

In February 1958, to commemorate the tenth anniversary of the founding of the KPA, Kim Il Sung made this statement: "The Marxist-Leninist army that is the KPA is the army of the Korean Workers' Party." As innocuous as it might sound to those not experienced in reading between the lines, this language signaled the beginning of massive purges in the party and the armed forces.[11] The Soviet and Yenan factions—Korean communist leaders who had close links with the Soviet and Chinese communist parties, respectively—were purged and replaced by officers who belonged to the Manchurian faction, or those aligned with Kim Il Sung.

"Like all other people's organizations, the armed forces can only survive under the orders of the party and cannot be elevated above the party," said Kim Il Sung in September 1960.[12] Thereafter, the KPA would be guided by two iron-clad principles: to serve as an instrument of the party and, by extension, to serve Kim Il Sung and later his son Kim Jong Il. The primordial mission of the KPA was not to safeguard the state but to pay allegiance to and serve the Kim dynasty.

After the postwar rebuilding, the North Korean military went through substantial modernization beginning in the 1960s. Kim Il Sung announced four military guidelines: (1) arming the entire people, (2) fortifying the entire nation, (3) strengthening the readiness of the entire armed forces, and

Figure 6: KPA Command and Control

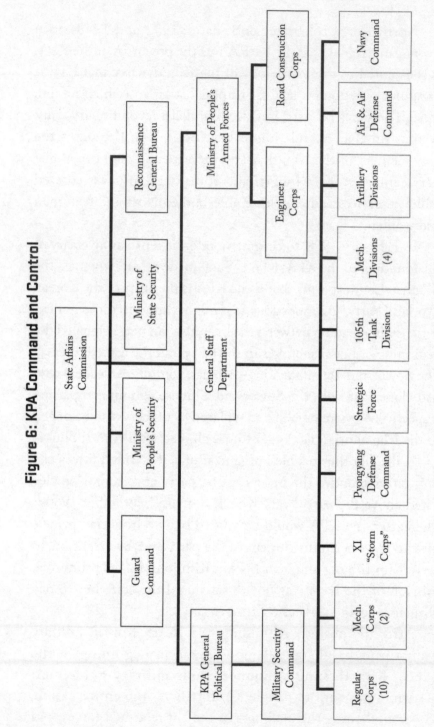

Source: "The Conventional Military Balance on the Korean Peninsula," International Institute for Strategic Studies, 2018, p. 14.

(4) modernizing the entire armed forces. The KPA expanded rapidly during this time, from 400,000 to about 700,000 troops, with commensurate modernization and creation of the 8th Army Corps for unconventional warfare.[13]

In parallel with the rise of Kim Jong Il as the anointed heir in the early 1970s, the KPA began the second phase of rapid expansion and modernization. "By 1979, North Korea surpassed South Korea in military manpower and the KPA's mobility increased rapidly through mechanization ... and in 1976, military development became one of the four core pillars of the people's economy."[14]

While the NDC was the most powerful organ in the North Korean government during the Kim Jong Il era, when *songun*, the military-first policy, was supreme, Kim Jong Un abolished the NDC and replaced it with the SAC, as noted in Chapter Five. Under his father, the KPA's grip had grown much too strong, and Kim Jong Un wanted to solidify his control over the armed forces, which he did through targeted purges of military personnel and by placing trusted lieutenants into key positions.

As supreme commander of the KPA and all military and paramilitary units in North Korea, Kim exerts nearly total control over the armed forces. The General Staff reports directly to him (see Figure 6) on military matters, while the Guard Command, Ministry of People's Security, Ministry of State Security, and Reconnaissance General Bureau also report solely to Kim.

The strength of North Korea's C4ISR (command, control, communications, computers, intelligence, and surveillance) lies in a rigorous hierarchy that enables the rapid mobilization and concentration of forces. Speed, firepower, and motivation are the hallmarks of the KPA. Yet its very organizational structure is also its inherent weakness. In the midst of a major war or a crisis, such intangible factors as flexibility, innovation, agility, and adaptability are essential to react to changes in the environment and to shape successful action. But given the multiple layers of political, intelligence, and surveillance oversight over each of the component commands in the KPA and the restricted information flows among them, severe bottlenecks could arise, with devastating effects.

Fine-tuning the party's penetration of all military units through its Central Military Commission (also headed by Kim Jong Un) while ensuring maximum military autonomy to the extent possible within the confines of the North Korean military system is a critical task. What sets the KPA apart from its counterpart in South Korea or even the U.S. military is that the KPA is organized, trained, and equipped to fight a blitzkrieg-type war in order to maintain the "correlation of forces," a translated Soviet term that encompasses all of the relevant components for a military operation to succeed, such as military and economic power, political stability, technological prowess, and military strategy, throughout the initial phases of combat.

> Consequently, its training system is designed to produce tough, intensively trained troops who can travel farther and faster with more equipment and less food than most of their counterparts in other armies. These troops are mentally and physically hardened, disciplined and taught to suffer privations that would challenge cohesion in other armies. Complementing this is a course of prolonged political and ideological training designed to produce well-indoctrinated soldiers who believe that because of their ideological training and moral superiority they can defeat a numerically and technologically superior enemy. Combat training emphasises individual fighting skills, mountain warfare, night combat, infiltration, unconventional warfare and achieving assigned objectives regardless of costs.[15]

The KPA's troops are underfed and poorly housed, and they have less sophisticated weapons than the ROK military. But lifelong indoctrination coupled with a messianic commitment to attacking and defeating the South if called to do so is the foundational essence of the KPA. Nothing else matters. Should another Korean War break out, ROK and U.S. forces would ultimately prevail, but at extremely high costs. The KPA is a finely tuned war machine, and while it may lose at the very end, it will also destroy everything in its path as it fights the next major war on the Korean Peninsula.

False Peace and the South-North Military Balance

Tens of thousands of KPA soldiers and civilians train for several months to hold the annual massive parade celebrating the founding of the KPA—although in 2018 there were two celebrations, the other marking the seventieth anniversary of the founding of the DPRK.

As the military units goose-step past Kim Jong Un, the soldiers turn their heads to the right in unison, acknowledging the Supreme Leader. North Korea also usually shows off its newest ballistic missiles, including ICBMs. In the February and September 2018 parades no ICBMs were visible. This was because Kim was in the midst of courting Trump with the help of Moon. Moreover, for the time being, there was no more need to show off the ICBMs, since the world knew he had them.

Trump quickly took credit for their absence, tweeting "Thank you to Chairman Kim. We will both prove everyone wrong! There is nothing like good dialogue from two people that like each other! Much better than before I took office."[16] Just because Kim didn't show off his ICBMs, it didn't mean he was on the verge of giving them up. As Jeffrey Lewis writes:

One explanation was that the lack of ICBMs may well have been China's price for sending Li Zhanshu, a member of China's Politburo [to represent Xi at the parade].... Beijing may well have asked North Korea to tone down the parade.... Kim has figured out that, having completed North Korea's nuclear deterrent, he can have his cake and eat it, too. By denucleariza- tion, Kim Jong-un doesn't mean giving up his nuclear weapons. Instead, he means a process by which nuclear weapons recede into the background. He's willing [to] forego nuclear testing and certain missile tests. He's also willing to stop showing off his nuclear-armed mis- siles in his parades. And in exchange, he's expecting the United States and its allies in Asia to stop com- plaining about it. In other words, he stops brandishing the bomb, and we pretend the problem is solved. He is asking the United States to accept North Korea's nu- clear status on the same terms that it does with Israel.[17]

In terms of sheer numbers, the KPA's conventional force, with its 1.2 million troops, overshadows South Korea's, with 670,000. Since Seoul lies only fifty kilometers from the DMZ, a major war using only conventional weapons would be devas- tating. If the KPA used biochemical weapons, as they would in a full-scale war, Seoul and other major urban areas would be effectively shut down.

What is more relevant, however, is the advantage of geog- raphy and how rapidly North Korea would be able to mount a massive attack against the South. After announcing the Pyong- yang Declaration in September 2018, including extensive mili- tary confidence-building measures, each side agreed to take down eleven guard posts within the DMZ—although North Korea started out with two and half times more guard posts than South

Korea. These guard posts are in the no-man's-land on both sides of the 38th parallel. The DMZ has the greatest concentration of land mines, heavy artillery, and tanks in the world, and initially, under the 1953 armistice agreement, no guard posts were allowed within it. But they continued to be built and maintained in order to ensure hair-trigger alert.

The South Korean Ministry of National Defense announced in November 2018 that "all weapons, military personnel, and equipment in the 11 GPs [guard posts] that were agreed to be dismantled through the South-North military agreement were tabulated on the 10th of last month, and from the 11th, dismantlement of the facilities were begun."[18] The Moon government emphasizes that such steps will result in fundamental changes in the North Korean military threat. Joint exercises between the U.S. Forces Korea and ROK forces have been curtailed or postponed to provide added incentives to North Korea. But North Korea's military posture and strategy toward the South hasn't changed.

Analyzing the severity and magnitude of multiple threats emanating from North Korea and calibrating the military balance between the two Koreas is more art than science. The bulk of the North's land forces are stationed very close to the 38th parallel in order to take advantage of the line's geographic proximity to Seoul. But analysts think that "although North Korea's armed forces are equipped with a wide range of conventional military systems, including large numbers of artillery pieces and multiple-launch rocket systems, its conventional forces have become weaker, compared with those of South Korea and its US ally."[19] This is precisely why North Korea has pursued robust asymmetrical weapons capabilities.

The South Korean troops are much better equipped, with better food and better living conditions. Conscripts serve nineteen months, compared to ten years for North Korean men. The

KPA isn't concerned about its soldiers' welfare or about preparing them for civilian life after their period of service. But on balance, the KPA's ability to endure hardships and to follow orders is invariably higher than that of their South Korean counterparts.

The Pentagon's 2017 annual report to Congress on military developments in North Korea noted that "reunification with the ROK, by force if necessary, is a key component of North Korea's national identity, validating its policies and strategies, and justifying the sacrifices demanded of the populace. However, North Korea's leaders almost certainly recognize that achieving forceful reunification under North Korea's control is unattainable so long as the ROK has greater military capabilities and an alliance with the United States."[20]

More problematic is the Moon government's belief that military tensions between the two Koreas are receding to the extent that Seoul can afford to relax its defensive stance. By 2022, South Korea's ground forces are slated to be cut by 118,000, owing partly to the falling number of service-eligible men and partly to the transition to a more technologically advanced but leaner force structure. However, it is also true that in the case of stability operations over North Korea—such as dismantling and controlling all nuclear and WMD sites, providing immediate humanitarian assistance, ensuring a viable civil security mechanism, and maintaining political stability—the ROK would need a minimum of 260,000 to 400,000 troops.[21]

To be sure, South Korea has made major strides forward in its defense. South Korea is one of the most powerful Asian economies, and the ROK forces are fully modernized and feature formidable defense and deterrence assets. Moreover, South Korean Air Force pilots fly an average of some 130 hours per year, compared to 30–40 hours for their North Korean counterparts. Critically, the 28,000-strong U.S. contingent is a key deterrent, with the ability to bring in strategic assets from U.S. bases in Japan,

Guam, Hawaii (headquarters of the Indo-Pacific Command), and the continental United States.

In July 2018, President Moon received briefings on Defense Reform 2.0, a plan that places inordinate emphasis on modernized firepower. But the reality is that within five years, as force cuts are implemented, the area of defense each division is responsible for is going to increase from twenty to forty square kilometers. "How the government is going to make up this deficit remains unclear. A defense policy that is premised on a belief that 'the outbreak of war is unlikely' is political populism. . . . It has also been reported that the framework of a new offensive operational concept has been put on hold."[22]

The underlying assumption behind Moon's decision to downgrade South Korea's offensive capabilities is simple: not pursuing such steps will upset North Korea and derail inter-Korean détente. An army's primary focus, however, must always remain on defeating the enemy by all possible military means. A gentler, kinder army isn't going to win the next Korean War.

1979: The Tipping Point

Park Chung-hee's assassination in 1979 resulted in massive political disruptions in South Korea, but it was also a major tipping point for the military balance on the Korean Peninsula. For Park, the most important national goal had been rapid economic modernization, and under his leadership, South Korea began its unparalleled economic transformation. Park was also an authoritarian leader who had become increasingly dictatorial after 1972. In October 1979, Park was killed by Kim Jae-kyu, a trusted aide and director of the Korean Central Intelligence Agency at the time.

As previously noted, by 1979 North Korea had surpassed South Korea in virtually all aspects of military power, with a focus on developing ballistic missiles and other asymmetrical assets. In

December 1979, Major General Chun Doo-hwan, who headed the powerful Defense Security Command—the military's key intelligence agency—engineered a coup against Acting President Choi Kyu-ha, who had succeeded to the presidency after Park's assassination. Choi had served as prime minister under Park but never exercised real power, nor did he have presidential ambitions.

The country was still nominally under civilian control, but real power lay with the generals, especially after the brutal military crackdown in Kwangju in May 1980 that resulted in the deaths of several hundred civilians. Chun created a military junta called the Special Committee for National Security Measures that was branded as an advisory body but served as one in name only. In reality, Chun ruled South Korea as head of the committee. Chun's military coup had key consequences for South Korean defense. Park had been determined to attain greater self-sufficiency in defense, given South Korea's critical dependence on the United States. Moreover, the withdrawal of the U.S. Seventh Infantry Division in 1971 as part of the so-called Nixon Doctrine (in which U.S. allies in the Asia-Pacific were asked to assume a greater share of defense) and the downfall of South Vietnam in 1975 had convinced Park that South Korea could not always rely on the United States. It was imperative, Park thought, to have indigenous capabilities, including ballistic missiles.

Chun's rise to power as president in August 1980 coincided with a heated presidential race in the United States, and as a result, the Carter administration didn't have much leverage over him. The incoming Reagan administration in January 1981 grudgingly accepted Chun's rise to the presidency, given the primacy of maintaining stability on the Korean Peninsula. At the same time, however, Washington also put immense pressure on Seoul to dismantle its ballistic missile program and forced it to sign a bilateral missile accord that tied Seoul's hands. Given his lack of political legitimacy, Chun was in no position to argue with the Reagan administration. The net result was that by the early 1990s, North Korea was working on a nuclear weapons program at precisely the moment when South Korea's ability to develop its own offensive capabilities against the North was stymied by its closest ally.

Although Chun always maintained that his military coup of December 1979 was motivated by worsening national security conditions following Park's assassination, there were no indications that a North Korean attack was imminent or that the South Korean government was on the verge of collapse.

General John Wickham, who served as the commander in chief of the U.S. Forces Korea from July 1979 to June 1982, recalled the harrowing days following Park's assassination and Chun's rise to power. Right after Chun began to grab power in the ROK military in December 1979, Wickham wrote that a very senior South Korean three-star general visited him unexpectedly. Without any aides or translator present, the South Korean general asked Wickham if the United States would be willing to support a countercoup against Chun and his ilk.

> Before responding, I took a moment to think through the ramifications. At a minimum, his group obviously wanted a tacit go-ahead for their endeavor, and it probably wanted an assurance that the United States would withhold the kind of withering criticism that was being heaped on Chun. . . . Obviously, I could not speak for the U.S. Government or Ambassador [William] Gleysteen. But we had already come close to civil war on the night of December 12 [when Chun's forces overpowered the chairman of the Korean Joint Chiefs of Staff]. The general's offer reopened that possibility with all of its inherent dangers, both for America to become

caught between several contending factions, and for North Korea to exploit the situation.[23]

Wickham replied that "the United States is not in the business of supporting coups and absolutely would not support any counteraction by the military faction [the general] represented or any other faction."[24] In hindsight, though, Wickham wondered if his firm negative response (which Ambassador Gleysteen agreed with) could have been construed as tacit support for Chun. "It was U.S. policy not to [support Chun] at the time, but rather to keep Chun at arm's length and to deal only with the legitimate authorities, although the faction the general represented undoubtedly perceived my response as a vote of support for Chun."[25]

North Korea understood that superior American firepower and an increasingly sophisticated ROK military could only be stopped with nuclear weapons and ballistic missiles. Even as South Korea's own missile program was being gutted at the beginning of the Chun government, North Korea was determined to develop its own nuclear weapons.

Glimpses of a Second Korean War

The biggest oxymoron in digesting military developments on the Korean Peninsula is the very phrase "demilitarized zone," which refers to a strip of land about 250 kilometers long and 4 kilometers wide that cuts across the Korean Peninsula at roughly the 38th parallel.

Why? Because the world's heaviest concentration of forces and firepower lies on either side of the DMZ. More than 800,000 North Korean ground forces and some 540,000 South Korean troops are positioned along or close to the DMZ, with thousands of long-range artillery pieces as well as numerous tanks, land mines, anti-tank barriers, and massive close air support.

War games are highly situation-specific, so even minor tweaks to a scenario will result in widely different outcomes. Among the many scenarios that American and South Korean forces plan and train for are those that involve very rapid escalation of tensions following a major crisis, such as another North Korean thermonuclear or ICBM test, the shooting down of a civilian airliner by North Korean missiles, or an indication that North Korea is about to launch a preemptive attack on the South in the belief that the United States—with or without the support of its South Korean allies—is planning an imminent attack on North Korea. The U.S. and ROK forces have developed a number of operational plans (OPLANs) that involve the KPA or a third country's military intervention. According to *Breaking Defense*, OPLAN 5027 is the primary battle plan for repelling and defeating a North Korean invasion.[26]

The exact contents of these and other OPLANs remain classified, but U.S. and ROK forces have also trained to take out North Korean WMD sites. An updated OPLAN 5027 was presumably made in 2016 to maximize counteroffensives against North Korea's massive conventional forces buttressed by WMD assets. According to GlobalSecurity.org, the most recently updated OPLAN 5027 includes "pre-emptive strike plans on North Korea's nuclear capable sites and weapons."[27] OPLAN 5015 has been described as a "decapitation strike" that would seek to "swiftly neutralize North Korea's top civilian and military leadership, as well as eliminate the threat of the country's weapons of mass destruction—including both nuclear and chemical stockpiles—and ballistic missiles."[28] In March 2016, the annual Key Resolve exercise was the biggest yet, with the participation of 300,000 ROK forces and 17,000 U.S. troops. According to press reports, this exercise was the first to test out OPLAN 5015.[29]

Most analysts argue that South Korea and the United States will prevail in another Korean War, but at an extremely high cost for the allies. In the initial phases of war, tens of thousands will die in Seoul, with up to a million casualties across South Korea.[30] If North Korea uses biochemical weapons, hundreds of thousands in Seoul alone will die. In the event of a nuclear attack, hundreds of thousands in Seoul and other population centers will die.

Estimating casualties entails huge data input and a wide range of variables. According to the Joint Staff,

> Calculating even the roughest "best-or-worst casu-alty estimates" for any conventional or nuclear attack is challenging. . . . Given Seoul's vulnerability, casualty estimates will vary significantly depending upon the nature, intensity, and duration of a North Korean at-tack. Further complicating the calculation of casualty estimates is the ability of our ROK–U.S. Alliance forces to respond to a North Korean attack with counter-battery fire and coalition airstrikes, missions for which we train constantly.[31]

This doesn't mean that ROK and U.S. forces will stand still. A massive counterattack will begin as soon as there is incontro-vertible intelligence that a North Korean invasion is imminent.

The state of military play on the Korean Peninsula can per-haps be best understood by thinking about a Rubik's cube. Look-ing only at one or two sides of the cube is like a two-dimensional drawing with limited insight into what Carl von Clausewitz called the "fog of war." Only by looking at it holistically, through a three-dimensional prism, can one imagine the outbreak and evolution of the world's fiercest battle.

The KPA enjoys four major advantages: numerical superior-ity coupled with rapid mobilization; long-range artillery that can pummel Seoul and adjacent targets; biochemical weapons; and special forces that can penetrate into key civilian and military targets in the South.

The first side of the Rubik's cube entails the world's biggest artillery barrage and ballistic missile attacks on Seoul, Incheon, and Busan in order to prevent incoming reinforcements from U.S. bases in Japan. Around 8,600 artillery pieces and 5,500 multiple rocket launchers will spew out millions of rounds to decimate South Korean defenses and kill as many civilians as possible. Some 200,000 special forces will infiltrate Seoul and other critical centers.

Tank columns and armored vehicles—about 6,700—will try to destroy South Korea's defense perimeter and take Seoul hostage. With civilian casualties in the South numbering in the tens of thousands, if not hundreds of thousands, Pyongyang's calculus is that by threatening the use of nuclear weapons, South Korea will sue for peace. This is the KPA's war plan: a vicious attack on Seoul and other major cities in order to force a termination of the conflict on North Korea's terms.

The KPA knows that once massive U.S. reinforcements begin to pour into South Korea, the game will be nearly over. Hence, destroying a large part of Seoul and the South Korean leadership *before* the augmentation of U.S. forces reaches the peninsula is the critical goal.

The second side of this Rubik's cube is the joint counteroffensive that will be mounted by better-trained and better-equipped South Korean forces and the U.S. Forces Korea, with rapid reinforcements that will spike up to nearly 700,000 U.S. ground, naval, and air force troops.[32] Initially, flexible deterrence options lay out the amount of U.S. reinforcements that will be necessary to deter North Korean provocations as crisis escalates on the Korean Peninsula. If these efforts fail, preplanned time-phased force deployment data will trigger U.S.-ROK combined operations.[33]

Together with the U.S. 7th Air Force, the ROK Air Force will mount a ferocious air campaign to take out advancing North

Korean forces, destroying long-range artilleries and wreaking havoc deep into enemy lines. Unlike previous military doctrines that called for absorbing the first wave of attacks before mounting counterattacks, North Korea's very probable use of WMD means that counterattacks must be launched almost simultaneously with a North Korean invasion. Attacking deeply, rapidly, and unrelentingly into the heartland of North Korea is the goal.

The North Korean air force has 810 fighters, but the majority are MiG-15s, MiG-17s, MiG-19s, and MiG-21s. Its most advanced fighter is the MiG-29, which entered service in the mid-1980s. According to the International Institute for Strategic Studies, "The obsolescence of the force has, in the last 15 years, prompted Pyongyang to engage in limited efforts to ameliorate this situation, including by introducing a modern automated air-defence C3I system, which provides overlapping coverage of the country, and developing the new Pongae-5 vertical-launched mobile SAM system and its associated radar."[34] Until the advent of a progressive government in 2017, South Korea's defense strategy was based on a triad: the so-called Kill Chain, or real-time responses to North Korean missile attacks, including possible preemptive strikes; the "Korea Air Missile Defense"; and the "Korea Massive Punishment and Retaliation" strategy.

In South Korea's *2016 Defense White Paper*, it was noted that "the Kill Chain is an attack system comprising a series of steps, from the real-time detection of enemy missile threats and identifying the target locations to deciding on the most effective means of strike and launching the strike."[35] Under the Moon government, the *2018 Defense White Paper* significantly softened the urgency of the military threat from North Korea. The defense ministry shifted its focus from a North Korea threat–centric strategy to a "strategic targeting system" that takes into account "deterrence against omnidirectional asymmetrical threats and deterrence by denial."[36]

The *2018 Defense White Paper* doesn't state that North Korea itself is a threat to South Korea; it states that the ROK faces a range of asymmetrical threats from North Korea. As the *Joongang Ilbo* editorialized in January 2019, "the most recent white paper has watered down and made ambiguous the very concept of a main adversary for our military," and "while North Korea's denuclearization and improving South-North relations are key tasks, massive military threats including nuclear weapons and WMD from North Korea remain as critical threats."[37]

The politicization of South Korea's threat perceptions and attendant military responses, as well as the Trump administration's haphazard stance on the overarching North Korean threat, will have long-term consequences, such as weakening South Korea's defense posture and ability to mount decisive counterattacks against North Korea in case of a major military conflict or selective North Korean military probes. In May 2019, when North Korea launched short-range missiles for the first time since 2017, Trump stated that "nobody's happy about it, but we're taking a good look. . . . The relationship continues, but we'll see what happens. I know they want to negotiate, they're talking about negotiating, but I don't think they're ready to negotiate."[38] In South Korea, the Moon government was initially wary of calling out North Korea for its missile test, and the ministry of unification stated that it would continue to provide humanitarian assistance to North Korea regardless of the missile test.[39]

The one area where the ROK has an advantage is in air superiority since it is augmented significantly by the U.S. 7th Air Force, stationed in South Korea. F-15Ks and F-16s constitute the bulk of South Korea's combat aircraft, with forty F-35s that will be deployed in the early 2020s. Apart from the U.S. 7th Air Force, the U.S. 5th Air Force in Japan will be almost immediately involved in a major Korean conflict, as will the U.S. strategic bombers based in Guam.

The most problematic dimension of the Rubik's cube is the third side: whether or not North Korea is going to use nuclear weapons if it's pushed into a corner or if it believes that a preemptive nuclear strike on South Korea will enable it to reunify the peninsula on its own terms.

Michèle Flournoy, former U.S. deputy secretary of defense for policy, has stated that another Korean War "would be nothing like Iraq. . . . It's not that the North Korean military is so good. It's that North Korea has nuclear weapons and other weapons of mass destruction—and is now in a situation where they might have real incentives to use them."[40] This is the biggest strategic challenge confronting South Korea and the United States in the event of a second Korean War.

Unlike under the doctrine of mutually assured destruction that prevailed between the United States and the Soviet Union during the Cold War, the current possibility of North Korea actually using nuclear weapons is much higher. There is no way to know short of an actual conflict if North Korea is going to push the nuclear button, but the strategic dividend from having deliverable nuclear weapons is huge. North Korea is deterred from launching another Korean War because U.S. involvement is virtually assured, with massive counterattacks. But every major military step South Korea and the United States take must now consider the horrors of a potential North Korean nuclear attack.

As important as this element is, what North Korea has achieved is quantitative superiority *plus* the added value of using WMD. According to *The Diplomat*, notwithstanding the superior military technology of the United States and South Korean forces compared to the KPA, "should a conflict break out, it is important to understand that this will not be a simple 'shock and awe' campaign ending with a bloody American victory, a leveled Pyongyang, and a chastised North Korea."[41]

In the end, the ROK and the United States will prevail in an-

other major conflict with North Korea. But technological dominance isn't going to guarantee victory. The United States' longest
war, in Afghanistan, and the ongoing struggle in Iraq attest to
how determined foes can wear down a technologically superior
force.

The Quest for Nuclear Weapons

North Korea's determination to pursue its own nuclear arsenal
began in earnest in the late 1970s, just when South Korea's own
short-lived nuclear weapons program was discontinued under
heavy pressure from the United States.

A combination of factors, including the withdrawal of the
U.S. 7th Infantry Division in 1971, the collapse of South Vietnam in 1975, and Jimmy Carter's initial pledge to withdraw U.S.
ground forces from the ROK, all contributed to a heightened
sense of anxiety and abandonment in South Korea. President
Park Chung-hee believed that only an independent nuclear
arsenal would enable South Korea to have a self-reliant defense
posture. Yet as domestic political turbulence mounted beginning
in early 1978, Park was forced to give up his dreams of acquiring
nuclear weapons. His assassination in October 1979 laid to rest
Seoul's aspirations to develop nuclear weapons, but even under
Park, South Korea never went beyond the conceptual phase.

In the late 1970s and early 1980s, the rest of the world was
more worried that South Korea and Taiwan wanted their own
nuclear deterrents than about any nuclear ambitions North Korea might harbor. On July 9, 1982, the CIA issued a report on
North Korea's new nuclear research reactor at the Yongbyon
nuclear center. The one-page assessment is heavily redacted but
concludes that "the reactor, which will not be completed for several years, is not designed to provide the quantities of plutonium
needed for a nuclear weapons program."[43] That same month,

the CIA issued National Intelligence Estimate 4-82, "Nuclear Proliferation Trends Through 1987." It looked at the conflict between India and Pakistan and how security would be affected if Pakistan acquired nuclear weapons after New Delhi's test of its "peaceful nuclear bomb" in 1974. Equally worrisome in the eyes of the CIA were South Korea and Taiwan: "US relations with South Korea and Taiwan will continue to be strained as both governments react to internal pressures to acquire sensitive nuclear fuel cycle facilities. Both will press the United States to help ensure their energy security, hoping for eventual US approval for their acquisition of such facilities."[44] According to the report,

> Both South Korea and Taiwan have provided assurances to the United States that they will not undertake nuclear weapons development—assurances dating from a period in the mid-1970s when the United States discovered evidence of dedicated programs to develop nuclear weapons. If US support remains strong over the next five years, lobbying for sensitive nuclear research in Seoul and Taipei is unlikely to move either government to renounce these assurances to the United States. Nevertheless, the governments are concerned that the constraints that the United States wishes to impose on their nuclear fuel cycle research threaten their future energy security.[45]

By the late 1980s, U.S. intelligence began to focus much more on nuclear developments in North Korea. Throughout the 1980s, North Korea made significant progress in its missile program—begun in the 1970s by reverse-engineering Soviet short-range missiles. In August 1998, however, North Korea surprised the world by test-firing the Taepodong-1 medium-range missile with an estimated range of 2,000–5,000 kilometers. Pyongyang was inching toward what the United States considered to be a real red line: missiles that could hit the United States with nuclear warheads.

What triggered North Korea to place the highest priority on developing nuclear weapons? First and foremost, North Korea developed nuclear weapons in order to directly threaten the United States, not just its forces based in South Korea, Japan, and Guam. Kim Il Sung saw the technological advancement of the U.S. military and vowed that he would match it. As South Korea began to outpace North Korea economically, with commensurate improvements in defense, attaining an irreversible asymmetrical advantage was crucial.

The collapse of the Soviet Union in 1991 and the dissolution of the Warsaw Pact signaled to North Korea that it could no longer rely on Russia. China remained a critical ally, but Beijing's policies also shifted after it embarked on unprecedented economic reforms in 1978. North Korea's insistence that it had a sovereign right to develop nuclear weapons was, in some sense, a way of standing up against its patron.

After Kim Jong Un became Supreme Leader in December 2011, his primary goal was to accelerate North Korea's nuclear weapons program—partly in order to fulfill the promise he had made to his father, but also to demonstrate his strategic acumen to his generals.

On November 28, 2017, North Korea successfully tested the Hwasong-15 ICBM, with a range of 8,500–13,000 kilometers and a road-mobile transporter erector launcher.[46] According to the *2018 Military Balance*, North Korea now has at least six ICBMs (Hwasong-13, Hwasong-14 in test, and Hwasong-16 in test), an unknown number of intermediate-range ballistic missiles (Hwasong-12 in test), about ten medium-range ballistic missiles (Nodong, Scud-ER, and Hwasong-10), and some thirty short-range ballistic missiles (Hwasong-5).[47]

Figure 7: North Korean Nuclear Program Timeline

12/1985	NK joins NPT but no safeguards
9/1991	US withdraws all tactical nuclear weapons
1/1992	Two Koreas sign non-nuclear pact
3/1993	NK announces NPT withdrawal
2/1994	NK makes agreement with IAEA / CIA Director, NK has 1–2 nuclear weapons
7/1994	Kim Il Sung dies
10/1994	Agreed Framework signed / Consortium agrees to construct 2 LWRs in NK
8/1998	NK tests Taepodong–1 IRBM
9/1999	US NIE: NK likely to develop ICBM by 2015 / NK could develop 200-kg warhead to target US
6/2000	Two Koreas hold 1st summit
10/2002	US Asst. Sec. James Kelly visits NK / US says NK admitted to HEU nuclear program
8/2003	Six Party Talks begin
10/2006	NK conducts 1st nuclear test, 0.7-2 kt
5/2009	NK conducts 2nd nuclear test, 2-5.4 kt
12/2011	Kim Jong Il dies
2/2013	NK conducts 3rd nuclear test, 6-16 kt
1/2016	NK conducts 4th nuclear test, 7-16.5 kt
9/2016	NK conducts 5th nuclear test, 15-25 kt
9/2017	NK conducts 6th nuclear test, 70-280 kt / 1st hydrogen bomb test

What is so striking about North Korea's nuclear program is that all measures failed to deter Pyongyang from crossing the nuclear threshold. Former South Korean presidents Kim Dae-jung's and Roh Moo-hyun's "sunshine policy" of overwhelming North Korea with incentives that would convince them not to develop or test nuclear weapons failed dismally. Sanctions and political pressures on North Korea were also unsuccessful in rolling back the country's nuclear capabilities.

Importantly, intelligence estimates on North Korea's nuclear weapons and ballistic missile capabilities have been behind the curve. South Korea's progressive governments consistently downplayed North Korea's nuclear capabilities. And despite overwhelming strategic intelligence assets, the United States also missed the rapid progress North Korea was making on nuclear weapons and ballistic missiles. According to David Sanger of the *New York Times*, when the Trump administration came into office in January 2017, it believed that there was "still ample time—upward of four years—to slow or stop its [North Korea's] development of a missile capable of hitting an American city with a nuclear warhead."[48]

In just over a quarter of a century—from September 1993, when North Korea threatened to withdraw from the Nuclear Non-Proliferation Treaty (NPT), until September 2017, when it tested its first hydrogen bomb—North Korea had developed the ability to place a miniaturized warhead on an ICBM (see figure 7). That was what allowed Kim Jong Un to announce: "From April 21 [2018], North Korea will stop nuclear tests and launches of intercontinental ballistic missiles"—a statement that elicited praise from Moon and Trump for his "bold" decision.[49] Kim, who knows that North Korea has reached a level where additional tests will only result in marginal technical improvements but even more onerous international sanctions, has played his nuclear card beautifully.

For the past twenty-five years, the United States and South Korea, as well as China and Japan, have wrestled with one major dilemma: is any country willing to go to war with North Korea to prevent it from attaining nuclear weapons? The short answer was, and remains, no. So many red lines have been announced by the United States and South Korea since the early 1990s that they've become a red carpet.

Practically, this has meant that despite the heavy-handed rhetoric that "all options are on the table"—code for possible military options—the United States and certainly South Korea have not wanted to risk another Korean War if that was the alternative to living with a nuclearized North Korea. *None* of the joint statements, announcements, agreements, and accords that have been signed with North Korea since the early 1990s have succeeded in deterring or rolling back North Korea's nuclear weapons ambition. Living with a nuclearized North Korea has been the strategic reality since Pyongyang's first nuclear test in October 2006.

Over many years, the North Koreans have outmaneuvered several American presidents—Republicans and Democrats alike—with technological advances that seemed highly threatening but not worth the risk of a war that could kill millions in South Korea and Japan. A beefed-up military presence off the North Korean coast, cyberattacks, sabotage of imported parts, and simulated bombing runs may have slowed the country's nuclear program but ultimately failed to stop it.

Many in the Pentagon see the failure to anticipate the North's recent breakthroughs as an ominous reminder of how much could go wrong. A successful preemptive strike by the United States, for example, might require precise knowledge of the locations of manufacturing facilities, nuclear plants, and storage areas, plus the confidence that cyberstrikes and electronic strikes would cripple Kim's ability to retaliate.[50]

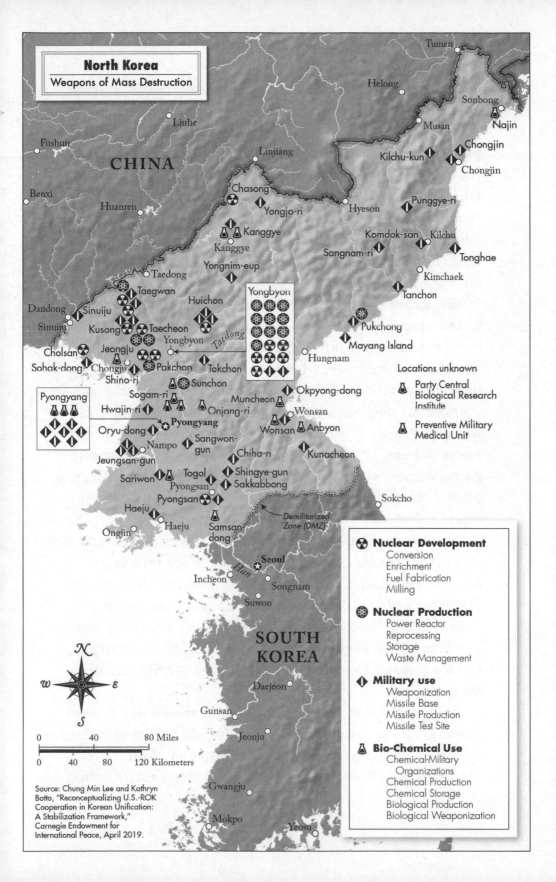

North Korea
Weapons of Mass Destruction

Locations unknown

⚗ Party Central Biological Research Institute

⚗ Preventive Military Medical Unit

☢ **Nuclear Development**
Conversion
Enrichment
Fuel Fabrication
Milling

⚛ **Nuclear Production**
Power Reactor
Reprocessing
Storage
Waste Management

◈ **Military use**
Weaponization
Missile Base
Missile Production
Missile Test Site

⚗ **Bio-Chemical Use**
Chemical-Military Organizations
Chemical Production
Chemical Storage
Biological Production
Biological Weaponization

Demilitarized Zone (DMZ)

CHINA

SOUTH KOREA

N
W E
S

0   40   80 Miles
0   40   80   120 Kilometers

Source: Chung Min Lee and Kathryn Botto, "Reconceptualizing U.S.-ROK Cooperation in Korean Unification: A Stabilization Framework," Carnegie Endowment for International Peace, April 2019.

Tumen
Helong
Sonbong
Najin
Musan
Liuhe
Chongjin
Chongjin
Kilchu-kun
Fushun
Benxi
Huanren
Linjiang
Chasong
Yongjo-ri
Hyeson
Punggye-ri
Komdok-san
Kilchu
Kanggye
Kanggye
Sangnam-ri
Tonghae
Yongnim-eup
Kimchaek
Taedong
Tanchon
Taegwan
Huichon
Yongbyon
Dandong
Sinuiju
Pukchong
Sinuiju
Kusong
Taecheon
Mayang Island
Jeongju
Yongbyon
Cholsan
Hungnam
Sohak-dong
Chongju
Pakchon
Tokchon
Shino-ri
Sunchon
Okpyong-dong
Sogam-ri
Muncheon
Hwajin-ri
Onjong-ri
Wonsan
Pyongyang
Wonsan
Anbyon
Oryu-dong
Nampo
Sangwon-gun
Kunacheon
Jeungsan-gun
Chiha-ri
Sariwon
Togol
Shingye-gun
Sakkabbong
Pyongsan
Pyongsan
Sokcho
Haeju
Haeju
Ongjin
Samsan-dong
Seoul
Incheon
Songnam
Han
Suwon
Daejeon
Gunsan
Jeonju
Gwangju
Mokpo
Yeosu

Pyongyang

In the parlance of nuclear arms control, only five countries—the United States, China, Russia, Great Britain, and France—are recognized as "nuclear weapon states." But these five, all permanent members of the UN Security Council, have contrasting views on a nuclearized North Korea. Two of them, China and Russia, are North Korea's key supporters, and despite their official position on denuclearization of the Korean Peninsula, they've also gained dividends by pressuring the United States, South Korea, and Japan through North Korea's nuclear weapons.

Regardless of whether the United States or other powers refuse to recognize North Korea as a nuclear weapon state, it comes down to semantics, since North Korea, like India, Pakistan, and Israel, is a nuclear power. Moreover, North Korea never had any intentions of giving up its nuclear arsenal. Contrary to the conventional wisdom among South Korea's leftists, Kim Jong Un isn't going to use it as a bargaining chip. The idea that North Korea will give up nuclear weapons in exchange for a security guarantee, normalization of relations with the United States, and other incentives such as massive foreign aid has been, and remains, a chimera.

A statement issued by the Institute for American Studies under North Korea's Ministry of Foreign Affairs on December 16, 2018, emphasized that "during the past six months since the Singapore DPRK-U.S. summit, the U.S. high-ranking politicians including the secretary of state have almost every day slandered the DPRK out of sheer malice, and the State Department and the Treasury Department have taken anti-DPRK sanctions measures."[51]

From the outset of nuclear talks with the United States, North Korea has insisted on the term "denuclearization of the Korean Peninsula" and not "denuclearization of North Korea." On December 20, 2018, KCNA released a commentary, under

the pen name of Jong Hyun, that addressed what denuclearization meant to North Korea. It emphasized that "when we refer
to the Korean peninsula, they include both the area of the DPRK
and the area of south Korea where aggression troops including
the nuclear weapons of the U.S. are deployed."[52]

This harks back to the 1991 South-North Joint Declaration
on Denuclearization, which stated that "South and North Korea
agree not to test, manufacture, produce, receive, possess, store,
deploy, or use nuclear weapons; to use nuclear energy solely for
peaceful purposes; and not to possess facilities for nuclear reprocessing and uranium enrichment."[53] Importantly, this is the
only document where the two Koreas made an explicit promise
not to develop, deploy, or use nuclear weapons, but in all other
statements released since that time, the term "denuclearization
of the Korean Peninsula" has been used as a catchall phrase. The
KNCA commentary went on to say:

> The United States must now recognize the accurate
> meaning of the denuclearization of the Korean Penin-
> sula, and especially, must study geography. . . . When we
> talk about the Korean Peninsula, it includes the terri-
> tory of our republic and also the entire region of [South
> Korea] where the United States has placed its invasive
> force, including nuclear weapons. When we talk about
> the complete denuclearization of the Korean Peninsula,
> it means the removal of all sources of nuclear threat,
> not only from the South and North but also from areas
> neighboring the Korean Peninsula.[54]

The nebulous term "denuclearization of the Korean Peninsula" has been used to paper over fundamentally different concepts
of denuclearization. Not once has North Korea ever agreed to
CVID, or the complete, verifiable, and irreversible dismantlement

of its nuclear weapons, although this remains the key goal of the United States, Japan, and to a lesser degree South Korea. For the Moon government, political factors make the creation of an irreversible peace regime on the Korean Peninsula much more important than achieving CVID, although it continues to pay lip service to the goal of dismantling North Korea's nuclear program. Under Trump, CVID has been renamed FFVD, or the final, fully verified denuclearization of North Korea's nuclear weapons.

The focus on unilateral peace by the Moon administration is dangerous because it equates North Korean *commitments* to denuclearization with tangible and verifiable progress toward CVID. In a September 2018 address, Moon stated that "the two Koreas agreed to a mutual cessation of hostilities on the entire Korean Peninsula. This is akin to a declaration to end the Korean War as it substantially eliminates the danger of war. Efforts will be made to demilitarize the heavily fortified Demilitarized Zone and the Joint Security Area and transform them into a symbol of peace. These are important strides towards the realization of a Korean Peninsula free from war."[55]

Alluding to ongoing steps to reduce tensions, he noted that South Korea and the United States have responded positively to the actions taken by North Korea. "Our two countries stopped large-scale joint military exercises involving the deployment of strategic assets. I expect there will be significant progress in denuclearization if the leaders of North Korea and the United States sit down together again."[56] However, the lack of a viable North Korea policy under the Trump administration coupled with Trump's penchant for the limelight and personal diplomacy has resulted in vastly different perceptions in the United States and North Korea of what was agreed to in the June 2018 Singapore summit. This became very apparent in Hanoi in February 2019 when Trump showed Kim a list of North Korean nuclear facilities that had to be dismantled if the talks were to go forward.

Neither Kim nor Trump was willing to make key concessions, and the second summit was abruptly terminated.

While Trump continues to hope for a groundbreaking nuclear deal with Kim Jong Un, it is critical to understand the deep gulf that persists between the United States and North Korea over denuclearization. Despite Moon's—or, for that matter, Trump's—hopes, North Korea won't give up nuclear weapons or other WMD. This is the new strategic reality that deserves undivided attention even if Trump and Kim ultimately agree on a tenuous nuclear accord for political expediency.

SEVEN

REGIONAL GIANTS AND THE KOREAN PENINSULA

The Return of the Celestial Empire

Kim Jong Un didn't make his first visit abroad as Supreme Leader until March 28, 2018, when he visited Beijing. Unlike his father and grandfather, who made regular pilgrimages to China, Kim Jong Un waited a long time before being invited by Chinese president Xi Jinping. The main reason was the four nuclear tests under Kim's leadership, which infuriated China. Xi expressed his displeasure by first visiting South Korea, in 2014.

Still, despite China's irritation at its much poorer, dangerous, and disruptive cousin, Beijing has propped up North Korea for its own security interests. While the Chinese leadership has chastised North Korea for testing nuclear weapons and ICBMs, every Chinese leader since Jiang Zemin believed that strategic dividends far outweighed any liabilities in the Sino–North Korean relationship. Xi Jinping isn't an exception.

North Korea's value to China as a buffer against South Korea, and by extension the United States and Japan, has ebbed in recent years because of the enormous disparity in all measures of power between China and North Korea and due to Beijing's growing ties with Seoul since the early 1990s. Clearly, South Korean, American, and Japanese reactions to a nuclearized North Korea, including greater attention to missile defense and more robust defense modernization programs, are inimical to Chinese interests.

Nevertheless, China's calculus is that it gains more than it loses from a North Korea that can threaten all of China's adversaries with nuclear weapons and ICBMs. Moreover, propping up the Kim Jong Un regime serves Chinese interests since Beijing doesn't want to see either a unified Korea under South Korea's leadership or a highly destabilized North Korea. Chinese officials and pro-government scholars often criticize North Korea in private settings, but such views hardly represent Beijing's realpolitik views on North Korea. For China, a North Korea that keeps China's adversaries at bay highlights Pyongyang's intrinsic value as a very useful proxy.

Just prior to the first Moon-Kim summit in April 2018, Xi Jinping finally allowed Kim Jong Un to come to Beijing for an official visit in March of that year. Pyongyang was saying that it was prepared to halt nuclear and ballistic missile tests, and as the Moon administration placed the highest of priorities on fostering South-North cooperation, Beijing wanted to reaffirm its leverage over North Korea.

In May 2018 the *Global Times*—sister paper of the *People's Daily* and an influential mouthpiece for the PRC—opined, "China is a crucial driving force of the progress on the peninsula. On the one hand, China's strength and geopolitical position is obvious to all. On the other, North Korea is a fully independent country." Yet the next sentence carried the real message: "China does not have a decisive influence on the affairs of the peninsula, yet without

China, major decisions in the region can hardly take shape or be implemented in a stable way."[1] As it has done for the past millennium, China was really saying that North Korea—and, for that matter, South Korea—couldn't move away from China's imperial shadow.

In that first visit in March 2018, Xi welcomed Kim Jong Un in an indoor ceremony in the Great Hall of the People. Surrounded by a wraparound mural of the Great Wall, Kim stood next to Xi as the head of the Chinese honor guard took six and a half steps toward the dais, legs swinging high with each step. He unsheathed his ceremonial sword and stepped back slightly toward his left, all the while inclining his head toward the two leaders. Xi gestured with his left hand as Kim inspected the People's Liberation Army (PLA) honor guard.

After the first formal meeting was over, Xi hosted a banquet in Kim's honor. As the leaders sat down, a video was shown highlighting the "unbreakable bonds" between the PRC and the DPRK. Footage of Kim Il Sung embracing Mao Zedong and Deng Xiaoping was shown in addition to Kim Jong Il's bear hugs with former presidents Jiang Zemin and Hu Jintao. The official North Korean video commemorating this visit shows Kim Jong Un smiling when he sees a video clip of his father's meeting with Xi.

Korea specialist Fei Su stressed that this visit showed that talk of China's declining leverage over North Korea was overblown: "The meeting appeased [North Korea's] only ally, ensured Chinese leverage on North Korea, and helped repair their frosty relations."[2] Fei Su further notes that China should maximize the opportunities resulting from the fact that North Korea has limited security alternatives:

> North Korea will need Chinese support to increase
> its leverage in those negotiations, and under certain

conditions, China is willing to oblige in order to ensure
Chinese interests are represented even with the North's
other bilateral arrangements. This dynamic was evident
during Kim's first visit to China in March 2018, where
both Xi and Kim recognized the development of the
China–North Korea friendship as a "strategic choice"
and jointly stated that their bond would remain unchanged.[3]

This bond goes back to July 11, 1961, when North Korea
signed the Mutual Aid and Cooperation Friendship Treaty with
China, right after signing a similar treaty with the USSR. While
the North Korea–USSR treaty became defunct after the collapse
of the Soviet Union, the Sino–North Korean treaty, which includes a mutual defense clause, has been renewed every twenty
years. The latest renewal was in 2001, and there is every indication that in 2021 it will be renewed for another twenty years.

As we have seen, North Korea would not exist, at least not in
its present form, had it not been for China's military intervention
in October 1950, when Kim Il Sung's forces were in retreat and
facing certain military defeat. In November 1953, Mao Zedong
addressed a North Korean delegation that had come to Beijing
to sign an economic and cultural cooperation agreement, and
he praised the gallantry of the North Korean people and their
resilience. "The Korean people are brave. They can handle suf-
fering; [they are] courageous; [they are] disciplined; [they are]
not afraid of hardship," said Mao, and "we [the Chinese peo-
ple] cannot match them in these respects. We should learn from
[their example]."[4] According to Chinese sources, 180,000 Chinese People's Volunteers died in the Korean War, although actual
casualties are likely to be higher.[5] Some of the 3 million Chinese
troops who fought in the Korean War were former Kuomintang
or nationalist forces that fought against the Chinese communists

but were captured in mainland China or chose not to escape to Taiwan in 1949. Mao's own son was killed in that war. Yet in this speech, Mao made the claim that North Korea was helping to save China.

> In the fight against imperialist invasion—in the fight against the imperialist's invasion of China—the Korean people helped us. Without the heroic struggle of the Korean people, China would not be secure. Had the enemy not been beaten back away from the Yalu River, China's development would not be secure. The Chinese People's Volunteer Army and the Korean People's Army, as well as the people of Korea, struggled together and achieved victory together; [our] assistance was mutual. [The victory in the Korean War] helped the Soviet Union, China, and the entire democratic camp, as well as peace loving people all over the world. This point should be taught to the people.[6]

Over the years, the Sino–North Korean relationship has fluctuated as Pyongyang played Moscow against Beijing in order to maximize its leverage. When Nikita Khrushchev denounced Stalin in February 1956, it caught Kim Il Sung off guard, even as his own cult of personality was reaching new heights; he knew that any similar trend toward demythologization threatened his power. North Korea denounced Moscow's revisionism and tilted toward Beijing. Throughout the Sino-Soviet split in the 1960s and into the 1970s, North Korea hedged between its two major patrons.

After the Soviet collapse, however, North Korea was left with only China. The sharp drop in Soviet aid and North Korea's famine in the 1990s resulted in even greater dependence on Chinese assistance and trade. In 2016, China accounted for a staggering

92.7 percent share of North Korea's total trade volume.[7] North Korea's total trade volume decreased by 15 percent from 2016 to 2017, to $5.5 billion ($1.7 billion in exports and $3.8 billion in imports), owing to international sanctions.[8] In terms of North Korea–China trade from 2014 to 2018, North Korean exports to China dropped from $2.8 billion to $221 million, and imports from China declined from $4 billion to $2.5 billion.[9]

Since China accounts for so much of North Korea's total trade, it makes little sense to compare it with any of North Korea's other top ten trading partners; the three largest after China are Russia ($77 million), India ($55 million), and the Philippines ($19 million).[10]

China also helps North Korea to skirt those very international sanctions. A UN report on North Korean sanctions released in September 2017 noted that "the Democratic People's Republic of Korea continued to violate sectoral sanctions through the export of almost all of the commodities prohibited in the resolutions, generating at least $270 million in revenue during the reporting period."[11] The report noted that several UN member states have "wittingly and unwittingly" provided assistance to North Korean front companies and banks. The report provided numerous examples of Chinese banks and commercial entities that have facilitated North Korea's financial transactions, setting up ledgers and opening North Korean businesses in China, including Hong Kong, although Chinese authorities deny any official knowledge and assert that no Chinese company has the "business authorization and qualification to establish and operate banks in the Democratic People's Republic of Korea."[12] The UN report noted:

> Moreover, foreign companies maintain links with financial institutions of the country established as subsidiaries or joint ventures in violation of the resolutions. Involvement of diplomatic personnel of the Democratic

People's Republic of Korea in commercial activities and
the leasing of embassy property generate substantial
revenue and are aided by multiple deceptive financial
practices. These illicit financial activities benefit from
the lack of appropriate domestic legal and regulatory
frameworks which would give effect to the resolutions,
including in many States in Asia.[13]

Officially, despite the fact that almost all of North Korea's
trade, both legal and illicit, goes through China, Beijing insists
that it has little leverage over North Korea. Despite such claims,
William Newcomb, a former deputy coordinator of the U.S. State
Department's North Korea Working Group, argues, "China has
an extraordinarily good security service. I don't believe for a minute that they don't know who the North Koreans are and what
they're up to and who's working with them but we don't see any
kind of follow-up."[14]

Pulling the Koreas into China's Orbit

As North Korea's only ally and major political and economic
sponsor, China enjoys unique leverage over Kim Jong Un. For Xi,
the task is to also rope in South Korea—the one country in its
immediate periphery that has a robust military alliance with the
United States, and the only place on the Asian mainland where
U.S. ground troops are stationed.

Since 1992, when China normalized relations with South
Korea, bilateral ties between Seoul and Beijing have flourished.
China now accounts for 24 percent of South Korean exports
and 22 percent of imports, allowing China significant leverage.
People-to-people exchanges surged after normalization as well,
and many in Seoul began to believe that Beijing had tilted toward Seoul while Pyongyang was busy embarrassing Beijing

with increasingly provocative nuclear tests. It's true that Beijing warmed up to Seoul, but even though China enjoyed significant economic ties with South Korea, that didn't mean the PRC was willing to drop support for North Korea.

Indeed, China's heavy-handedness toward South Korea was vividly displayed in Beijing's vicious opposition to Seoul's decision to deploy the Terminal High Altitude Area Defense (THAAD) system following North Korea's fifth nuclear test in 2016. China continues to argue that THAAD denigrates China's counterattack capabilities and thus weakens China's deterrent capabilities. The depth of Chinese opposition stems from a combination of factors, including a desire to prevent the expansion to South Korea of a de facto ballistic missile defense system that involves the United States and Japan. As one U.S. Sinologist noted:

> For most Chinese, the THAAD deployment decision also represents a kind of betrayal by South Korea and a related strengthening of Washington's overall effort to counter or contain China. The sense of South Korean betrayal (termed by some Chinese as a "stab in the back") results from the strong Chinese view that, by accepting the THAAD system, a friendly Seoul had joined a growing U.S.-led anti-China security network in Asia centered on an invigorated U.S.-Japan alliance. Despite some ups and downs in recent years, Beijing had viewed Seoul as a developing partner of sorts, a U.S. ally, yes, but more independent than Japan and holding very similar, wary views regarding Japanese defense modernization.[15]

Seoul and Beijing resolved the THAAD controversy in October 2017, when South Korea agreed to abide by the so-called

Three Nos: (1) no additional deployment of THAAD batteries, (2) no participation in a regional missile defense system, and (3) no military alliance between the United States, Japan, and South Korea.

Numerous Chinese officials, including Beijing's envoys to Seoul, have openly threatened South Korea if it continues to support THAAD deployment. In February 2017, for example, the *People's Daily* overseas edition noted, "If THAAD is really deployed in South Korea, then China–South Korea relations will face the possibility of getting ready to cut off diplomatic relations."[16] In the face of unrelenting Chinese political and economic pressures, not to mention Beijing's gross intervention in South Korean politics, the Moon administration caved in to China's demands: "Beijing, which claims the system's radar can be used by the United States to spy on China, retaliated against the deployment of the Terminal High Altitude Area Defense (THAAD) system with unofficial sanctions against the South. Seoul has now agreed to accept military constraints in return for the lifting of those sanctions, creating a worrying precedent for Beijing's rivals in the region."[17]

The biggest opportunity cost arising from Seoul's capitulation is that no matter what steps South Korea takes to enhance its deterrence and defense posture, such as developing longer-range ballistic missiles or next-generation submarines, China will argue that such measures aren't acceptable, since they could negatively affect Chinese or North Korean security. While China has regularly condemned North Korea's nuclear tests, it has never said openly that such tests directly affect South Korean security. Indeed, China has continued to argue that South Korea and the United States shouldn't overreact to North Korea's nuclear tests.

China's desire to enhance its leverage over the two Koreas is hardly surprising, since it has always deemed the Korean Peninsula as part of its "near abroad." Xi has also calculated that in light of Trump's increasingly erratic foreign policy, including his sudden move to improve relations with North Korea, a unique opening was available to the PRC: weakening America's strategic posture on the Korean Peninsula and, by extension, the U.S.-led alliance system in East Asia.

Trump's rash comments on the need to withdraw U.S. troops from Japan and South Korea during the 2016 campaign and his subsequent claims that these two allies are defense "free riders"— which isn't true, although Trump never lets facts get in the way— was a godsend for China and North Korea. Jimmy Carter had advocated the withdrawal of U.S. ground forces from South Korea when he became president in 1977, but subsequently reversed his position when U.S. intelligence estimates showed the KPA was much larger than previously thought. Unlike Carter, however, Trump sees everything through his own fantasy mind-set and a zero-sum transactional mentality. Now China and North Korea are dealing with a U.S. president who has almost no knowledge or appreciation of history and who insists that alliances are, at best, one-way political, military, and economic burdens that should be fundamentally altered. By June 2018, China's official media was highlighting the importance of a "brighter" Sino–North Korean relationship. The *Huanqui Shibao* editorialized on June 19, 2018:

> Chairman Kim Jong Un visited China three times in three months; that attests to the ongoing improvement in Sino–North Korean ties, and this is an objective fact. We have to support such a development and believe that there's no need to think about it in a complicated manner. Regardless of whether one devotes a lot of thought to this issue or imposes several meanings, such an effort is totally useless . . . the Sino–North Korean relationship is developing very strongly, and the future is bright. The future of the Sino–North Korean relationship is

proceeding simultaneously with the future of Northeast
Asia. At a minimum, neither North Korea nor China
wants either of these two futures to be mutually exclusive. The Sino–North Korean relationship has already
emerged from the structures left from the Cold War
and embodies this era's open-mindedness and external cooperation. We hope that countries in the broader
world will transmit their friendly support to the Sino–
North Korean relationship.[18]

For Xi Jinping, meeting with Kim Jong Un twice before the
June 2018 U.S.–North Korea summit and once immediately
thereafter enabled him to demonstrate China's ongoing influence
over North Korea—and also to warn North Korea that Kim has
only limited strategic maneuverability.

Furthermore, Beijing wanted to stress the critical Chinese role
in shaping Kim's policies. According to the *Global Times*, "Chinese
media reporting was not subtle on this point—highlighting that
China's dual suspension plan, which consisted of a pause of U.S.
military exercise for a freeze in North Korean nuclear testing,
was basically adopted in Singapore. According to Chinese media,
this demonstrates China's role as 'a responsible great power' and
that progress on the Korean nuclear issue 'is indeed inseparable
from China's efforts.'"[19] Moreover, China was able to highlight
its bond with North Korea as a symbol of its regional might and
as expediting the weakening of the U.S. military presence in and
around the Korean Peninsula.

China wants to solidify progress towards a reduced U.S.
military presence on the peninsula. Along these lines,
the United States stopping joint exercises is only the
first step. Beijing will likely begin to push for peace
treaty talks that would undermine the legitimacy of a

continued U.S. presence on the peninsula. China may even push Kim to bring up the U.S. deployment of the THAAD system to South Korea in the next round of talks, which could put the United States in a tough position.[20]

"Return of empire" may be the phrase that best describes China's "new look" toward the Korean Peninsula. For the past thousand years, especially during the Joseon Dynasty (1392–1910), Korea was a vassal state whose leadership placed the highest of values on emulating China. Because it borders the Middle Kingdom, Korea's geopolitical fate has always been intertwined with whoever rules mainland China, and no other power has had such a profound impact on Korea.

With the collapse of China's Qing Dynasty in 1911—just a year after the end of Korea's Joseon Dynasty—colonization, civil wars, and great-power rivalries and interventions would engulf China and Korea until the middle of the twentieth century. Throughout the period of Japanese colonization, a weakened China continued to interact with various elements of a colonized Korea, including the setting up of the Korean Provisional Government in Shanghai in 1919.

After the formation of the two Koreas in 1948 and the PRC in 1949, South Korea had no official ties with China until 1992. The absence of such formal ties with China was a historical aberration. Under Xi Jinping, not only has China regained its global status, but it has begun to show its imperial traditions once more. From Beijing's perspective, both Seoul and Pyongyang have to be drawn closer to China's orbit.

A reunified Korea is acceptable so long as it doesn't impinge upon China's core national interests. For Xi, ensuring that the two Koreas moved closer to China was just a continuation of long-established historical tradition. China was reminding the two Koreas that in the long run, they have no choice but to accept Chinese hegemony and dominance. Just like the good old imperial days.

Expanding Moscow's "Greater Eurasian" Space

In the flurry of shuttle diplomacy that marked developments on the Korean Peninsula in 2018, Russia seemed like the odd man out. Russia's role on the Korean Peninsula has declined sharply since the heyday of Soviet communism. The most profound change affecting Russia's strategic calculus not only on the Korean Peninsula but throughout East Asia is the once unthinkable specter of a much more powerful China.

It is true that Vladimir Putin pumped up Russia's military prowess with irredentist foreign policies such as annexing Crimea, undertaking military intervention in Ukraine, and pressuring the Baltic states. Indeed, according to the *U.S. News & World Report*'s power rankings for 2017, Russia was second only to the United States, with China just behind it.[21] The main reason is geopolitical, since Russia spans the Eurasian landmass, a position that provides it with unique advantages.

Nevertheless, it is a sobering fact that the hard-power gap between Russia and China is irreversible. In 2018, China's nominal GDP was $12 trillion, and Russia's was only $1.5 trillion—just about the same as South Korea's. In per capita GDP, Russia fared better, with $11,000 versus $8,500 for China.

Russia spent $45 billion on defense in 2017, compared with China's $150 billion (although U.S. estimates of actual Chinese spending are much higher), and while Russia has an advanced defense industrial complex as a legacy from the Soviet era, the Chinese are catching up rapidly. "The building of defence and civil-military science, technology and industrial capabilities intersect two of Xi's most prized policy priorities: strengthening

China's defence capabilities and making innovation the primary locomotive of China's long-term development."[22]

The creation of the Central Military Commission Science and Technology Commission (CMC-STC) was one major step forward for the Chinese military in pursuing its desire to reach technological parity with, and in time even leap over, the United States. Unlike the Defense Advanced Research Projects Agency (DARPA), which has been at the leading edge of U.S. defense innovation and disruptive technologies, "the CMC-STC is tightly integrated into the PLA hierarchy, with a two-star lieutenant-general in charge, whereas DARPA enjoys considerable autonomy by being outside of the uniformed chain of command."[23]

Even if Chinese economic growth slows, perhaps considerably, going into the 2020s, Russia will never catch up economically with China. Given this stark disparity, Putin has attempted to maximize the opportunities made possible by the alignment of strategic interests between Russia and China. In what Putin has called the "Greater Eurasian Partnership," the idea is to integrate Russia's Eurasian Economic Union (EEU) with China's Belt and Road Initiative (BRI). According to Russia's leading think tank, IMEMO, "The grand project announced by President Vladimir Putin, which seeks to integrate the EEU with the BRI, shows and reinforces the profound interdependence of the Eastern and Eurasian vectors of Russian strategy."[24]

Putin is betting that while Russia will never catch up economically with China, the Middle Kingdom can ignore Russia only at its peril. Should bilateral ties worsen and return to acrimonious relations reminiscent of the Sino-Soviet split, Russia would still be powerful enough to force China to reallocate vital military assets along the Sino-Russian border. At a time when China is flexing its muscle in the South China Sea and remains focused on reaching maritime parity with the United States by the late 2020s, the last thing China needs is to have to keep watching its back and worrying about Russian counteroffensives.

The Kremlin's Korean Window

It is in such a broad strategic context that Moscow perceives its limited leverage over the Korean Peninsula. Historically, Russia has wanted to maintain a balance of power on the peninsula so that it wouldn't threaten Russian interests by tilting to any of the other major powers.

This precept survived into the Soviet era. In preparation for the Cairo Conference in 1943, which would address what to do about Korea after Japan's defeat (with the goal being that "in due course, Korea will become free and independent"), a Soviet diplomatic memorandum noted that Korea might well be under the joint administration of the major powers for a long time. The note stressed the penultimate importance of ensuring that Japan "must be forever excluded from Korea, since a Korea under Japanese rule would be a constant threat to the Far East of the USSR."[25] Central to Russian interests was the emergence of a post-liberation state that didn't threaten Russia.

> The independence of Korea must be effective enough to prevent Korea from being turned into a staging ground for future aggression against the USSR, not only from Japan, but also from any other power which would attempt to put pressure on the USSR from the East. The surest guarantee of the independence of Korea and the security of the USSR in the East would be the establishment of friendly and close relations between the USSR and Korea. This must be reflected in the formation of a Korean government in the future.[26]

Seventy-four years after that memorandum was written, Russian interests on the Korean Peninsula remain surprisingly consistent. The major caveat is Russia's severely weakened leverage over the two Koreas compared to the Cold War years, when Moscow enjoyed significant influence over Pyongyang. By enticing the two Koreas to join in developing the Russian Far East, Putin is hoping to deepen Russian influence in Northeast Asia. The peninsula serves as a useful conduit for Russia's ongoing ambition to develop its sparsely populated Far Eastern region.

Moscow has four main interests vis-à-vis the Korean Peninsula. First, Moscow believes that its overall footprint in Northeast Asia can be enhanced by strengthening ties with North Korea (which has led to Russia being scrutinized for the possible transfer of WMD technologies and component parts to North Korea). Second, Russia can extricate itself partially from Western sanctions by turning its attention to developing the Far Eastern region, and it believes that Japanese and South Korean participation is critical. Third, while Russian-Chinese interests converge at the global level—that is, in terms of joining efforts against the United States—it doesn't follow that bilateral interests coincide at the regional level. Indeed, because China's economic power vastly outpaces Russia's, it is also in Russia's interest to counterbalance China's exponentially increasing influence in East Asia. Fourth, Russia sees a need to develop closer security ties among Russia, China, and North Korea in response to the alignment of interests among the United States, South Korea, and Japan.[27]

Kim Jong Il's final foreign visit was to Siberia on August 21, 2011, where he met with President Dmitry Medvedev, although at that time the real power behind the throne was former president and then prime minister Putin. At that meeting, initial discussions began on North Korea's potential participation in a South Korean–North Korean–Russian gas pipeline, which gained traction in June 2012 when Russia wrote off 90 percent of North Korea's debt, to the tune of $11 billion.[28] Contrary to the belief of some that this meant Kim Jong Il was on the cusp of announcing major economic projects with Russia, however, nothing concrete emerged from his visit.[29]

The heyday of Russian influence on North Korea is irreversibly gone, but Russia can maximize the dividends flowing from three key sources of influence. First, as a permanent member of the UN Security Council, Russia, together with China, can swing the vote on any major political change on the Korean Peninsula to protect North Korea's interests. Although Russia doesn't have China's hard power, including military assets in the Far East, it has enough presence to deter South Korea and the United States (as well as Japan) from steps that could be deemed detrimental to North Korean interests. Second, since North Korea wants to lessen its all-pervasive dependence on China, forging stronger political and economic ties with Russia buttresses Pyongyang's maneuverability. If Kim Jong Un is serious about developing North Korea, Russian energy is essential. Third, strengthening Pyongyang's ties with Moscow offers North Korea added geopolitical weight. "Overall," notes Elizabeth Economy of the Council on Foreign Relations, "Russia plays a critical role as a behind-the-scenes negotiator, spoiler, and unholy ally. It is not front and center, but it is central."[30]

In November 2018, the Russian news agency TASS reported that Russia's ambassador to North Korea, Alexander Matsegora, had met with North Korea's vice foreign minister, Choe Son Hui, and that the two sides agreed that current problems must be resolved "on a phased and synchronized approach"—code suggesting that Russia would be supporting North Korea's and the PRC's positions on denuclearization and other issues.[31] Russia has argued that sanctions on North Korea must be reduced before progress is made on denuclearization.

"It is becoming more and more important to elaborate security guarantees," said Mikhail Ulyanov, Russia's permanent representative to the International Atomic Energy Agency. Furthermore, "reliable international security mechanisms are necessary in the region to prevent recurrence of the situation which has developed around the Joint Comprehensive Plan of Action on the Iranian nuclear program."[32] Russia continues to claim that Washington's desire for Pyongyang to disarm itself prior to real negotiations is a pipe dream.

Anton Khlopkov, director of Russia's Center for Energy and Security Studies, has said that "Washington and South Korea need to understand that Pyongyang's unilateral back-down is totally ruled out." He also noted that "the scenario suggested by a number of South Korean experts, under which North Korea gives up its nuclear ambitions and South Korea remains under the US nuclear umbrella, is unrealistic."[33]

> Moscow's greatest strength is its relatively equal relationship with both North Korea and South Korea. While the United States, Japan, and China maintain closer ties with one side of the demilitarized zone (DMZ) or the other, Russia has maintained steady economic and political relations with both sides of the DMZ. . . . Ultimately, Russia's most important and often overlooked role with regard to North Korea may be its shared willingness to use chemical weapons. While the United States and the rest of the world have focused attention on addressing the nuclear threat posed by North Korea, North Korea's stockpile of chemical weapons and failure to sign the Chemical Weapons Convention also pose a significant threat to global security.[34]

Given the disparities in Chinese and Russian power, Moscow has no illusions that it can ever displace China on the Korean Peninsula. What Moscow realizes, however, is that it has a boutique role to play vis-à-vis the two Koreas.

For example, Putin has been openly critical of international sanctions on North Korea. (Russia itself, of course, is under Western sanctions.) "Sanctions of any kind would now be useless and ineffective," said Putin in September 2017, referring to international responses to North Korea's most powerful nuclear test, and he emphasized that North Koreans would "rather eat grass than abandon their [nuclear weapons] programmes unless they feel secure."[35]

Moreover, despite Western criticism of human rights abuses in Russia, Putin has also continued to support the stationing of North Korean workers in Russia—a key source of hard-currency earnings for Kim Jong Un. Russia has also followed North Korea's lead in repatriating North Korean escapees. In November 2018, press reports said that Russia arrested, tried, and repatriated a former North Korean soldier, twenty-nine-year-old Jun Kyung Chul, back to North Korea, where he is likely to face imprisonment in a gulag for his crimes.[36]

By the summer of 2018, Russia was extending an open invitation to Kim Jong Un. "I would like to re-extend, and ask you to convey to the leader of North Korea Kim Jong Un, our invitation to visit Russia," said Putin in a meeting with Kim Yong Nam, then chairman of the Presidium of the Supreme People's Assembly of North Korea and the nominal head of state.[37] On April 25, 2019, Putin met with Kim in Vladivostok for their first face-to-face meeting. Perhaps the only interesting development during the summit was that the famously tardy Putin had to wait thirty minutes for Kim to arrive. Russia's main news agency TASS paraphrased Alexei Maslov, head of the School of Asian Studies at the Higher School of Economics, who said that while the summit was important for the leaders to sound each other out, "the meeting had no formal results even in the form of a communique."[38] Putin aired his support for reviving the six-party talks to resolve the North Korean nuclear problem, but he stressed that North Koreans need a "guarantee about their security. That's it. All of us together need to think about [it]."[39] Overall, however, the summit was a letdown. "In what may be a sign that North Korea and Russia did not see eye-to-eye on all issues discussed, state media fell short of saying the two sides reached complete consensus. It said the two leaders during their one-on-one meeting 'reached *satisfactory consensus* on imminent issues of cooperation.'"[40]

Elizabeth Economy writes, "Like China, [Russia] has its own set of complicated interests with regard to North Korea that do not align fully with those of the United States. Yet Moscow cannot be ignored. Despite its relatively low public profile as a player in the North Korea negotiations, Russia's behind-the-scenes ability to throw a wrench in the process should not be underestimated."[41]

Russia doesn't need to have overwhelming influence over North Korea, as it did from the 1950s until the 1970s. The global pecking order has changed, and with it Russia's strategic influence and importance. But Russia still has plenty of cachet in North Korea, and by extension the Korean Peninsula, where its interests and voices can't be ignored.

Russia is in exactly the spot it wants to be in: allowing China to pull much of the weight on the Korean Peninsula, thereby minimizing its political and military exposure; complicating American (and South Korean) responses to major crises on the Korean Peninsula with the possibility of joint Sino-Russian actions; expediting the decoupling of the United States from Japan and South Korea; and exercising whatever limited power it has to shape the contours of a future unified Korea. Given the compatibility of Moscow's and Beijing's interests, so long as Russia and China don't collide on the Korean Peninsula, Russia can live with letting China take the lead.

Tokyo's Complex Korea Prisms

Among all of Northeast Asia's key stakeholders, Japan has been the most vocal about North Korea's growing threat envelope. North Korea's provocations against Japan are manifest, including missiles that have fallen into Japanese waters or traversed Japanese airspace. Next to the United States, Japan has received the lion's share of North Korea's ire.

The Japanese–North Korean relationship is fraught with historical legacies and unresolved issues. Moreover, the complexity of Japanese policy toward the Korean Peninsula is even more pronounced because of Tokyo's critically important but also deeply divisive relationship with Seoul. Indeed, no other bilateral relationship between two mature, advanced democracies with centuries of interaction is as fragile and politically volatile.

As Brad Glosserman writes, "Even in the face of a potentially existential threat from North Korea, the relations between the two countries are better characterized as contentious rather than cooperative. Those frictions threaten to undermine the united front essential to counter and contain North Korea and change its behavior."[42] National identities built upon very strong ethnocentric worldviews in both countries, compounded by deeply embedded notions of victimization in South Korea, have contributed further to icy bilateral relations.

> Seoul has a progressive government, and the left in South Korea has historically been antagonistic toward the United States, used Japan as a cudgel in domestic political battles, and sought common cause with Pyongyang in the name of a united Korea. Only progressive presi-

dents have met with North Korean leaders and Japan worries that Moon Jae-in will be tempted to follow in their footsteps, even if it means breaking with Washington and Tokyo and abandoning the united front that is pressuring Pyongyang to change its behavior.[43]

For the United States, the fact that the relationship between its two most important allies in Asia, Japan and South Korea, is marked by bitter historical legacies and contrasting threat perceptions vis-à-vis North Korea has become a major impediment to sustaining and strengthening trilateral security cooperation.

In South Korea, domestic politics is rarely separate from its Japan policy. The deep scar left by Japan's brutal colonization of Korea from 1910 to 1945 is understandable from a South Korean perspective (and also from a North Korean one, although Pyongyang heavily propagandizes its anti-Japanese stance). Despite the closest of ties and irreversible linkages between South Korea and Japan, both sides spin their joint history for political ends. South Koreans argue that while successive Japanese governments have apologized for their colonial rule, the Japanese have never fully come to accept responsibility for wartime atrocities such as using Korean sex slaves to service members of the Japanese military and using forced laborers for wartime production.

> Japan implemented harsh and restrictive policies towards the Korean people throughout the colonial period, with policies of forcible assimilation hitting a peak as Japan expanded its empire during the 1930s and 40s. As Japan waged war throughout Asia and the Pacific, its government and military began to recruit Koreans (often coercively) to work at jobs left behind by Japanese conscripts, as well as Korean women to serve soldiers at military installations across its empire. Tokyo also

sought to forcibly assimilate Koreans into Japanese culture by assigning Koreans Japanese names, promoting
the exclusive use of the Japanese language, and banning
the teaching of Korea's language and history.[44]

The Japanese maintain that the 1965 basic treaty that normalized relations between Tokyo and Seoul covers all actions
prior to 1945 and that Seoul is constantly moving the goalposts
on the issues of so-called comfort women and forced labor. As
Japan has become more conservative, particularly under Prime
Minister Shinzo Abe, and leans toward a more robust defense
posture, South Korea's diplomatic bandwidth has fluctuated
widely depending on whether a leftist or a rightist government is
in power. Conservatives highlight the importance of maintaining
key security ties with Japan and, to the extent possible, deepening
trilateral security cooperation among the United States, Japan,
and South Korea.

This doesn't mean that previous conservative governments
neglected historical issues. Former president Lee Myung-bak's
visit to Dokdo in August 2012, the first visit to that island by a
South Korean president, was highly symbolic, since while South
Korea has jurisdiction and control over Dokdo, Japan also claims
rights over the island, which it refers to as Takeshima. As he
stepped off the presidential helicopter, Lee remarked, "Dokdo is
an invaluable place that must be defended at all costs."[45] Japanese
foreign minister Koichiro Gemba then called Lee's visit "utterly
unacceptable," and Tokyo temporarily recalled its ambassador to
Seoul.

Japanese claims on Dokdo are spurious. "This is clearly a Korean
island, it has effective control," said Robert Dujarric, director of the
Institute of Contemporary Asian Studies at Temple University's
Tokyo campus. "The Japanese government is very blind to the
historical, psychological background to this."[46]

When she was in office, President Park Geun-hye didn't hold any bilateral meetings with Prime Minister Abe for nearly three years, although her government signed a landmark agreement with Japan on the comfort women issue in December 2015. In that deal—hailed by the United States—Seoul and Tokyo agreed to form a Reconciliation and Healing Foundation with a $9 million payout by the Japanese government. However, the Moon administration decided to replace that money with its own funds.[47] While technically the agreement is still in force, for all practical purposes it has been nullified by the Moon government.

Another major issue that has further divided Seoul-Tokyo relations is the South Korean Supreme Court's decision in November 2018 that Japan's Mitsubishi Heavy Industries must compensate any surviving individuals who were forced laborers during World War II. Earlier, the Supreme Court had ruled that Nippon Steel and Sumitomo Metal Corporation were liable for wartime forced labor too.[48] Tokyo responded forcefully, insisting that "all claims arising from the years of Japan's colonial rule of the Korean Peninsula were 'settled completely and finally' in the June 1965 treaty."[49] The Japanese Foreign Ministry announced after the ruling:

> Japan once again conveys to the Republic of Korea its position as elaborated above, and strongly demands that the Republic of Korea take appropriate measures, including immediate actions to remedy such breach of international law.... Furthermore, if appropriate measures are not taken immediately, Japan will continue to examine all possible options, including international adjudication and counter measures, and take resolute actions accordingly from the standpoint of, inter alia, protecting the legitimate business activities by Japanese companies.[50]

While the Korean Supreme Court argued that the 1965 agreement between South Korea and Japan didn't cover forced laborers, the South Korean foreign ministry, in order to avoid a worsening of bilateral relations with Japan, has been working to minimize the fallout with Tokyo. On November 7, 2018, South Korean prime minister Lee Nak-yeon issued a formal statement noting that "the judiciary's ruling is not a diplomatic issue. The judiciary hands down legal rulings and it is a fundamental precept of democracy of a government's non-interference in the judiciary's decisions. I believe that Japanese leaders are also aware of this point."[51]

Japan's North Korea Angst

From a Japanese perspective, the security environment around Japan has worsened since the end of the Cold War due to the convergence of three major threats: the accelerated rise of China and the PLA's unparalleled power projection capabilities in the East China Sea and the South China Sea; North Korea's nuclear weapons program, with mature ballistic missile capabilities that endanger Japanese security; and a Sino-Russian strategic entente coming on the heels of Russia's revamping of its military forces.

More recently, Japan's relationship with the United States has soured because of Trump's imposition of steel and aluminum tariffs on Japan and his incessant harping about Japan and South Korea as defense free riders. As a matter of fact, Japan assumes more than 85 percent of the costs of maintaining U.S. Forces Japan and commits $1.7 billion annually for host nation support based on the Special Measures Agreement.[52]

In addition, Japan is a major importer of U.S. arms. From 1950 to 2017, Japan imported a total of $64 billion in arms, and almost all of them were U.S. purchases.[53] In 2017, Japan imported $4.8 billion in U.S. arms (the corresponding figure for South Korea was $4.5 billion).[54]

On December 18, 2018, the Japanese government announced the newest Mid-Term Defense Program (MTDP), earmarking some $243 billion for defense procurements over the next five years. "The biggest news to come out of the MTDP was the confirmation that Japan will seek to add to its buy of an additional 105 Lockheed Martin F-35 Lightning II Joint Strike Fighters, which would include 42 F-35B short-takeoff-and-vertical-landing aircraft, although this was not much of a surprise."[55]

While Japan is very troubled by China's accelerated military buildup, particularly the PLA's ability to conduct offensive operations in and around the Senkaku Islands (also claimed by China, which refers to them as the Diaoyu Islands), Tokyo perceives a greater threat from North Korea's WMD programs. Six nuclear tests and more than forty ballistic missile tests since 2016 "pose an unprecedentedly serious and imminent threat to the security of Japan," noted Japan's defense ministry in its *Defense White Paper 2018*.[56] The report also stated that "North Korea's possession of nuclear weapons cannot be tolerated. At the same time, sufficient attention needs to be paid to the development and deployment of ballistic missiles, the military confrontation on the Korean Peninsula, and the proliferation of WMDs and ballistic missiles by North Korea."[57]

The Japanese defense ministry announced a military budget of $46 billion for FY2019, and, combined with Japan's increasingly alarmed views on Chinese defense, "Abe has cited Pyongyang's race to develop nuclear weapons and ballistic missiles as proof that Japan must bolster its defence capabilities and loosen some of the constitutional shackles imposed after the second world war on its self-defence forces."[58] These two threats have resulted in approval of the biggest defense budget in history for FY2019. "This will be the sixth consecutive year that the defense budget has risen, with the amounts sharply increasing since Abe took office in 2012. But rather than a reflection of the prime minister's desire to revise Japan's pacifist, war renouncing constitution, the increase is more in response to mounting military tensions in East Asia, chief among them North Korea's increasingly provocative behavior."[59]

In one of the most symbolic demonstrations of Japan's military muscle, the Japanese government also decided to put into service two *Izumo*-class aircraft carriers manned with F-35 fighters. These are the largest ships in the Maritime Self-Defense Force. "The review of the new defense guideline is extremely meaningful to show the Japanese people and the world what is truly necessary in our defense to protect the people and to serve as the cornerstone of the future" for the Japan Self-Defense Forces, said chief cabinet secretary Yoshihide Suga.[60]

The *Japan Times* noted right after the June 2018 Trump-Kim Singapore summit that Japan needed to maximize the opportunities resulting from the reduction in tensions involving North Korea. Trump's assurances notwithstanding, North Korea continues to threaten Japan.[61] In a rebuke to Trump, the paper wrote:

> Trump's penchant for hyperbole and his indifference to detail (and often facts themselves) is sufficiently well established that his claim upon returning from the Singapore summit with North Korean leader Kim Jong Un that "there is no longer a nuclear threat from North Korea" was roundly dismissed. Skepticism was deserved: The Singapore joint statement was striking in its lack of detail and Pyongyang has not made any gestures that indicate a change in its thinking about nuclear weapons.[62]

Critics of Japan's increased defense budget, the right to collective defense, and ongoing force modernization programs, such as China, have criticized Japan roundly for exploiting the

North Korean threat as a cover for Tokyo's militarization. Given South Korea's overlapping linkages and shared interests with Japan, Seoul has been much more constrained in questioning Japan's growing power projection capabilities. Still, not only is Abe on the verge of becoming the longest-serving postwar Japanese prime minister, but he has ushered in key defense policy changes that would have been unthinkable a decade ago.

Responding militarily to North Korea's threat, however, is just one component of Japan's North Korea policy. North Korea's abduction of Japanese nationals in the 1970s to teach North Korean spies about Japanese culture and language is arguably the single most important unresolved dispute, and one that resonates strongly with the Japanese public. In November 1977, Japanese middle school student Megumi Yokota was kidnapped by North Korean agents, and the Japanese government believes that abductions occurred until the early 1980s. In May 1997, the Japanese government officially noted a "strong possibility" that ten Japanese nationals had been kidnapped by North Korea.[63] When Prime Minister Junichiro Koizumi visited Pyongyang for a one-day meeting with Kim Jong Il in September 2002, Kim admitted for the first time that "rogue agents" had indeed kidnapped Japanese nationals, giving the number as thirteen; Kim said eight had died and five were still alive. Koizumi secured the release of those five, who were reunited with their parents in May 2004.[64]

Japan held a number of discussions with North Korea over the abductee issue, but no final resolution was achieved. As tensions mounted after North Korea's first nuclear test in 2006, efforts at normalizing Japan–North Korea relations floundered. Pyongyang has continued to insist that the abductee issue isn't a central impediment to normalizing ties with Tokyo. Rather, it argues that Japan has to come clean on its own role during the colonial period. Speaking at a conference in Seoul in November 2018,

Ri Jong Hyok, vice chairman of the Korean Asia-Pacific Peace Committee—one of North Korea's many front organizations—stated that "we, the entire Korean people, strongly demand Japan's sincere and frank reflection, apology, and sufficient compensation" and harshly criticized Japan for "crimes that violated human rights."[65]

Japan has been a key actor in calling out North Korea for its blatant human rights abuses in recent years. North Korea's KCNA lambasted Japan in October 2018 after Japan pushed for a UN human rights resolution focusing on North Korean abuses: "It is a mockery and insult to justice and human rights that Japan, which committed the unethical crimes against the Korean nation and other Asian countries but has made no apology for them, is taking the lead in the 'human rights' campaign."[66]

Prime Minister Abe has tried to engage North Korea in order to retain Japan's leverage amid ongoing developments, even as other powers expend significant political capital on dialogue with North Korea. But Trump's erratic North Korea policy has weakened the international community's ability to maintain a hardline posture. In a scathing diatribe, the North Korean party newspaper *Rodong Sinmun* wrote that Japan "has been left alone in the region, being branded as a country of pygmy politicians engaged in abnormal view on things and phenomena, anachronistic thought and stupid and unbecoming conduct."[67]

Looking over the Horizon

Japan's longer-term interests on the Korean Peninsula are shaped by how a unified Korea would interact with Japan and the extent to which such a state could negatively affect Japan's core interests. Tokyo's preference is for a unified Korea that is democratic, with a flourishing market economy, multiple linkages with the global community, and strong support for a liberal international order. In short, Japan wants a unified Korea that is an extension of the ROK.

Whether a unified Korea would actually illustrate such traits is going to depend critically on the survivability of North Korea, the process by which unification occurs, the degree to which China opts to intervene, the sustainability of American policy, and South Korea's depth of political will and strategic acumen. In none of these areas, however, does Japan have critical leverage, though it does have an indirect influence on America's role in the unification process. Its limited capacity is almost wholly a product of Japan's historical legacy. If there is a common theme that resonates in the two Koreas, it is that Japan should have no direct role in the process leading up to unification. The depth of anti-Japanese sentiment is such that, short of a North Korean attack on South Korea, which would trigger Japan's role as the most important rear base for U.S. military operations, none of the key actors wants Japanese involvement.

Historically, Japan has viewed the Korean Peninsula as a dagger pointed toward Japan—not by virtue of Korean power, but as an extension of Chinese power. Instability on the peninsula was deemed anathema to Japanese interests, and Tokyo chose to expand its zone of operations into Korea by fighting two major wars: the Sino-Japanese War of 1894–1895 and the Russo-Japanese War of 1904–1905. Both resulted in Japanese victories and enabled Japan first to assume control of Korean foreign and defense policies in 1905 and then, in 1910, to annex Korea outright.

For the time being, though, Japan sees North Korea as its most existential external threat. "Threat perceptions are greater over North Korea today than the Soviet Union during the Cold War," writes Kazuto Suzuki of Hokkaido University, and he cites four reasons: "the unpredictability of Kim Jong-un's regime; the possible 'de-coupling' of the US-Japan alliance; fear of a massive refugee crisis; and the potential for increased Chinese influence in the event of conflict."[68]

Abe's preferred strategy involves beefing up Japan's military capabilities not only to counter the PLA's leapfrogging strategies but also to ensure that should a major North Korean crisis develop, Japan will have credible military options. As the world's third-largest economic power, Japan has a vital role to play in assisting North Korea's denuclearization. Estimates of how much it would cost to dismantle North Korea's WMD and pave the way for reconstructing North Korea vary widely depending on timelines and scenarios, but some financial analysts have put the price tag at $1 trillion over a decade, including funds for secure dismantlement, the construction of light water reactors, and economic assistance.[69]

"I think it would be fair to say that dismantling and cleanup of a substantial part of the North Korean nuclear complex (not even considering the missile complex) would cost many billions and take 10 years or so," said Siegfried Hecker, a Stanford University nuclear specialist who visited the Yongbyon nuclear facility in 2010.[70] In response to Trump's assertion that Japan and South Korea should assume the lion's share of denuclearization costs, Japan has pledged to do its part.

For Japan, the worst possible outcome on the Korean Peninsula is a unified Korea ruled by the North—highly unlikely, but not totally impossible. Hence, sustaining the status quo while managing North Korea's nuclear and WMD threats is the best option for Tokyo. Developments on the Korean Peninsula have always had a direct bearing on Japanese security, and Tokyo wants a capabilities-based Korea policy that sufficiently protects Japan's core interests regardless of the scenario. At a time when bilateral ties with Washington are at an all-time low due to Trump's incompetence, Japan's anxiety will continue to remain high and lead to a greater reliance on its own capabilities.

The United States and Korea: Unplanned but Critical Allies

The slogan for the U.S.-ROK Combined Forces Command is *katchi kapshida*, "Let's go together," which symbolizes the uniqueness of the most integrated military partnership currently in operation. Since the Korean War, the Korean-American alliance has evolved from South Korea's near-total dependence on the United States to a much more equal partnership. Seoul's rise from the bottom of the economic barrel to the eleventh-largest economy in the world wouldn't have been possible without a robust alliance that kept North Korea at bay.

What is truly remarkable about the alliance, however, is that it was neither designed nor intended to be so successful. History shows how the United States became a vital but accidental stakeholder on the Korean Peninsula.

In 1905, following Washington's mediation in the Russo-Japanese War, the United States agreed with Japan that Korea's foreign and defense policies would henceforth be administered by Japan. Five years later, Korea was colonized by Japan. In effect, Washington washed its hands of Korea. This is seen by many Koreans as a major diplomatic blunder by the United States, but from Washington's perspective, Korea was not a vital interest in the Far East at that time.

Having lost its power to conduct foreign relations, Korea made last-ditch efforts to inform the United States that the treaty of November 1905 had been signed under duress. When special envoy "without credentials" Min Young-chan called on Secretary of State Elihu Root in December 1905, he was informed that the official Korean chargé d'affaires had already formally acknowledged the United States' withdrawal of its ambassador to Korea."[71] Root told Min:

> In view of this official communication, it is difficult to see how the Government of the United States can proceed in any manner upon the entirely different view of the facts which you tell us personally you have been led to take by the information which you have received. It is to be observed, moreover, that the official communications from the Japanese Government agree with the official communications from the Korean Government, and are quite inconsistent with your information. . . . Under all these circumstances, I feel bound to advise you that the Government of the United States does not consider that any good purpose would be subserved by taking notice of your statements.[72]

The former Korean legation building in Washington, D.C., was bought by the Japanese government for $5 in 1910 and promptly sold off. After the liberation of Korea from Japanese control in August 1945, a trusteeship was imposed for three years by the United States and the Soviet Union through their respective zones of occupation across the 38th parallel. On January 12, 1950, Secretary of State Dean Acheson gave what many consider to be the most fateful speech prior to the outbreak of the Korean War in June 1950. Referencing the need to protect Japan in the aftermath of its defeat and disarmament, Acheson stated:

> I can assure you that there is no intention of any sort of abandoning or weakening the defenses of Japan and that whatever arrangements are to be made either through permanent settlement or otherwise, that de-

fense must and shall be maintained. . . . This defensive perimeter runs along the Aleutians to Japan and then goes to the Ryukyus. We hold important defense positions in the Ryukyu Islands, and those we will continue to hold. In the interest of the population of the Ryukyu Islands, we will at an appropriate time offer to hold these islands under trusteeship of the United Nations. But they are essential parts of the defensive perimeter of the Pacific, and they must and will be held. . . . So far as the military security of other areas in the Pacific is concerned, it must be clear that no person can guarantee these areas against military attack. But it must also be clear that such a guarantee is hardly sensible or necessary within the realm of practical relationship.[73]

As noted in Chapter Four, Kim Il Sung was eager to get approval from Stalin and Mao, but especially the former, to launch an attack against the South. Acheson's speech didn't give the green light for a North Korean invasion. Rather, it was part of a series of events that convinced Kim, and later Stalin, that the United States didn't consider Korea a central strategic asset. In 1949, the U.S. Joint Chiefs of Staff recommended that all U.S. troops should be withdrawn from South Korea except for a handful of military advisors. In late 1949, the U.S. House of Representatives opted to cut vital economic aid to South Korea, prompting the ROK government to ask the Truman administration to reverse the House decision.

Militarily, the nascent South Korean armed forces were supplied and trained by the United States, but they were in no shape to defend South Korea against a North Korean attack, much less deter one. The Korea Military Advisory Group, which supervised U.S. military aid to South Korea, reported in January 1950 that military assistance to South Korea would have to be limited to $9.8 million.[74]

Much more important, however, was the prevailing belief that the South Korean military shouldn't be too strong, lest it become a threat to the North. "The objective of this program is to strengthen the existing Security Forces without providing means for an increase in numerical strength," wrote Brigadier General W. L. Roberts, head of the Korea Military Advisory Group. The equipment that was being provided was "an attempt to equalize the range and weight of weapons in South Korea with those known to be in North Korea."[75]

Roberts did stress, however, the critical importance of providing combat aircraft to the South Korean forces, since those were thought to be "absolutely necessary for the defense of South Korea."[76] When war broke out in June 1950, however, the ROK military didn't have a single fighter airplane. Combined, all of these developments led Kim Il Sung to think that he didn't really have to worry about massive and immediate American military intervention on behalf of South Korea.

Historian Kathryn Weathersby writes:

> In the spring of 1950 Stalin's policy toward Korea took an abrupt turn. During meetings with Kim Il Sung in Moscow in April, Stalin approved Kim's plan to reunify the country by military means and agreed to provide the necessary supplies and equipment for the operation. The plan to launch the assault on South Korea was Kim's initiative, not Stalin's. The Soviet leader finally agreed to support the undertaking only after repeated requests from Kim. Furthermore, Stalin's purpose was not to test American resolve; on the contrary, he approved the plan only after having been assured that the United States would not intervene.[77]

The Truman administration wanted to avoid being pulled into another major Asian war, an attitude Acheson supported. At the same time, however, once Kim Il Sung attacked South Korea, Truman felt compelled to respond forcefully because of the prevailing view that such an attack could be a harbinger of equally serious attacks against a young NATO in Western Europe.

Washington and the Emerging Korean Question

The urgency of coping with the North Korean nuclear issue has dominated U.S. policy toward the Korean Peninsula since the early 1990s. What is happening now, however, is equally if not more compelling: the convergence of powerful political forces reminiscent of the early 1900s and late 1940s that changed the course of Korean history, and America's involvement in that journey.

On June 16, 2009, presidents Barack Obama and Lee Myung-bak released a joint statement that outlined what type of a unified Korea was desirable, the first time the leaders of the United States and South Korea had outlined such a vision: "Through our Alliance we aim to build a better future for all people on the Korean Peninsula, establishing a durable peace on the Peninsula and leading to peaceful reunification on the principles of free democracy and a market economy."[78] South Korea's progressives criticized the statement for stating explicitly that a unified Korea should be a free democracy; they were upset because such a goal implies the collapse of North Korea or unification by absorption.

As important as the North Korean nuclear issue is, however, the United States has much wider and deeper interests on the Korean Peninsula. South Korea is the only country in mainland Asia where U.S. forces are deployed, and China, Russia, and North Korea have long wanted to see those forces withdrawn.

Decoupling South Korea from the United States is another shared interest. Deterring a second Korean War remains an essential element of U.S. strategy on the Korean Peninsula and enables the United States to maintain a longer-term military footprint.

The most vexing task confronting the United States is how it would manage the transition from the existing status quo to a unified Korea. On the nuclear front, Washington, Beijing, and Moscow share a common interest in ensuring denuclearization and preventing South Korea from inheriting nuclear weapons and long-range ballistic missiles.

A far more contentious issue is how each of the major powers would respond to the dynamic forces involved in a relatively gradual unification process—or, alternatively, to the high political volatility and uncertainty that would be triggered if there was massive political disruption in North Korea, such as would accompany regime collapse. In the latter case, the final outcome would be shaped by a combination of factors, such as the degree of military intervention by the major powers, the depth of South Korean preparation and willingness to execute rapid responses, and of course the aftermath of the North Korean implosion. It's critical to bear in mind that even if regime collapse occurs in the North, it doesn't mean that millions of North Koreans will rush to the South.

The worst outcome of Korean unification for China and Russia would be unification along the lines of the German model—that is, absorption of the North by the South. For the United States, by contrast, a Korean Peninsula led by the ROK is the preferred outcome. This is hardly assured, however. Chinese intervention in the case of a major North Korean crisis is virtually inevitable. Furthermore, prospects for joint Chinese-Russian operations in support of North Korea or against the ROK and the United States also can't be ruled out. From September 11 through September 17, 2018, Russia held the Vostok (Asia) 2018 military games, with 297,000 Russian forces, 36,000 pieces of equipment, and more than 1,000 combat aircraft—72 percent of all combat-capable Russian aircraft. What made this exercise noteworthy was the participation of 3,200 PLA troops and an unknown number of Mongolian forces.[79] According to *The Hill*, this drill covered Russia's nine military districts and was the biggest military exercise since Zapad-1981, which simulated the Warsaw Pact's invasion of Poland.

> China's presence allowed the Russian armed forces to judge *in situ* the level of preparedness and adaptation to modern warfare of a country that has not had combat experience in decades, and draw conclusions. The same can be said for Beijing, as there are many sectors where both armies can learn from each other and explore further military and technical cooperation. Vostok also showed off Russia's "combat-proven" military hardware which could help it secure additional defence contracts with Beijing.[80]

Given the historical mistrust between Russia and China and growing PLA capabilities, there is no assurance that these two major powers would actually conduct joint military operations in a real crisis. Nevertheless, in the event of substantial turbulence in North Korea stemming from regime collapse or a rapid deterioration in inter-Korean ties leading to significant military clashes, the United States can no longer assume that there won't be military pushback by China, Russia, or both.

None of the key scenarios leading up to a unified Korea is going to be easy. Peaceful integration is the most desirable outcome but at the same time the most unlikely. If a North Korean collapse occurs, it won't look like the collapse of communist regimes in

Eastern Europe in 1989 and 1990. And if North Korea launches another invasion, it would be followed by massive U.S. and South Korean retaliation, possibly spurring Pyongyang to go for broke and use nuclear weapons. Again, the United States must consider Chinese or even Russian military intervention, and to a lesser extent involvement by Japan, in any serious crisis management scenarios.

Significant Sino-American cooperation on major contingencies on the Korean Peninsula is going to be essential in order to avoid unwanted spillovers. For China, a unified Korea that has a robust military alliance with the United States is unacceptable, just as a unified Korea under North Korea is unacceptable to the United States. Narrowing this gap with minimal friction is going to pose the greatest challenge to U.S. diplomacy and crisis management since the outbreak of the Korean War in 1950.

The Primacy of Politics and Common Perceptions

Managing an outcome favorable to the ROK and the United States is going to depend crucially on the degree of political cooperation between Seoul and Washington, but such cooperation is by no means a certainty. In the post–Korean War era, the United States has faced numerous Korea-related crises, such as the capture of the USS *Pueblo* by North Korea in 1969; the murder of two American soldiers in Panmunjom by North Korean soldiers in 1976; the assassination of Park Chung-hee in 1979 and the ensuing political turmoil in South Korea; the killing of eighteen senior ROK officials in Rangoon, Burma, by North Korean agents in 1983; and the downing of Korean Air Lines flight 007 also in 1983 by the Soviet Union.

Deterring major conflict on the Korean Peninsula has been the cornerstone of U.S. policy since the middle of the twentieth century, but ever since North Korea's first nuclear test in 2006, and even more so since its September 2017 hydrogen bomb test, deterrence has become markedly more difficult. The North Korean nuclear crisis has been one of the longest-running crises in the post–Cold War era; the specter of massive political dislocation in the event of a North Korean collapse means an exponential increase in all sorts of risks on top of the nuclear threat.

Three dimensions need to be taken into account in thinking about how the United States would cope with a major Korean crisis. First, while the United States likes to think of German unification as providing a model for Korea, that model isn't really applicable in the Korean context. The unification of West Germany and East Germany occurred just before the collapse of the Soviet Union and at the height of American power. In Korea, unification is going to occur, if it occurs at all, when China is at the apex of its power. This single geopolitical factor alone is a potential game changer on the Korean Peninsula.

Second, while the United States has unsurpassed hard power at its disposal, North Korea has no plans to go quietly. If North Korea instigates another war, there is no doubt that it will be defeated, but at a huge cost for South Korea and the United States. Clearly, one can fall into the trap of overestimating the KPA's capabilities given its sheer numerical advantages on top of its WMD arsenal. But just as dangerous is overestimating the advantages of superior U.S. military technologies, as seen in the costly counterterrorism and counterinsurgency operations needed against Al Qaeda, the Taliban, and ISIS in Iraq and Afghanistan.

Third, the geopolitical stakes are far greater than they were with German unification given the possibility of Chinese or Russian intervention in a major Korean crisis. Not since the Korean War has the United States fought the PLA, but the Chinese military of the early 1950s was a mere shadow of what it is today. The United States has to play three-dimensional chess on the

Korean Peninsula in order to achieve four simultaneous goals: ensuring maximum operational jointness between U.S. and ROK forces throughout the phases of conflict or major crises, deterring North Korea's potential use of nuclear weapons, avoiding military clashes with China (and to a lesser extent with Russia) but prevailing if the United States is forced to engage, and maximizing the opportunities for a political settlement that favors American and South Korean interests while not denigrating China's core security concerns.

If a major crisis breaks out in North Korea over the next several years, what would be required of the United States is a whole-of-government effort. Political awareness and agility at the highest levels of leadership, an abiding appreciation of core institutions, centrality of alliance management, and, most important, a constant focus on creating a unified Korea that preserves liberty and democracy will be essential. The United States and South Korea can't afford to fail.

CONCLUSION
Three Gateways

Kim Jong Un Is on Top—And Why He's Not

On the last day of 2018, Kim Jong Un sent letters to two leaders he needed to cajole into an agreement: U.S. president Donald Trump and South Korean president Moon Jae-in. The contents of the letters weren't made public, but his message wasn't hard to guess: *My offer of "complete denuclearization" remains on the table, but this is only going to happen if you listen to my demands.*

For the first time since he rose to power, Kim was at the top of his game. China and Russia backed him; Donald Trump's national security team was floundering, with no cohesive North Korea strategy; and Moon was more than happy to join hands with Kim in watering down international sanctions and building an irreversible inter-Korean peace regime.

Kim Jong Un delivered his 2019 New Year's address sitting on a sofa in front of two huge pictures of Kim Il Sung and Kim

Jong Il. In contrast to the finely tailored Mao suit he usually favors, this time he wore a black Western suit with a gray tie. It was Pyongyang's version of a fireside chat.

"I am ready to meet the US president again anytime, and will make efforts to obtain without fail results which can be welcomed by the international community," Kim said, emphasizing his openness to a dialogue with Trump. He also stressed that "if the United States does not keep the promise it made in the eyes of the world, and out of miscalculation of our people's patience, it attempts to unilaterally enforce something upon us and persists in imposing sanctions and pressure against our Republic, we may be compelled to find a new way for defending the sovereignty of the country and the supreme interests of the state and for achieving peace and stability of the Korean Peninsula."[1]

According to veteran South Korean journalist Shin Seok-ho, who has covered North Korea for seventeen years, Kim was telling Trump that while he wants to "fulfill the denuclearization aspiration of his father"—something Pyongyang always emphasizes, to burnish its commitment to giving up nuclear weapons—he can do so only if the United States satisfies North Korea's conditions.

In other words, Kim has no intention of giving up his nuclear weapons, but he is tempting Trump with denuclearization, something that has eluded every U.S. president beginning with Bill Clinton. So long as Kim keeps up the act, playing to Trump's ego and his desire for personal victories (even if they are illusory or self-delusional), he knows that time is on his side. Despite Trump's rhetoric about bombing North Korea back to the Stone Age if Pyongyang doesn't give up nuclear weapons, even Trump won't be able to start a second Korean War without the full support of his generals. Equally important, no sitting South Korean president is going to agree to a preemptive strike on North Korea.

Kim Jong Un's concerted psychological operations against

South Korea and the United States wouldn't have been possible without Trump's unexpected victory in November 2016 and the inauguration of Moon in May 2017. A U.S. president who sees little value in stationing U.S. troops in South Korea or Japan, who says that joint military exercises are threatening to North Korea, and who constantly denigrates his closest allies, such as Japan, was a godsend for Kim Jong Un.

As he tested Trump throughout 2017 with thermonuclear and ICBM tests, Kim ran the risk of triggering a military response by the United States. However, his willingness to push the envelope paid off handsomely, as Kim was able to put into place a game plan that began with his 2018 New Year's address and involved bringing Moon into his fold, reassuring Xi Jinping and securing his backing (and Vladimir Putin's), enticing Trump with the deal of the century, and ignoring Japan. The only reason Trump didn't give Kim everything he wanted during their first summit in June 2018 was because Defense Secretary James Mattis, National Security Advisor H. R. McMaster, and CIA Director Gina Haspel, among others who were alarmed at Trump's naiveté, joined in efforts to exert pressure on him.

In a New Year's tweet at the beginning of 2019, Trump wrote, "Kim Jong Un says North Korea will not make or test nuclear weapons or give them to others. . . . I also look forward to meeting with Chairman Kim who realizes so well that North Korea possesses great economic potential!"[2] On January 2, 2019, as he chaired his first cabinet meeting in the new year, Trump showed off a letter from Kim Jong Un. "Kim Jong Un, they've [North Koreans] never written letters like that. This letter is a great letter, we've made a lot of progress," Trump said, and stressed that since Kim Jong Un wanted another summit, just as he did, Trump was looking forward to seeing him.[3] Trump also made the claim that were it not for his administration, there would have been a catastrophic war on the Korean Peninsula:

If another administration came in instead of this administration, namely, Mike and myself and the group around this table, you'd be at war right now. You'd be having a nice big fat war in Asia and it wouldn't be pleasant. And instead of that, we're getting along fine. I'm not in a rush. All I know is that there is no rocket and there is no testing. . . . I was watching PBS and they really covered it accurately . . . on Chairman Kim's speech, he really wants to get together, he wants to denuclearize, and a lot of good things are happening, and they covered it very, very nicely.[4]

As reported in the *Dong-a Ilbo*, what North Korea wants from Trump is something no U.S. president has been willing to give in a package: (1) end all U.S.-ROK joint military exercises; (2) stop all transfers of U.S. strategic assets and war matériel into South Korea; (3) begin multilateral negotiations to replace the current armistice agreement; (4) restart the Kaesong Industrial Complex and Mount Kumgang tours; (5) remove all U.S. influence from South-North relations; (6) recognize North Korea's earnest first steps, such as shutting down the Pungye-ri test site, with commensurate measures from the United States, such as ending all military pressures; and (7) future negotiations based on mutual respect and fair principles.[5]

Given that north and south committed themselves to advancing along the road of peace and prosperity, we maintain that the joint military exercises with foreign forces, which constitute the source of aggravating the situation on the Korean peninsula, should no longer be permitted and the introduction of war equipment including strategic assets from outside should completely be suspended. . . . We will never tolerate the interference and intervention of outside forces who stand in the way of national reconciliation, unity and reunification with the design to subordinate inter-Korean relations to their tastes and interests.[6]

Based on some of his public pronouncements, Trump has seemed inclined to give Kim at least some of these concessions. He has complained bitterly about the United States flying B-2 bombers from Guam to South Korea for exercises or as a demonstration of U.S. resolve and commitment to South Korea's defense. He dismissed the need to hold joint U.S.-ROK military drills, called for the withdrawal of U.S. forces from South Korea and Japan because they were too expensive, and asserted that the nuclear threat from North Korea was over thanks to his diplomatic prowess. Moreover, since Moon doesn't want to provoke Kim, Seoul has heartily welcomed the postponement of U.S.-ROK joint military exercises and even the downsizing of unilateral South Korean military war games.

Watching all this from Pyongyang, Kim must be heartened by Washington's and Seoul's willingness to accommodate his demands. While Trump hasn't implemented any withdrawal of U.S. forces from South Korea or removed the U.S. nuclear umbrella from Seoul (and if he did that, presumably he would withdraw protection from Tokyo as well), he has done more political damage to the alliance between the United States and South Korea than any other American president. The fact that President Moon joined hands with Kim to present a new united front hardly augurs well for the U.S.-ROK alliance. Kim Jong Un is confident that Trump is ultimately going to give him sanctions relief, which will mean jettisoning the maximum-pressure strategy against North Korea.

Kim is also banking that Moon is going to focus on South-North reconciliation as the cornerstone of his administration, especially since the South Korean economy will continue to flounder. The South Korean economy is expected to grow by less than 2.6 percent in 2019, according to a forecast made by the Korea Development Institute, South Korea's premier economic think tank—a result of slowing domestic demand and plateauing exports.[7] The Capital Market Institute noted that, "After peaking during the third quarter of this year, the economy is likely to show a phase of moderate contraction till the first half of 2020 [and] South Korea's economic growth is falling as corporate capital and construction investments remain weak amid exports' dwindling contribution."[8]

There has been a constant push and pull between autonomy, alliance, and even abandonment in the U.S.–South Korea relationship throughout the post–Korean War era. At no point until the present, however, have there ever been occupants of the Blue House and the White House whose interests coincided in the way they do now—for very different political ends, but with potentially far-reaching implications for the U.S.-ROK alliance and the future of the Korean Peninsula.

Kim Jong Un believes that he can control South-North relations to his advantage, given the alignment of interests between Moon and Trump. In the end, however, Kim won't be able to foresee, much less control, the eruption and convergence of new political forces within North Korea. And while it's hard to imagine that the Kim dynasty is going to collapse anytime in the near future, North Korea is at a crossroads precisely because Kim can't—as much as he might want to—stem the tide of two potent forces: information seeping into North Korea about both the outside world and the reality of life within the North Korean state, and the awakening of the North Korean people.

In the months before the fall of the Berlin Wall in November 1989, virtually no one predicted its collapse and the rapid dissolution of the Iron Curtain. Until the very end, the East German authorities felt that they could maintain control of the levers of power. While it's virtually impossible to imagine that North Koreans are going to march in droves to protest against the regime, Kim wouldn't bat an eye if he had to kill thousands or tens of thousands of citizens to show that he's fully in charge. Fear, mutual suspicion, the burden of making ends meet, and resignation have all combined to create a nation in prison. But this prison won't last forever.

Forces Beyond Control

Unsurprisingly, the two Koreas have spent a considerable amount of time thinking about and preparing for unification. Although they both agree on key principles such as noninterference by foreign powers and peaceful reintegration of the two Koreas, Seoul's and Pyongyang's respective unification blueprints have little else in common. In large part this is because of the intensely nationalistic and normative nature of the unification issue. Both Koreas place the highest political value on national reunification. But their plans to overcome deeply entrenched political, ideological, socioeconomic, cultural, and even linguistic differences remain more in the realm of wishful thinking than grounded reality.

As mentioned earlier, however, regardless of how the Korean Peninsula transitions in the years or decades ahead, one undeniable fact is that Korean unification, when it occurs, will happen at the apex of Chinese power. Conversely, German unification occurred at the nadir of Soviet power. This distinction is crucial because even though Moscow had deep reservations about a West German–led unification process (as did Great Britain and France), President George H. W. Bush understood the historical significance of the moment and cajoled each of the major stakeholders into accepting a unified Germany that was an extension of the Federal Republic of Germany.

Crucially, Bush didn't embarrass Soviet leader Mikhail Gorbachev by figuratively dancing on top of the Berlin Wall; he deliberately chose not to celebrate the defeat of East Germany or, later on, the collapse of the Soviet Union. In the Korean context, however, irrespective of unification pathways, the China factor is going to rule supreme. A unified Korea will be possible only after China is assured that such a state won't impinge upon its strategic and economic interests. In fact, a 2015 Washington think tank report raised the possibility that "a unified Korea [would be] treated as a modern tributary state of Beijing."[9]

Contrary to conventional wisdom in South Korea, where unification is often thought of as a peaceful process based on webs of inter-Korean cooperation and engagement, peaceful unification through a grand compromise, although the most desirable outcome, is also the most unlikely scenario. Peaceful unification ignores the inevitable existential fight for North Korea's and South Korea's very identity as sovereign states. While the circumstances are totally different, peaceful unification might be thought of as akin to a peaceful merger between Apple and Huawei in which the outcome is a single corporate entity that nevertheless retains elements of each company's DNA. The most likely reality, however, is that unification will resemble a ferocious clash of titans fighting for their very existence. Only one party is going to emerge victorious.

A second widely hoped-for scenario involves North Korean collapse followed by absorption by South Korea. This model closely resembles German unification, since East Germany imploded rapidly after Mikhail Gorbachev no longer wanted to, or was able to, support the German Democratic Republic. Such a possibility can't be discounted, but "a collapsed North Korea would be a watershed event, unleashing dynamics that would redefine the geopolitical landscape and test the future of the region. The regional powers—South Korea, China, Japan, Russia, and the U.S.—are all ill prepared to handle short- and long-term challenges to their vital interests emerging from a collapsed North Korea."[10]

Finally, the pathway that everyone wants to avoid is unification through war or conflict. South Vietnam's capitulation in 1975 is the closest real-life example. When the Nixon administration signed the Paris Peace Accord in January 1973, no one really believed that South Vietnam would be able to win the peace. In a phone conversation between National Security Advisor Henry Kissinger and White House chief of staff Al Haig on March 15, 1973, barely two months after the agreement was signed, Kissinger told Haig, "We know the goddamned agreement will probably not work, but we've got to be in a position where if it doesn't work, it will be the result of the other side."[11]

Overall, the unification process is going to be volatile and unpredictable, with high levels of uncertainty. Though South Korea has a commanding economic lead over the North, that doesn't mean South Korea is going to dominate the unification process. As Bruce Bennett of the RAND Corporation has written, the three main limitations on South Korean thinking about unification are "(1) a heavy focus on peaceful unification and little discussion of other unification paths, (2) an assumption that unification will succeed once it is started, and (3) a failure to address cases involving unification under North Korean control."[12]

Unification strategies and policies are much more integrated into the DPRK's goals than the ROK's given the prominence of unification in the context of North Korea's monolithic ideology. Crucially, unifying the Korean Peninsula under North Korean rule remains the defining element of Pyongyang's national security strategy. This is, of course, an outcome that is anathema to South Korea, at least to those who continue to attach value to a unified Korea that is free and democratic. However, for the extreme left in South Korea, unification doesn't necessarily have to emphasize liberty and freedom, since the overwhelmingly important goal on both sides is to reunite a divided nation.

For the left in South Korea, recapturing the "oneness" of the Korean nation and the Korean race is the goal of unification. Exclusion of the great powers is a must. In this view, only after Korea recovers its true national identity, which has been hijacked by generations of a corrupt ruling class in the South and tainted by foreign cultures, will it be possible to say that Korea has really become whole. As a 2015 Center for a New American Security report noted, one possible geostrategic implication "of unification's impact . . . [is] the possibility of a united Korea as an outlet for Korean nationalism."[13]

Peaceful unification is the holy grail of the two Koreas. However, it is also the most uncertain pathway, since it is premised on negotiated outcomes. While neither Pyongyang nor Seoul admits it, unification is going to be the end result of an epic political struggle. A unified Korea can emerge only if one of the two Koreas ceases to exist. And the entire fabric of North Korea's political psychology, the raison d'être for the Kim dynasty, depends on the peninsula coming under the North's rule. A parallel principle holds sway in South Korea, although there are many more contending voices. For the vast majority of South Koreans, however, a unified Korea that doesn't guarantee individual rights and freedoms isn't worth the effort. As much as South Koreans are nationalistic, they've tasted the fruits of freedom for far too long. For them, ensuring that all Koreans on both sides of the 38th parallel enjoy liberty, freedom from persecution, and the ability to say no to tyranny is what unification must be about.

In a survey conducted by the Asan Institute for Policy Studies in March 2018 that asked Koreans how South Korea's ties with North Korea and the United States will change in the future, 66.4 percent said that relations with North Korea will improve, while only 16.5 percent replied that ties will worsen and 11.7 percent said that relations will remain the same.[14] With respect to ties with the United States, 57.8 percent responded that ties would improve, 23.6 percent believed that they would worsen, and 13.5 percent said they would stay the same.[15] The significant number who feel that relations with the United States will worsen is largely a product of Trump's views on free trade and his obsession with getting South Korea (and Japan) to pay more money for the stationing of U.S. forces in the region.

Other polls have revealed shifts in South Korean attitudes toward the North. In 2011, 46.4 percent of South Koreans felt that North Korea was "one of us/neighbor" versus 36 percent who felt that North Korea was a "stranger/enemy." But in 2017, 55.8 percent believed that North Korea was a neighbor, while 31.9 percent felt that North Korea was an enemy.[16]

What is notable about South Korean attitudes toward North Korea and unification, however, is that members of the younger generation are more concerned about maintaining security than pushing for unification. For example, an Asan poll conducted in April 2018 showed that 57.4 percent of those in their twenties felt that war was likely on the Korean Peninsula, compared to 47.7 percent in their fifties and 64.4 percent in their sixties and older.[17] As far as indifference to unification is concerned, 23 percent of those in their twenties were indifferent, while those in their thirties registered the highest figure of 31.3 percent; 12.7 percent of South Koreans in their fifties and 14.9 percent in their sixties and older were indifferent.[18]

Despite the potency of nationalism on both sides of the 38th parallel, the fact remains that the two Koreas have chosen very different trajectories since 1948. In South Korea, only 12.3 percent of those polled believe that unification will serve to restore the unity and identity of the Korean people, whereas 27.4 percent feel that unification is good because it will lower the threat of war, 22 percent believe that the South's technology and the North's labor force can create a powerful synergy, and 14.6 percent see unification as a means to reuniting separated families.[19]

No one knows how North Koreans truly feel about unification, of course, since there are no public opinion surveys and no free press. There is little doubt that Koreans share a common heritage, history, and culture, but the "great divergence" that began in 1948 with the creation of the two Koreas is deeper and more pervasive than Koreans like to admit. In the end, though, totalitarianism can't beat freedom and democracy. As much as the Trump presidency has tarnished these two basic precepts of liberty, they are, after all, the weapons of mass destruction that Kim Jong Un fears most.

Little Cracks in the Wall

Nothing remains the same forever, and North Korea—the most totalitarian state on the planet—isn't an exception. The regime remains strong on the outside, but five forces are converging, and they're beginning to create little cracks in the system: (1) marketization from below, which Kim Jong Un can't reverse; (2) crossborder movement between North Korea and China, despite Kim's crackdown on defectors; (3) a regime and a system that are rotten at the very core and feeding on corruption to maintain the veneer of control; (4) the inflow of information that contravenes North Korea's Ten Commandments, something the regime can't roll back; and (5) ideological erosion, despite brain-numbing cultist indoctrination.[20]

Kim's ruthless dictatorship seems to be at the apex of its power, especially since it is now a nuclear power. The regime shows no signs of closing its gulags or tearing down the police state. Fear, repression, and ignorance will still enable the Kim dynasty to rule North Korea into the foreseeable future. In the long run, however, all revolutions begin with little cracks.

As the *jangmadang* generation demonstrates, North Korean society is not monolithic. There are 25 million avatars in the country, but beneath each avatar is a real person. Hundreds of thousands of them work diligently to preserve and strengthen Big Brother, as they are its beneficiaries. But all the others suffer from it. One day, however, when one brave North Korean refuses to continue living behind an avatar, he or she will shout, *"Deoneun andoe!"*

No more!

Like the lonely hero who stood in front of a column of tanks in Tiananmen Square in June 1989 and became a symbol of freedom and of the yearning for basic human dignity in China, a similar North Korean is going to appear in the future, there is no doubt. The KPA and security forces will kill him and thousands of others, as they have done with impunity since North Korea was founded in 1948. Like in the killing fields of Cambodia under the Khmer Rouge, the Kim dynasty will hold out until the bitter end.

At some point, however, Kim Jong Un will realize that he can't kill 25 million North Koreans. This will be the tipping point, when North Korea's prison walls begin to collapse, and with them, the longest-running family dictatorship the modern world has ever witnessed.

ACKNOWLEDGMENTS

I am most grateful to Adam Bellow from All Points Books at St. Martin's Press for guiding me throughout the writing of *The Hermit King*. Adam was an outstanding editor and encouraged me from the outset. A great team at St. Martin's Press supervised the production process, including managing editor Alan Bradshaw, Kevin Reilly, Jennifer Fernandez, and Laury Frieber, as well as Guy Oldfield and Greta Jung from Macmillan Audio. I also worked with an amazing agent, Roger Freet, from Foundry Media, who was indispensable, always gave me sound advice, and worked tirelessly on my behalf.

Many former South Korean officials shared their views and experiences with me in private, for which I am most thankful. It goes without saying, however, that all of the interpretations and shortcomings in this book are entirely my own. I have learned from a long list of North Korea watchers, including Andrei Lankov, Yang Un-chul, B. R. Myers, and the *Washington Post*'s Anna

Fifield. I'd like to thank all my former teachers, but especially Dr. Kim Dalchoong for introducing me to the world of diplomatic history and the Korean academic community, and the late Dr. Lee Ki-taek for inspiring my lifelong fascination with national security and intelligence affairs. My association with the Seoul Forum for International Affairs and the Carnegie Endowment for International Peace have benefited me greatly.

I have been very fortunate to engage with leading experts and colleagues from the International Institute for Strategic Studies for twenty-five years. Many friends offered critical suggestions, including Hyun In-taek, David Straub, Choi Kang, Lee Geun, Han Seok-hee, and Shin Beom-chul. The idea for writing *The Hermit King* goes back to the summer of 2017 when members of the Air Power Policy Seminar in Washington, D.C., including Bill Rosenau, Sean McFate, and Chip Rodgers, urged me to write a book on North Korea's complex political-military configuration. I am also indebted to Michael Raska at the RSIS in Singapore, Katie Botto, and Sujin Kim for their incisive views and research support.

For more than thirty years, Don Brown has been an unstinting friend, and this book wouldn't have been completed without his encouragement. Don, Choi Jong-moon, and Lee Seok-soo are lifelong brothers. I'm also grateful to Choe Jong-hyun and Ariel Levite for their friendship, and I was deeply saddened by the sudden passing of Charles M. Perry just as I began work on the book.

I am especially cognizant of my late mother's absence and most thankful to my father for all that he has taught me. My two sisters, Chuly and Hyangly, and my niece and nephew, Tanya and Andreas, have given so much more than I could have ever asked for. As in my previous books, I remain especially thankful to my wife, Minjeong, and my daughter, Jean, for their love and support.

CHUNG MIN LEE
Washington, D.C.
August 2019

LIST OF ABBREVIATIONS

BRI Belt and Road Initiative
CIA Central Intelligence Agency
CMC-STC Central Military Commission Science and Technology
    Commission
CPC Communist Party of China
CVID Complete, Verifiable, Irreversible Dismantlement
DARPA Defense Advanced Research Projects Agency
DMZ Demilitarized Zone
DPRK Democratic People's Republic of Korea
EEU Eurasian Economic Union
FFVD Final, Fully Verified Denuclearization
GDP Gross Domestic Product
ICBM Intercontinental Ballistic Missile
IMEMO Institute of World Economy and International Rela-
    tions
KCNA Korea Central News Agency
KCP Korean Communist Party
KPRA Korean People's Revolutionary Army
KPA Korean People's Army

KWP Korean Workers' Party

MPS Ministry of People's Security

MSS Ministry of State Security

MTDP Mid-Term Defense Program

NGO Non-Governmental Organization

NKVD People's Commissariat for International Affairs (Soviet secret police)

NIS National Intelligence Service

NPT Nuclear Non-Proliferation Treaty

OPLAN Operation Plan

PVA People's Volunteer Army

PLA People's Liberation Army

PRC People's Republic of China

ROK Republic of Korea

SPA Supreme People's Assembly

THAAD Terminal High Altitude Area Defense

USSR Union of Soviet Socialist Republics

VCP Vietnamese Communist Party

WMD Weapons of Mass Destruction

NOTES

Introduction

1   Chris Mills Rodrigo, "Trump Discussed Using Nuclear Football on North Korea During Puerto Rico Trip," *The Hill*, March 28, 2019, https://thehill .com/homenews/administration/436401-trump-discussed-using-nuclear -football-on-north-korea-during-2017.

2   "Kim Jong Un's 2019 New Year Address," The National Committee on North Korea, January 1, 2019, North Korea, https://www.ncnk.org /resources/publications/kimjongun_2019_newyearaddress.pdf/file_view.

3   Huong Le Thu, "Can Vietnam's Doi Moi Reforms Be an Inspiration for North Korea?," Australian Strategic Policy Institute, August 23, 2018, https://www.aspi.org.au/opinion/can-vietnams-doi-moi-reforms-be -inspiration-north-korea.

One: Life in Earth's Paradise

1   "Nambukhaneui juyo gyeongjaejipyo bigyo" [Comparison of South and North Korea's key economic indicators], Bank of Korea, https://www.bok .or.kr/portal/main/contents.do?menuNo=200090.

2   "The Happiest People on Earth: North Korea, Rulers, Citizens and Official Narrative," RT, 2017, https://www.youtube.com/watch?v=7ZMB _TxyuNM. The quotations from the factory manager and university student were translated by the author from this documentary.

3   Radio Free Asia, *North Korean Prison Camps* (Amazon Digital Services, June 9, 2016), Kindle loc. 284.

4   Jung Yong-su, "Kim Jong Un ganbu sukcheongwa cheohyeong jaegae" [Kim Jong Un restarts purging and execution of officials], *Joongang Ilbo*,

November 2, 2017, https://news.joins.com/article/22078573. In North Korea, *hyeokmyunghwa* or "revolutionized" means a specific form of punishment that involves being sent to a reeducation camp or sentenced to hard labor for a period of several months to several years, depending on the severity of the alleged crime. Leaders from Kim Il Sung on down have used this mechanism as a way of implementing the principle of divide and rule, so that no one individual becomes too powerful, and as a way of instilling party discipline.

5   Steven Borowiec, "'Under the Sun' Documentary Catches North Korea with Its Guard Down," *Los Angeles Times*, July 6, 2016, https://www.latimes.com/entertainment/movies/la-et-mn-under-the-sun-north-korea-doc-20160705-snap-story.html.

6   Fyodor Tertitskiy, "The Party's 10 Principles, Then and Now," *NK News*, December 11, 2014, https://www.nknews.org/2014/12/the-partys-10-principles-then-and-now/.

7   Steven Borowiec, "'Under the Sun' Documentary Catches North Korea with Its Guard Down."

8   "North Korea Documentary 'Under the Sun' Reveals Inner Workings of Propaganda Machine," CBC, June 30, 2016, https://www.cbc.ca/radio/thecurrent/the-current-for-june-30-2016-1.3659432/north-korea-documentary-under-the-sun-reveals-inner-workings-of-propaganda-machine-1.3659436.

9   Ibid.

10 Choe Sang-Hun, "Defector to South Korea Who Became a Celebrity Resurfaces in the North," *New York Times*, July 18, 2017.

11 Choe Sang-Jun, "North Korean Defector in South Seeks Vietnam's Help to Return Home," *New York Times*, March 7, 2016, https://www.nytimes.com/2016/03/08/world/asia/north-korean-defector-in-south-seeks-vietnams-help-to-return-home.html.

12 Anna Fifield, "North Korean Defectors Are Crucial—but Sometimes Unreliable—Witnesses," *Washington Post*, January 19, 2015, https://www.washingtonpost.com/news/worldviews/wp/2015/01/19/north-korean-defectors-are-crucial-but-sometimes-unreliable-witnesses/?utm_term=.fdac7a90fecf.

13 Interview with Lee in Seoul, January 15, 2016.

14 Hyeonseo Lee, "Escape from North Korea," TED Talk, April 29, 2014, https://www.ted.com/talks/hyeonseo_lee_my_escape_from_north_korea/transcript.

15 Anna Fifield, "This Journalist Didn't Just Interview North Korean Defectors, He Followed Them on Their Escape," *Washington Post*, June 20, 2015, https://www.washingtonpost.com/news/worldviews/wp/2015/06/20/this-journalist-didnt-just-interview-north-korean-defectors-he-followed-them-on-their-escape/?utm_term=.ca7df4c0bed8.

16 Anna Fifield, "Life Under Kim Jong Un," *Washington Post*, November 17, 2017, https://www.washingtonpost.com/graphics/2017/world/north-korea-defectors/?utm_term=.45a3a86356a2.

17 Kim Suk, "Talbukjaga namseo sagidanghangeotdo bangsong ... geureoni bukaeseo deogwanshim" [Reporting even on stories of North Korean defectors' scammed in the South, that's why there's greater interest in North Korea], *Munwha Ilbo*, April 25, 2018, http://www.munhwa.com/news/view .html?no=2018042501033503007001.

18 Thae Yong Ho, *Tae Yong-hoeui jeungeon: 3cheung seogishileui amho* [Thae Yong Ho's testimony: the secret code of the third floor secretariat] (Seoul: Gipirang, 2018), 333.

19 Yun Il-geon, "Cheohyeongdoen Ri Yong-ha, Jang Su-gileun nugu inga" [Who were the executed Ri Yong-ha and Jang Su-gil], *Yeonhap News*, December 3, 2013, https://www.yna.co.kr/view/AKR20131203179 200014.

20 Ibid.

21 Choe Sang-Hun, "North Korean Defector Says Kim Jong-Un's Control Is Crumbling," *New York Times*, January 25, 2017, https://www.nytimes.com /2017/01/25/world/asia/north-korea-defector.html.

22 Thae, *Tae Yong-hoeui jeungeon*, 387.

23 Ibid., 399.

24 Ibid., 399–400.

25 Brian Hook, "The Parasites Feeding on North Koreans," *New York Times*, November 24, 2017, https://www.nytimes.com/2017/11/24/opinion/north -korea-songbun.html.

26 As quoted in Jeon Gyeong Ung, "JSA gwisun Oh Cheong Seong ... 'Ilbongangetdo mollatdaneun tongilbu'" [Joint Security Area defector Oh Cheong Seong, "Ministry of Unification didn't know he went to Japan"], *New Daily*, November 19, 2018, http://www.newdaily.co.kr/site/data/html /2018/11/19/2018111900130.html.

27 "Gwisun Oh Cheong Seong, 'bukhan senghwalbojang patan sangtae'" [Defector Oh Cheong Seong, "North Korea's guaranteeing of livelihood in shatters"], VOA Korea, November 17, 2018, https://www.voakorea.com /a/4662726.html.

28 Alec Luhn, "Russia Hiring North Korean 'Slave' Workers Despite UN Sanctions," *Telegraph*, August 3, 2018, https://www.telegraph.co.uk/news /2018/08/03/russia-hiring-north-korean-slave-workers-despite-un -sanctions.

29 Jason Aldag, "How North Korea Takes a Cut from Its Workers Abroad," *Washington Post*, November 1, 2017, https://www.washingtonpost.com /world/asia_pacific/how-north-korea-takes-a-cut-from-its-workers -abroad/2017/10/31/98728d28-b98d-11e7-9e58-e6288544af98_story .html.

30 Ibid.

31 Tim Sullivan, "NKorean Workers Prep Seafood Going to US Stores, Restaurants," Associated Press, October 5, 2017, https://www.apnews.com /8b493b7df6e147e98d19f3abb5ca090a.

32   Ibid.

33   UN Security Council, Resolution 2375 (2017), September 11, 2017, 5.

34   "North Korean Workers Return to China in Defiance of UN Restrictions,"
     Radio Free Asia, April 4, 2018, https://www.rfa.org/english/news/korea
     /workers-04042018134944.html.

35   Andrew Higgins, "North Koreans in Russia Work 'Basically in the Situa-
     tion of Slaves,'" *New York Times*, July 11, 2017, https://www.nytimes.com
     /2017/07/11/world/europe/north-korea-russia-migrants.html.

36   Ibid.

37   Nicole Stinson, "North Korea Slaves: Workers Forced to Eat Rubbish as
     Kim Tries to Raise Case for Missiles," *Express*, April 16, 2018, https://
     www.express.co.uk/news/world/947043/North-Korea-slaves-Kim-Jong
     -un-nuclear-missile-programme-BBC-Panorama.

38   Alexandra Ma, "North Korean Slaves Found Working Abroad Where They
     'Give Up Being Human' to Prop Up Kim Jong Un's Life of Luxury," *Business
     Insider*, April 16, 2018, https://www.businessinsider.com/lives-of-north
     -korea-slaves-working-in-abroad-to-prop-up-kim-jong-un-2018-4.

39   UN Human Rights Council, "Report of the Commission of Inquiry on
     Human Rights in the Democratic People's Republic of Korea," February
     7, 2014, 11–12.

40   *Trafficking in Persons Report* (Washington, D.C.: Department of State, June
     2018), 255, https://www.state.gov/documents/organization/282798.pdf.

41   UN Human Rights Council, "Report of the Commission of Inquiry on
     Human Rights in the Democratic People's Republic of Korea," 12.

42   Ibid., 14. Emphasis added.

43   "Democratic People's Republic of Korea," *Country Reports on Human Rights
     Practices for 2018* (Washington, D.C.: Department of State, 2018), https://
     www.state.gov/j/drl/rls/hrrpt/humanrightsreport/index.htm#wrapper.

44   David Hawk with Amanda Mortwedt Oh, *The Parallel Gulag, North Korea's
     "An-Jeon-Bu" Prison Camps* (Washington, D.C.: Committee for Human
     Rights in North Korea, 2017), 6.

45   Ibid., 11.

46   War Crimes Committee of the International Bar Association (IBA), "Re-
     port: Inquiry on Crimes Against Humanity in North Korean Political
     Prisons," December 2017, 23, file:///C:/Users/admin/Desktop/2017-12,pe
     rcent20Reportpercent20onpercent20Crimespercent20Againstpercent20H
     umanitypercent20inpercent20Northpercent20Koreanpercent20Politicalp-
     ercent20Prisons.pdf.

47   Radio Free Asia, *North Korean Prison Camps* (Kindle loc. 230–233).

48   War Crimes Committee of the International Bar Association (IBA), "Re-
     port: Inquiry on Crimes Against Humanity in North Korean Political
     Prisons," 39.

49   Ibid., 96.

50 Lee Jin-seo, "Bukhan jeongchitnyongso teukjip 1bu: jiokeui suyongso" [Special report on North Korea's political prisons: the hellish camps, part 1], Radio Free Asia, May 19, 2015, https://www.rfa.org/korean/special-programs /prisoncampsp-05192015101247.html. Sung Hye Rim gave birth to Kim Jong Il's first son, Kim Jong Nam, but Kim Jong Il eventually lost interest in her; she died of cancer in Russia. Her sister's son defected to South Korea but was tracked down and assassinated by North Korean agents.

51 Ibid.

52 "Bukhan jeongchibeomsuyongso teukjib 4bu: jeongchibeom suyongsoeui sugamja gwaliwa unyeongshiltae" [Special report on North Korea's political prisons: treatment of prisoners and management], Radio Free Asia, May 22, 2015, https://www.rfa.org/korean/special-programs/prisoncampsp -05212015153012.html.

53 Ibid.

54 Seong Bo-mi, "Talbukjadeuli jigjeobgeurin 'bukhan suyongso'eui kkcumjjikhan shiltae (10jang)" [Ten pictures of 'North Korea's hellish political prisons' drawn by North Korean defectors], Insight, September 11, 2016, https://m.insight.co.kr/newsRead.php?ArtNo=74971.

55 Robert Collins, Denied from the Start: Human Rights at the Local Level in North Korea (Washington, D.C.: Committee for Human Rights in North Korea, 2018), 87.

56 Anna Fifield, "North Korea's Prisons 'Worse' than Nazi Camps, Judge Who Survived Auschwitz Concludes," Independent, December 13, 2017, https:// www.independent.co.uk/news/world/asia/north-korea-prisons-nazi-camp -auschwitz-thomas-buergenthal-kim-jong-un-a8105896.html.

57 Kim Sae Jin, "Buk 'donju' keupseongjang, 1baekoek wondae neomeo" [Rapid growth in North Korea's 'donju,' more than 100 $1 million net worth individuals], MBC News, December 4, 2016, http://imnews.imbc .com/replay/2016/nwdesk/article/4176497_19842.html.

58 Anna Fifield, "North Korea's One-Percenters Savor Life in 'Pyonghattan,'" Washington Post, May 14, 2016, https://www.washingtonpost.com/world /asia_pacific/north-koreas-one-percenters-savor-life-in-pyonghattan /2016/05/14/9f3b47ea-15fa-11e6-971a-dadf9ab18869_story.html.

59 Kim Ji Hwan, "[Hanbandoga gyeongjeda 2] doni dolgo sijang yeolrin bukhan . . . horangee deunge tan 'urishik gaehyeok'" [(The economy in the Korean Peninsula, 2), North Korea opens up as money goes around . . . riding the tiger's back in "our type of reforms"], Kyunghyang Shinmun, January 9, 2019, http://news.khan.co.kr/kh_news/khan_art_view.html ?art_id=201901090600025.

60 Travis Jeppesen, "Shopping in Pyongyang, and Other Adventures in North Korean Capitalism," New York Times, February 14, 2019, https://www .nytimes.com/2019/02/14/magazine/north-korea-black-market-economy .html.

61 "Donju Are Princes of North Korean Economy," *Joongang Daily*, October 10, 2018, http://koreajoongangdaily.joins.com/news/article/article.aspx?aid=3054069.

62 Travis Jeppesen, "A Consumer Class Wields New Power in North Korea," *Wall Street Journal*, June 1, 2018, https://www.wsj.com/articles/a-consumer-class-wields-new-power-in-north-korea-1527867489.

63 Travis Jeppesen, *See You Again in Pyongyang* (New York: Hachette Books, 2018), 130.

64 Ibid.

65 Hwang Sung Joon, "Bukhan donjueui geokjeong" [The worries of North Korea's "donju"], *Donga Ilbo*, March 5, 2019, http://www.munhwa.com/news/view.html?no=2019030501033011000002.

66 Daniel Tudor, *Ask a North Korean: Defectors Talk About Their Lives Inside the World's Most Secretive Nation*, trans. Elizabeth Jae, Nara Han, Ashley Cho, and Daniel Tudor (Tokyo: Tuttle, 2017), 139.

67 *Bukhan Ihae* [Understanding North Korea] (Seoul: Unification Education Institute, 2018), 145.

68 "Connection Denied: Restrictions on Mobile Phones and Outside Information in North Korea," Amnesty International, 2016, p. 20, https://www.amnesty.org.uk/files/final_en_connection_denied_full_report1.pdf?J04HTd6iz3Dfur3FQf6iFBNXW2LJcEGW=.

69 Fifield, "Life Under Kim Jong Un."

70 Ibid.

71 Tudor, *Ask a North Korean*, 139.

72 Ibid., 43.

73 Jieun Baek, "Can Smuggled TV Shows Change North Korea?," *New York Times*, December 13, 2016, https://www.nytimes.com/2016/12/13/opinion/can-smuggled-tv-shows-change-north-korea.html.

74 Jieun Baek, *North Korea's Hidden Revolution: How the Information Underground Is Transforming a Closed Society* (New Haven, CT: Yale University Press, 2017), 153.

75 Ibid., 180.

76 All of the quotations that follow are from the documentary *The Jangmadang Generation*, video available on the *Washington Post* website, December 15, 2017, https://www.washingtonpost.com/video/world/watch-the-Jangmadang-generation-documentary/2017/12/15/23a3b83c-e0de-11e7-b2e9-8c636f076c76_video.html?utm_term=.1e421bae531f.

Two: Will the Real Kim Jong Un Please Stand Up?

1 This section is based on a National Geographic documentary about life in North Korea by Lisa Ling and illustrates how North Koreans have to behave in front of party cadres and especially foreigners. The documentary is available through YouTube. Lisa Ling, *Under Cover in North Korea*,

National Geographic, 2006, https://documentaryheaven.com/inside-north
-korea/.

2 "Overview of North Korea," NTI, June 2018, https://www.nti.org/learn
/countries/north-korea/

3 Fujimoto Kenji, *Kim Jong Ileui yorisa* [Kim Jong Il's chef], trans. Shin Hyeon Oh (Seoul: Monthly Chosun, 2003), 136.

4 Fyodor Tertitskiy, "Songbun and the Five Castes of North Korea," *NK
News*, February 26, 2015, https://www.nknews.org/2015/02/songbun-and
-the-five-castes-of-north-korea/.

5 "Sahoe gyecheung gujo" [Social class structure], North Korean Information
Portal, Ministry of Unification, http://nkinfo.unikorea.go.kr/nkp/overview
/nkOverview.do?sumryMenuId=SO303.

6 B. R. Myers, *The Cleanest Race: How North Koreans See Themselves
and Why It Matters* (Brooklyn, NY: Melville House, 2010), Kindle loc.
935–937.

7 "Kim Il Sung-Kim Jong Il jueui" [Kim Il Sung–ism and Kim Jong Il–ism],
North Korean Information Portal, Ministry of Unification, http://nkinfo
.unikorea.go.kr/nkp/overview/nkOverview.do?sumryMenuId=PO003.

8 Ruediger Frank, "North Korea's Economic Policy in 2018 and Beyond:
Reforms Inevitable, Delays Possible," *38 North*, August 8, 2018, https://
www.38north.org/2018/08/rfrank080818/.

9 Ibid.

10 Interview with Young-ja Park, Korea Institute for National Unification,
Seoul, September 7, 2018.

11 Frank, "North Korea's Economic Policy in 2018 and Beyond."

12 Leslie Stahl, "President Trump on Christine Blasey Ford, His Relation-
ships with Vladimir Putin and Kim Jong Un and More," *60 Minutes*, October 15, 2018, https://www.cbsnews.com/news/donald-trump-interview-60
-minutes-full-transcript-lesley-stahl-jamal-khashoggi-james-mattis-brett
-kavanaugh-vladimir-putin-2018-10-14.

13 Ibid.

14 Masaji Ishikawa, *A River in Darkness: One Man's Escape from North Korea*
(Seattle, WA: Amazon Crossing), 1–2.

15 Ibid., 60.

16 Barbara Crossette, "Korean Famine Toll: More Than 2 Million," *New York
Times*, August 20, 1999, https://www.nytimes.com/1999/08/20/world
/korean-famine-toll-more-than-2-million.html.

17 Daniel Goodkind and Loraine West, "The North Korean Famine and Its
Demographic Impact," *Population and Development Review* 27, no. 2 (June
2001): 234.

18 "How Did the North Korean Famine Happen?," Wilson Center, April
30, 2002, https://www.wilsoncenter.org/article/how-did-the-north-korean
-famine-happen.

19   Stephan Haggard and Marcus Noland, "Hunger and Human Rights: The
      Politics of Famine in North Korea," U.S. Committee for Human Rights in
      North Korea, 2005, 10, https://www.hrnk.org/uploads/pdfs/Hunger_and
      _Human_Rights.pdf.

20   Jordan Weissmann, "How Kim Jong Il Starved North Korea," *The Atlantic*,
      December 20, 2011, https://www.theatlantic.com/business/archive/2011
      /12/how-kim-jong-il-starved-north-korea/250244.

21   Quoted in "How Did the North Korean Famine Happen?," Wilson
      Center.

22   Weissmann, "How Kim Jong Il Starved North Korea."

23   Ibid.

24   Later, in 1997, Hwang would become the highest-ranking North Korean
      official to defect to South Korea, along with his deputy. Hwang was one
      of the key figures who developed *Juche* and one of North Korea's leading
      political thinkers.

25   "Kim Jong Ileui 'sanghai cheonjigaebyeok' baleon" [Kim Jong Il's "Shang-
      hai's fundamental transformation" remarks], *NK Chosun*, April 26, 2001.
      The term "cheonjigaebyeok" (天地開闢) literally means "profound changes
      in the heavens and earth" and is often used to describe truly remarkable
      developments.

26   "Kim Jong Il jungguk baljeonsangae chunggyeok bamjam seolchoetda"
      [Kim Jong Il unable to sleep after seeing China's shocking development],
      Joongang Ilbo, March 30, 2006, https://news.joins.com/article/2246569.

27   Nicholas Eberstadt, "What Is Wrong with the North Korean Econ-
      omy," American Enterprise Institute, July 1, 2011, http://www.aei.org
      /publication/what-is-wrong-with-the-north-korean-economy.

28   Ibid.

29   "World Military Expenditures and Arms Transfers 2017," U.S. Depart-
      ment of State, https://www.state.gov/t/avc/rls/rpt/wmeat/2017/index.htm.

30   Ruediger Frank, "The North Korean Parliamentary Session and Budget
      Report 2018: Cautious Optimism for the Summit Year," *38 North*, April
      19, 2018, https://www.38north.org/2018/04/rfrank041918.

31   "Less Than 1 Aircraft Carrier? The Cost of North Korea's Nukes," Voice of
      America, July 20, 2017, https://www.voanews.com/a/north-korea-nuclear
      -program-costs/3951886.html.

32   Fujimoto, *Kim Jong Ileui yorisa*, 136.

33   Kenji Fujimoto, *Wae Kim Jung Un inga?* [Why Kim Jong Un?], trans. Han
      Yu Hee (Seoul: Maks Media, 2010), 125.

34   Ibid., 131.

35   "New Stories Emerge from North Korean Dictator Kim Jong-un's Swiss
      School Days," *News.com.au*, January 16, 2018, https://www.news.com.au
      /finance/work/leaders/new-stories-emerge-from-north-korean-dictator
      -kim-jonguns-swiss-school-days/news-story/4d49237a5dbe99d421bb8e
      c7ae60974c.

36 Pat Ralph, "Kim Jong Un's High School Teacher Says the North Korean Leader Probably Knows English and Just Pretends Not To," *Business Insider*, June 11, 2018, https://www.businessinsider.com/kim-jong-un-high-school-teacher-switzerland-2018-6.

37 "Statement by President Moon Jae-in at a Joint Press Conference Following the 2018 Inter-Korean Summit in Pyeongyang," Cheongwadae, September 19, 2018, http://www.korea.net/Government/Current-Affairs/National-Affairs/view?subId=680&affairId=750&pageIndex=1&articleId=163666.

38 "Remarks by President Moon Jae-in at a Cabinet Meeting," Cheongwadae, October 8, 2018, http://english1.president.go.kr/BriefingSpeeches/Speeches/76.

39 Ibid.

40 Choe Sang-Hun, "Will Kim Jong-un Trade His Nuclear Arsenal to Rebuild Economy?," *New York Times*, April 21, 2018, https://www.nytimes.com/2018/04/21/world/asia/north-korea-kim-jong-un-nuclear-tests.html.

41 Kim Wae Hyeon, "Kim Jeong Un, nongeop hyeondaehwa-cheoldo geonseolduchuk sama geyeongjae gaehyeok ikkeuldeut" [Kim Jong Un likely to lead economic reforms through two pillars of farming modernization and railway construction], *Hankyeoreh Shinmun*, June 20, 2018, http://www.hani.co.kr/arti/international/china/849919.html.

42 Park Su-hyeon, "Kim Jeong Un 'gyeongjae baljeoneuiji' eoneujeongdoilkka . . . nunmul heulineun yeongsangkkaji jaejak" [How strong is Kim Jong Un's "devotion to economic development" . . . even making a movie that shows him shedding tears], *Chosun Ilbo*, May 30, 2018, http://news.chosun.com/site/data/html_dir/2018/05/30/2018053002620.html.

43 Andrew Salmon, "Getting to Grips with Law and Business in High-Risk North Korea," *Asia Times*, December 3, 2018, https://www.asiatimes.com/2018/12/article/getting-to-grips-with-law-and-business-in-high-risk-north-korea.

44 Ibid.

45 Andrew Salmon, "Going Native in the Hermit Kingdom," *Asia Times*, December 4, 2018, https://cms.ati.ms/2018/12/going-native-in-the-hermit-kingdom.

46 "Bukhaneui gyeongjaejeongchek hyunhwawa gaehyeokgaebang jeonmang" [Changes in North Korea's economic policy and prospects for reforms and openness], Ministry of Unification, North Korea Information Portal, http://nkinfo.unikorea.go.kr/nkp/overview/nkOverview.do?sumryMenuId=EC204.

47 Ibid.

48 Ibid.

49 Martyn Williams, "North Korea Moves Quietly onto the Internet," *Computerworld*, June 10, 2010, https://www.computerworld.com/article/2518914/north-korea-moves-quietly-onto-the-internet.html.

50 Priscilla Moriuchi, "North Korea's Ruling Elite Adapt Internet Behavior to Foreign Scrutiny," Recorded Future, April 25, 2018, https://www.recordedfuture.com/north-korea-internet-behavior/.

51 Insikt Group, "Shifting Patterns of Internet Use Reveal Adaptable and Innovative North Korean Ruling Elite," Recorded Future, October 25, 2018, https://www.recordedfuture.com/north-korea-internet-usage/.

52 Ibid.

53 Cited in Anthony Fensom, "North Korea Far from Following Vietnam," *The Diplomat*, June 11, 2018, https://thediplomat.com/2018/06/north-korea-far-from-following-vietnam.

54 Gang Min-su, "Dandok: Buk gyehyeokgaebang jeondam jojik sinseol . . . jung gongsandangae jiwon yocheong" [Sole report: North Korea creates new organization on reform and openness . . . asks China's Communist Party for support], KBS News, November 6, 2018, http://news.kbs.co.kr/news/view.do?ncd=4067885&ref=A.

55 Peter Ward, "North Korea as the Next Vietnam? It's Unlikely," *NK News*, May 15, 2018, https://www.nknews.org/2018/05/north-korea-as-the-next-vietnam-its-unlikely.

Three: The Supreme Leader Enters the World

1 "Less than 1 Aircraft Carrier? The Cost of North Korea's Nukes," *Voice of America*, July 20, 2017, https://www.voanews.com/a/north-korea-nuclear-program-costs/3951886.html.

2 Based on confidential interviews in Seoul.

3 Melissa Chan, "Kim Jong Un's Sister Is Making History at the Winter Olympics. Here's What We Know About Her," *Time*, February 9, 2018, http://time.com/5142290/kim-yo-jong-kim-jong-un-sister-winter-olympics.

4 Peter Baker and Choe Sang-Hun, "Trump Threatens 'Fire and Fury' Against North Korea if It Endangers U.S.," *New York Times*, August 8, 2017, https://www.nytimes.com/2017/08/08/world/asia/north-korea-un-sanctions-nuclear-missile-united-nations.html.

5 Ibid.

6 Javier E. David, "Trump Administration Steps Up Pressure on North Korea, Says Choice of Force or Diplomacy 'Up to the Regime,'" CNBC, October 1, 2017, https://www.cnbc.com/2017/10/01/trump-tells-tillerson-not-to-waste-time-on-north-korea-talks-well-do-what-has-to-be-done.html.

7 Ali Vitali, "Trump Threatens to 'Totally Destroy' North Korea in First UN Speech," NBC News, September 19, 2017, https://www.nbcnews.com/politics/white-house/trump-un-north-korean-leader-suicide-mission-n802596.

8 Ben Brimelow, "Trump Doesn't Have a 'Nuclear Button'—Here's What He Would Do to Fire a Nuke," *Business Insider*, January 3, 2018, https://www.businessinsider.com/does-trump-have-a-nuclear-button-2018-1.

9   Kanga Kong and Margaret Talev, "Trump Says His Nuclear Button Is Bigger than North Korea's," *Bloomberg*, January 2, 2018, https://www.bloomberg.com/news/articles/2018-01-03/trump-boasts-of-bigger-nuclear-button-in-retort-to-kim-jong-un.

10 Lee Min-jeong, "Jeonmun, buk Kim Jung Un 2018nyun shinnyunsa" [Complete transcript: North Korea's Kim Jong Un's 2018 New Year's speech], *Joongang Ilbo*, January 1, 2018, https://news.joins.com/article/22250044.

11 Ibid.

12 Ibid.

13 Bae Hyun-jung, "Full Text of Moon's Speech at the Korber Foundation," *Korea Herald*, July 7, 2017, http://www.koreaherald.com/view.php?ud=20170707000032.

14 Ibid.

15 "Address by President Moon Jae-in at May Day Stadium in Pyongyang," Cheongwadae, September 20, 2018, http://english1.president.go.kr/BriefingSpeeches/Speeches/70.

16 Ibid.

17 Charlie Campbell, "'The Korean War Is Over.' Kim Jong Un Begins 'Writing a New History' as the First North Korean Leader to Visit the South," *Time*, April 27, 2018, http://time.com/5257062/north-korea-south-dmz-kim-jong-un-summit. The formal delegation roster for the North included nominal head of state Kim Yong Nam; Kim Yong Chol, vice chairman of the KWP and former head of the Reconnaissance General Bureau (the main intelligence agency), who was in charge of the operation that sank a South Korean vessel in April 2010; Choe Hwi, vice chairman of the KWP and head of the national sports organization; Ri Son Gwon, chairman of the Committee for the Peaceful Reunification of the Nation; Ri Myong Suu, chief of the General Staff of the KPA; Ri Yong Ho, foreign minister; Ri Su Yong, vice party chairman of international affairs; and Pak Yong Sik, minister of the People's Armed Forces. The South Korean delegation consisted of national security advisor Chung Eui-yong; director of the NIS Suh Hoon; unification minister Cho Myoung-gyon; chief of staff Im Jong-seok; Kang Kyung-wha, minister of foreign affairs; and defense minister Song Young-moo. For additional details, see Ji-weon Park, "North and South Korea Summit: Who's Who in Each Delegation," ABC News, April 26, 2018, https://abcnews.go.com/International/north-south-korea-summit-delegation/story?id=54751525.

18 Park Sang-ki, "Nambuk jeongsanghwedam gwanjeonbob 1tan, Kim Jong Uneui hyubsang jeolryak bunseok" [Point 1: assessing the South-North summit: examining Kim Jong Un's negotiating strategy], *Sisa Journal*, April 30, 2018, http://www.sisajournal.com/journal/article/175081.

19 "Hanbandoeui pyunghwawa beonyeong, tongileul wihan Panmunjom seoneon" [Peace and prosperity on the Korean Peninsula, the Panmunjom

Declaration for Unification], Cheongwadae, April 27, 2018, https://www1
.president.go.kr/articles/3138.

20 Ibid. It is critical to remember that *all* of the naval clashes in the Western Sea (Yellow Sea) were instigated by North Korea. The sinking of the
ROK's naval vessel *Cheonan* in April 2010 and the bombing of Yeonpyeong
Island in December 2010 were also carried out by the North Korean navy
and army. Although the Northern Limitation Line (NLL) was confirmed
as the maritime boundary after the Korean War, North Korea has insisted
on changing the NLL to narrow South Korea's claims.

21 Kenneth B. Dekleva, "'Getting Past No' with Kim Jong Un: The Psychology of Negotiation, and Kim's 'Art of the Deal,'" 38 North, May 21, 2018,
https://www.38north.org/2018/05/kdekleva052118.

22 Mark Landler, "Trump Pulls Out of North Korea Summit Meeting with
Kim Jong Un," *New York Times*, May 24, 2018, https://www.nytimes.com
/2018/05/24/world/asia/north-korea-trump-summit.html.

23 Cited in Austin Bay, "How Trump's 'Maximum Pressure' Strategy Got
North Korea to the Table," *Observer*, March 13, 2018, http://observer.com
/2018/03/how-donald-trump-got-north-korea-open-to-giving-up-its
-nuclearweapons.

24 Ashish Kumar Sen, "Trump and North Korea: From 'Fire and Fury' to Diplomacy," Atlantic Council, March 9, 2018, https://www.atlanticcouncil.org/blogs
/new-atlanticist/trump-and-north-korea-from-fire-and-fury-to-diplomacy.

25 "Joint Statement of President Donald J. Trump of the United States of
America and Chairman Kim Jong Un of the Democratic People's Republic of Korea at the Singapore Summit," White House, June 12, 2018,
https://www.whitehouse.gov/briefings-statements/joint-statement
-president-donald-j-trump-united-states-america-chairman-kim-jong-un
-democratic-peoples-republic-korea-singapore-summit.

26 Ibid.

27 Ibid.

28 Jennifer Williams, "Read the Full Transcript of Trump's North Korea Summit Press Conference," *Vox,* June 12, 2018, https://www.vox.com/world
/2018/6/12/17452624/trump-kim-summit-transcript-press-conference
-full-text.

29 "Joint Statement."

30 "President Trump Sits Down with George Stephanopoulos: Transcript,"
ABC News, June 12, 2018, https://abcnews.go.com/Politics/president
-trump-sits-george-stephanopoulos-transcript/story?id=55831055.

31 Donald J. Trump, ". . . back home where they belong . . . ," Twitter, January 24, 2019, 5:34 a.m., https://twitter.com/realdonaldtrump/status
/1088429823561814017.

32 Clint Work, "The US-North Korea Summit: All Flash, Little Substance,"
The Diplomat, June 15, 2018, https://thediplomat.com/2018/06/the-us
-north-korea-summit-all-flash-little-substance.

33 Lee Cheol-jae and Park Yong-han, "Olhae gukbangbaekseo sakjae jeon-mang, jeonggwonttara bakkwineun pyohyeon" [This year's defense white paper expected to excise the term 'North Korean enemy,' changing references to North Korea by new governments], *Joongang Ilbo*, August 22, 2018, https://news.joins.com/article/22906628.

34 Steve Herman, "Trump: No More Nuclear Threat from North Korea," *Voice of America*, June 13, 2018, https://www.voanews.com/a/trump-no-more-nuclear-threat-from-north-korea-/4436759.html.

35 "North Korea Unlikely to Give Up Nuclear Weapons: U.S. Spy Chief Coats," Reuters, January 29, 2019, https://www.reuters.com/article/us-usa-northkorea-nuclear/north-korea-unlikely-to-give-up-nuclear-weapons-us-spy-chief-coats-idUSKCN1PN1Y7.

36 Rebecca Morin, "Pompeo Says North Korea Remains Nuclear Threat," Politico, February 24, 2019, https://www.politico.com/story/2019/02/24/pompeo-north-korea-nuclear-threat-1182560.

37 "Kim Jong Un's Train Journey to Trump Summit Is a Nod to His Grandfather," NBC News, February 26, 2019, https://www.nbcnews.com/news/world/kim-jong-un-s-train-journey-trump-summit-nod-his-n976076.

38 Amanda Macias, "Trump: Obama Told Me That He 'Was So Close to Starting a Big War with North Korea,'" CNBC, February 15, 2019, https://www.cnbc.com/2019/02/15/trump-obama-told-me-that-he-was-close-to-starting-a-big-war-with-north-korea.html.

39 Deirdre Shesgreen, "Trump: Obama Was Brink of 'a Big War' with North Korea. Not True, Ex-Obama Aides Say," *USA Today*, February 15, 2019, https://www.usatoday.com/story/news/2019/02/15/ex-obama-aides-refute-trumps-claim-big-war-north-korea/2880839002/.

40 "Japan's PM Nominated Trump for Nobel Peace Prize on U.S. Request: Asahi," Reuters, February 16, 2019, https://www.reuters.com/article/us-northkorea-usa-trump-japan/japans-pm-nominated-trump-for-nobel-peace-prize-on-us-request-asahi-idUSKCN1Q6041.

41 Robin Wright, "After All the Swagger, Trump's Talks with North Korea Collapse," *New Yorker*, February 28, 2019, https://www.newyorker.com/news/our-columnists/after-all-the-swagger-trumps-talks-with-north-korea-collapse.

42 "Remarks by President Trump in Press Conference, Hanoi, Vietnam," White House, February 28, 2019, https://www.whitehouse.gov/briefings-statements/remarks-president-trump-press-conference-hanoi-vietnam.

43 Ibid.

44 Ibid.

45 Ibid.

46 Christine Hauser, "Responding to Trump, Otto Warmbier's Parents Blame Kim Jong-un and 'Evil Regime' for Son's Death," *New York Times*, February 28, 2019, https://www.nytimes.com/2019/02/28/world/asia/trump-otto-warmbier.html.

47 Dartunorro Clark, "Trump Under Attack After Letting Kim Off the Hook for Warmbier's Death," NBC News, February 28, 2019, https://www.nbcnews.com/politics/politics-news/trump-under-attack-after-letting-kim-hook-warmbier-s-death-n977731.

48 "Transcript: National Security Adviser John Bolton on 'Face the Nation,'" CBS News, March 3, 2019, https://www.cbsnews.com/news/transcript-national-security-adviser-john-bolton-on-face-the-nation-march-3-2019.

49 Ibid.

50 Amy Held, "In Rare News Conference, North Korea Offers Its Own Version of Summit Collapse," NPR, February 28, 2019, https://www.npr.org/2019/02/28/699006894/in-rare-news-conference-north-korea-offers-its-own-version-of-summit-collapse.

51 Ankit Panda, "What to Make of North Korean Threats to Withdraw from Diplomacy with the U.S.," NK Pro, March 15, 2019, https://www.nknews.org/pro/what-to-make-of-north-korean-threats-to-withdraw-from-diplomacy-with-the-u-s.

52 David Welna, "Fact Check: U.S. and North Korea After Their Singapore Summit," NPR, July 31, 2018, https://www.npr.org/2018/07/31/634387644/fact-check-u-s-and-north-korea-after-their-singapore-summit.

Four: A New King Rises

1 "Official North Korea State TV Announcement of Death of Kim Jong Il," NHK World, YouTube, December 19, 2011, https://www.youtube.com/watch?v=6ibYfuzcGkY.

2 Richard Shears, "North Korean Official Is Executed by Mortar Shell for Drinking During 100-Day Mourning Period for Late 'Dear Leader' Kim Jong Il, *Daily Mail*, October 24, 2012, http://www.dailymail.co.uk/news/article-2222442/North-Korean-official-executed-drinking-100-day-mourning-late-Dear-Leader-Kim-Jong-il.html.

3 J. Dana Stuster, "And Then There Were Two ... Kim Jong Il's Dwindling Inner Circle," *Foreign Policy*, December 13, 2013, https://foreignpolicy.com/2013/12/13/and-then-there-were-two-kim-jong-ils-dwindling-inner-circle.

4 "Buk, aedosok nogolhwadoen 'Kim Jeongeunusanghwa'" [North, blatant personality cult around Kim Jong Un in the midst of mourning], KBS News, December 21, 2011, http://mn.kbs.co.kr/news/view.do?ncd=2407667.

5 Ibid.

6 Hwang Jang Yop, *Bukhaneui jinsilgwa heowi* [North Korea's truths and falsehoods] (Seoul: Shidaejeongshin, 2006), 104–105.

7 Ibid., 52.

8   C. Christine Fair, "The Only Enemy Pakistan's Army Can Beat Is Its Own Democracy," *Foreign Policy*, August 9, 2017, https://foreignpolicy .com/2017/08/09/the-only-enemy-pakistans-army-can-beat-is-its-own -democracy.

9   Mafia Family Tree, FBI, https://www.fbi.gov/file-repository/mafia-family -tree.pdf/view.

10 Matthew Carney, "Defector Reveals Secrets of North Korea's Office 39, Raising Cash for Kim Jong Un," ABC News, January 5, 2018, http://www .abc.net.au/news/2018-01-06/north-korea-defector-reveals-secrets-of -office-39/9302308.

11 Lalit K. Jha, "North Korean Hackers Behind \$81m Cyber Theft from Bangladesh Bank," *Dhaka Tribune*, February 4, 2018, https://www.dhakatribune .com/bangladesh/2018/02/14/n-korean-hackers-81m-bangladesh-bank -heist.

12 "Secrets of 'Office 39': North Korean Leader Kim Gets Russian Fuel via Singapore Dealers, Says Defector Who Fled China," *South China Morning Post*, June 28, 2017, https://www.scmp.com/news/asia/east-asia/article /2100310/secrets-office-39-north-korean-leader-kim-gets-russian-fuel.

13 Joey Millar, "Inside North Korea's Room 39—How Kim Sells Fake Cash and Viagra to Fund Lavish Lifestyle," *Express*, July 22, 2017, https://www .express.co.uk/news/world/831573/north-korea-latest-news-room-39 -kim-jong-un-black-market.

14 Tom Burgis, "North Korea: The Secrets of Office 39," *Financial Times*, June 24, 2015, https://www.ft.com/content/4164dfe6-09d5-11e5-b6bd -00144feabdc0.

15 "Hanmi, 2008nyun buk Kim Jong Il noejoljung CT bwatseotda—yeosend 3-5nyun pandan" [South Korea and the United States saw pictures of Kim Jong Il's stroke-related CT in 2008, assessed future life span between 3–5 years], *Yonhap News*, February 23, 2016, http://www.yonhapnews.co .kr/bulletin/2016/12/23/0200000000AKR20161223028300073.HTML.

16 Based on author's discussions with a source in 2016 who had intimate knowledge of intelligence operations in North Korea.

17 Kim Bond-seop, "Sajin: Kim Il Sung dalmeun Kim Jong Un choet deungjang eolron 1myun jangshik" [Picture: first picture of Kim Jong Un appears on front page resembling Kim Il Sung], Daily NK, September 27, 2010, https://www.dailynk.com/korean/read.php?cataId=nk00500&num =92391.

18 Ri Il Nam, *Ri Il Nam Sugi* [Ri Il Nam's recollections] (Seoul: Unification Media Group, 2011), ch. 17, http://www.uni-media.net/program_read.php ?n=302.

19 Max Fisher, "Even by North Korean Standards, This Announcement of Jang Song Thaek's Execution Is Intense," *Washington Post*, December 12, 2013, https://www.washingtonpost.com/news/worldviews/wp/2013/12

/12/even-by-north-korean-standards-this-announcement-of-jang-song
-thaeks-execution-is-intense/?utm_term=.bf5de132b629.

20 Based on discussions with a former high-ranking South Korean national
security official in 2015.

21 John Hudson and Josh Dawsey, "Trump and Kim Battled Subordinates
Ahead of Spike in Tensions," *Washington Post*, May 9, 2019, https://www
.washingtonpost.com/world/national-security/trump-and-kim-battled
-subordinates-ahead-of-spike-in-tensions/2019/05/09/9cfd59b3-5f06
-483f-a64a-a52793d21789_story.html?utm_term=.8ca5f6bba6fd.

22 Lee Cheol-jae, "Gukjeongwon, Jungguk, Kim Jong Nam gajok boho"
[NIS, 'China protecting Kim Jong Nam's family], *Joongang Ilbo*, February
16, 2019, https://news.joins.com/article/21265080.

23 Ibid.

24 Kim Jong Nam's son Han Sol, in a perceptive interview with Finnish TV
in 2012, even explicitly called his uncle Kim Jong Un a dictator and talked
about someday going back to North Korea to "make it easier for the people there." "Kim Han Sol interviewed by Elisabeth Rehn" (1/1), YouTube,
October 16, 2012, https:www.youtube.com/watch?v=T_uSuCkKa3k.

25 Noh Jeong Min, "Radio Saesang: Komi Yuji Inteobyu 2—Kim Jong Nam,
bukhaneul bakkwobogo sipeun maeumi itjianatseulkka?" [Radio Saesang:
Komi Yuji interview 2—Kim Jong Nam, wouldn't he have thought about
changing North Korea?], Radio Free Asia, July 17, 2012, https://www.rfa
.org/korean/weekly_program/radio-world/radioworld-07172012160823
.html.

26 Scott Neuman, "Kim Jong Nam Had Antidote in Bag When He Died
in Nerve Agent Attack," NPR, December 1, 2017, https://www.npr
.org/sections/thetwo-way/2017/12/01/567688162/kim-jong-nam-had
-antidote-in-bag-when-he-died-in-nerve-agent-attack.

27 Adam Taylor, "Antidote Kim Jong Nam Might Have Carried Was Probably Useless Against Nerve Agent That Killed Him, Experts Say," *Washington Post*, December 1, 2017, https://www.washingtonpost.com/news
/worldviews/wp/2017/12/01/antidote-kim-jong-nam-may-have-carried
-was-probably-useless-against-poison-that-killed-him-experts-say/?utm
_term=.3bc1fc3303a0.

28 Richard C. Paddock, "Woman Convicted in Kim Jong Nam's Killing Is
Freed in Malaysia," *New York Times*, May 2, 2019, https://www.nytimes
.com/2019/05/02/world/asia/kim-jong-nam-assassination-vietnam.html.

29 North Korea cites January 8, 1982, as Kim Jong Un's official birthday.
However, South Korean officials believe that he was born in 1981 and that
North Korea changed the date so that it was seventy years after the birth
of his grandfather Kim Il Sung and forty years after his father, Kim Jong
Il, was born. The U.S. Treasury Department cites his birthday as January
8, 1984. See Paul Szoldra and Veronika Bondarenko, "How North Korean
Leader Kim Jong-un, 33, Became One of the World's Scariest Dictators,"

Independent, April 19, 2017, https://www.independent.co.uk/news/world
/how-north-korean-leader-kim-jong-un-33-became-one-of-the-worlds
-scariest-dictators-a7691396.html.

Five: The Kim Dynasty and Pyongyang's Power Elites

1   Son Sae-il, "Pyeongyangsimindaehoee natanan 'Kim Il Sung janggun'"
    [The appearance of "General Kim Il Sung" in the Pyongyang citizens gath-
    ering], *Monthly Chosun,* August 2008, http://monthly.chosun.com/client
    /news/print.asp?ctcd=I&nNewsNumb=201008100064.

2   Robert A. Scalapino and Chong-Sik Lee, *North Korea: Building of the
    Monolithic State* (Seoul: KHU Press, 2017), 19–20.

3   Ibid., 20.

4   Joo Sung-ha, "Mi seongyosa jungmaero taeeonan Kim Il Sung" [Kim Il
    Sung born through the arranged marriage introduction of American mis-
    sionary], Radio Free Asia, February 3, 2017, https://www.rfa.org/korean
    /weekly_program/joosungha/co-sh-02032017083700.html.

5   Ibid.

6   "The Identity of Kim Il Sung," Central Intelligence Agency, September
    1949, 1, https://www.cia.gov/library/readingroom/docs/CIA-RDP80
    -00809A000600270269-4.pdf.

7   Ibid.

8   Ibid.

9   Based on discussions with Andrei Lankov in Washington, D.C. in
    June 2019.

10 "Soviet Report on Communists in Korea, 1945," 1945, History and Public
    Policy Program Digital Archive, AGShVS RF. F. 172. OP 614631. D. 23
    pp. 21-26. Translated by Gary Goldberg. https://digitalarchive.wilsoncenter
    .org/document/114890.

11 *Jeungeon: Kim Il Sungeul malhada* [Testimony: talking about Kim Il Sung]
    (Seoul: Hankook Ilbo, 1991), 25.

12 Ibid., 28.

13 The Korean Communist Party was founded in 1925, but the Soviets were
    extremely disappointed by its internecine factionalism, and the party was
    expelled from the Comintern in 1928.

14 Quoted in Michael Fry, "National Geographic, Korea, and the 38th Paral-
    lel," *National Geographic,* August 4, 2013, https://news.nationalgeographic
    .com/news/2013/08/130805-korean-war-dmz-armistice-38-parallel
    -geography; Andrei Lankov, "Terenti Shtykov: The Other Ruler of Na-
    scent N. Korea," *Korea Times,* January 25, 2012, http://www.koreatimes.co
    .kr/www/news/nation/2012/01/363_103451.html.

15 Fry, "National Geographic, Korea, and the 38th Parallel."

16 Shannon McCune, "The Thirty-Eighth Parallel in Korea," *World Politics* 1,
    no. 2 (January 1949): 225.

17 Ibid.

18   Lankov, "Terenti Shtykov."

19   Scalapino and Lee, *North Korea: Building of the Monolithic State,* 27.

20   Shim Ji Yeon, "Bukjoseonrodonddangeui changribgwa noseon" [The creation and guidelines of the North Korean Workers' Party], in *Bukhanchejeeui suribgwajeong 1945–1948* [The formation process of the North Korean system, 1945–1948] (Seoul: Kyungnam University, Institute for Far Eastern Affairs, October 1991), 99.

21   Central Intelligence Agency, "Implementation of Soviet Objectives in Korea," ORE, November 18, 1947, 1–2.

22   Central Intelligence Agency, "The Current Situation in Korea," ORE 15-48, March 18, 1948, 2.

23   Central Intelligence Agency, "Consequences of US Troop Withdrawal from Korea in Spring 1949," ORE 3-49, February 28, 1949, 1.

24   "Meeting Between Stalin and Kim Il Sung," March 5, 1949, History and Public Policy Program Digital Archive, AVP RF, f. 059a, op. 5a, d. 3, p. 11, ll. 10–20, and RGASPI, f. 558, op. 11, d. 346, ll. 0013–0023, https://digitalarchive.wilsoncenter.org/document/112127.

25   "Telegram from the Leader of the Group of Soviet Specialists in Northeast China to the Chairman of the USSR Council of Ministers About the Results of the Chinese-Korean Talks on Military Cooperation," May 18, 1949, History and Public Policy Program Digital Archive, AP RF, f. 4. op. 1. d. 331, pp. 59–61. Translated by Gary Goldberg. http://digitalarchive.wilsoncenter.org/document/114898.

26   Central Intelligence Agency, "Current Capabilities of the Northern Korean Regime," ORE 18-50, June 19, 1950, 1.

27   Ibid.

28   Ibid.

29   Nikita S. Khrushchev, "The Secret Speech—On the Cult of Personality, 1956," Modern History Sourcebook, February 7, 2012, http://www.ht.lu.se/media/utbildning/dokument/kurser/EUHA14/20121/Nikita_S._Khrushchev__The_Secret_Speech_On_the_Cult_of_Personality_1956.pdf.

30   Ibid.

31   Ibid.

32   Hwang Jang Yop, *Bukhaneui jinsilgwa heowi* [North Korea's truths and falsehoods] (Seoul: Sidae Jeongsin, 2006), 164.

33   Ibid., 161.

34   Kim Cheol Ju, "Kim Il Sung sengga munjjakeul tongjjaero tteueogan kim-mocheongnyun, gyulguk 3daega myeoljok" [Three generations of a young man's family executed who stole Kim Il Sung's birthplace's doorway], *Chosun Ilbo,* February 6, 2014, http://premium.chosun.com/site/data/html_dir/2014/02/06/2014020601189.html. Killing three generations of a person's family, including in-laws, was the most gruesome punishment meted out by the king during the Joseon Dynasty. This was done to literally wipe

a person and his extended family from the face of the earth in the name of preventing possible payback or to demonstrate the seriousness of the crime or offense that was allegedly committed. North Korea has extended this barbaric penal code into the twenty-first century.

35 Chinese president Xi Jinping is also fond of massive military parades. When the People's Liberation Army prepares for a very important parade, such as the seventieth anniversary of the end of World War II in August 2015, units are trained using rows of strings so that their movements are completely synchronized.

36 Fyodor Tertitskiy, "How the North Is Run: The State Affairs Commission," NK Pro, February 2, 2018, https://www.nknews.org/pro/the-history-and -evolution-of-north-koreas-state-affairs-commission.

37 *Kim Jong Un jeonggwoneui unyounggujowa gyeongjaesiltae bunseok* [Analysis of the Kim Jong Un regime's operating mechanism and economic condition] (Seoul: Institute for National Security Strategy, 2017), 2.

38 Ibid., 3.

39 Ibid.

40 "North Korea's Kim Jong Un Shuffles Leadership and Consolidates Power," CNBC, April 12, 2019, https://www.cnbc.com/2019/04/12 /north-koreas-kim-jong-un-shuffles-leadership-and-consolidates-power .html.

41 "Bukhaneui nodongdang joongangwiwonhoe jeonwonhoe 7gi 4cha hoeeuiwa choegoinminhoeeui 14gi 1cha hoeui teukjing bunseok" [Analysis of special characteristics of the 4th Plenum, 7th Term meeting of North Korea's Workers' Party's Central Committee and 14th Plenum, 1st Session of the Supreme People's Assembly], *INSS Issue Brief*, no. 123, April 4, 2019, p. 1.

42 Ibid., p. 2.

43 "Gongwhaguk muryeok choegosaryeonggwan hochingae daehan euimi bunseok" [Analysis of the meaning behind the term 'the Republic's Supreme Armed Forces Commander'], *INSS Issue Brief*, no. 122, April 24, 2019, p. 1.

44 "4th Plenum of the WPK Central Committee Held," *North Korea Leadership Watch*, April 11, 2019, http://www.nkleadershipwatch.org/2019/04/11 /4th-plenum-of-the-the-wpk-central-committee-held/.

45 Ra Jong-il, *Jang Seong Thaekeui gil* [Jang Seong Thaek's path] (Seoul: Alma Chulpansa, January 2016), 237.

46 Ibid., 238.

Six: War Machine and Nuclear Weapons

1 "North Korea Nuclear Test: Hydrogen Bomb 'Missile-Ready,'" BBC News, September 3, 2017, https://www.bbc.com/news/world-asia -41139445.

2 "U.S. Nuclear Commander Assumes North Korea Tested H-bomb, Sept. 3," CBS News, September 15, 2017, https://www.cbsnews.com/news/u-s -nuclear-commander-assumes-north-korea-tested-h-bomb-sept-3.

3 Ethan Siegel, "This Is How North Korea Will Develop a Hydrogen Bomb," *Forbes*, July 6, 2018, https://www.forbes.com/sites/startswithabang /2018/07/05/this-is-how-north-korea-will-develop-a-hydrogen-bomb /#51817c944ef9.

4 David E. Sanger and Choe Sang-Hun, "North Korean Nuclear Test Draws U.S. Warning of 'Massive Military Response,'" *New York Times*, September 2, 2017, https://www.nytimes.com/2017/09/03/world/asia/north-korea -tremor-possible-6th-nuclear-test.html.

5 Ibid.

6 "Why North Korea's Nuclear Test Is Still Producing Aftershocks," BBC, December 11, 2017, https://www.bbc.com/news/world-asia-42305161.

7 Ibid.

8 Kim Hyung-eun, "Jeong Sae Hyun jeon tongilbu janggwan: 'bukhani dae- hwaae naonge jaeje ttemuniraneun senggakeun keun osan'" [Former min- ister of unification Jeong Sae Hyun: assumption that "North Korea seeks dialogue due to sanctions" is big mistake," BBC News Korea, March 29, 2018, https://www.bbc.com/korean/news-43579759.

9 Fyodor Tertitskiy, "The Unusual History of North Korea's Military Foun- dation Day," *NK News*, February 8, 2018, https://www.nknews.org/2018 /02/the-unusual-history-of-north-koreas-military-foundation-day.

10 Ibid.

11 Kwon Yang-ju, *Bukhankunsaeui ihae* [Understanding the North Korean military] (Seoul: KIDA Press, 2010), 64.

12 Ibid.

13 Yu Yong-won, Shin Beom-chul, and Kim Jina, *Bukhangun sikeurit ripoteu* [Secret report of the North Korean military] (Seoul: Planet Media, 2013), 22.

14 Ibid., 23.

15 IISS, "The Conventional Military Balance on the Korean Peninsula," In- ternational Institute for Strategic Studies, 2018, 14, https://www.iiss.org /blogs/research-paper/2018/06/military-balance-korean-peninsula.

16 Josh Smith, "North Korea Military Parade Features Floats and Flow- ers, Not Missiles," Reuters, September 9, 2018, https://www.reuters.com /article/us-northkorea-anniversary-military-parad/north-korea-military -parade-features-floats-and-flowers-not-missiles-idUSKCN1LP045.

17 Jeffrey Lewis, "North Korea's Nuclear Disappearing Act," *The National Interest*, September 10, 2018, https://nationalinterest.org/feature/jeffrey -lewis-north-koreas-nuclear-disappearing-act-30942.

18 Choi Sung-jin, "GPsibeomcheolsuneun ijae choejongdangaeeh jinib- hetda" [Preliminary dismantlement of GP in final stages], *Huffington Post*

Korea, November 12, 2018, https://www.huffingtonpost.kr/entry/story_kr
_5be90b3ce4b0e84388996ae0.

19   IISS, "The Conventional Military Balance on the Korean Peninsula," 11.

20   *Military and Security Developments Involving the Democratic People's Republic of Korea* (Washington, D.C.: Department of Defense, 2017), 5.

21   Yu Yong-won, "Byeongryeok gamchuk, bokmu danchuk . . . 16manmyeong
julgaedoe 'gun unyongchaegae heundeul'" [Force reductions and cutting
back on length of service results in 160,000 reduction with side effects
for military's operational system], *Chosun Ilbo*, July 7, 2018, http://news
.chosun.com/site/data/html_dir/2018/07/07/2018070700275.html.

22   "Saseol: hekmujang 120man bukhangun abaeseo byeongryeok 12man ju-
lindaneun gukbang shilheom" [Editorial: a military experiment based on
reducing 120,000 forces in the face of a nuclearized North Korea with
1.2 million troops], *Chosun Ilbo*, July 28, 2018, http://news.chosun.com
/site/data/html_dir/2018/07/27/2018072703565.html.

23   John A. Wickham, *Korea on the Brink: From the "12/12 Incident" to the
Kwangju Uprising, 1979–1980* (Washington, D.C.: National Defense University Press, 1999), 77–78.

24   Ibid., 78.

25   Ibid.

26   Mark Cancian, "Korean War 2.0? The Signs to Watch," *Breaking Defense*,
August 15, 2017, https://breakingdefense.com/2017/08/korean-war-2-0
-the-signs-to-watch/.

27   "OPLAN 5017 Major Theater War-West," GlobalSecurity.org, https://
www.globalsecurity.org/military/ops/oplan-5027.htm.

28   Joseph Trevithick, "North Korean Hackers Stole US and South Korea 'Decapitation' Plans Months Ago," *The Warzone*, October 10, 2017, http://www
.thedrive.com/the-war-zone/15009/north-korean-hackers-stole-us-and
-south-korea-decapitation-plans-months-ago.

29   Franz-Stefan Gady, "Largest Ever US-Korea Military Drill Focuses on
Striking North Korea's Leadership," *The Diplomat*, March 8, 2016, https://
thediplomat.com/2016/03/largest-ever-us-korea-military-drill-focuses-on
-striking-north-koreas-leadership.

30   Robin Wright, "What Would War with North Korea Look Like?," *New
Yorker*, September 6, 2017, https://www.newyorker.com/news/news-desk
/what-would-war-with-north-korea-look-like.

31   Michael J. Dumont, Rear Admiral, U.S. Navy, Vice Director, Joint
Staff, Letter to the Honorable Ted W. Lieu, U.S. House of Representa-
tives, October 27, 2017, https://lieu.house.gov/sites/lieu.house.gov/files
/Response%20to%20TWL-RG%20Letter%20on%20NK.pdf.

32   *2016 Defense White Paper* (Seoul: Ministry of National Defense, 2016), 53.

33   Ibid.

34   IISS, "The Conventional Military Balance on the Korean Peninsula," 20.

35 *2016 Defense White Paper*, 68.

36 *2018 Gukbang baekseo* [2018 Defense White Paper] (Seoul: Ministry of National Defense, 2018), 53.

37 "[Saseol] deudieo 'bukhangun=jujeok'eul sakjaehan uri gukbang baekseo" [Editorial: Our Defense White Paper that cut out 'North Korean military = main adversary'], *Joongang Ilbo*, January 16, 2019, https://news.joins.com /article/23294006.

38 David E. Sanger, William J. Broad, Choe Sang-Hun, and Eileen Sullivan, "New North Korea Concerns Flare as Trump's Signature Diplomacy Fails," *New York Times*, May 9, 2019, https://www.nytimes.com/2019/05 /09/world/asia/north-korea-missile.html.

39 Ham Cheol-min, "Moon Jae-in jeongbu 'bukhani dangeori misail' balsa haetjiman 'sikryang jiwon' gyeheok byeonham eopda" [Moon government "no change in plans to provide food aid to North Korea despite short-range missile test"], *Insight*, May 10, 2019, https://www.insight.co.kr/news/226903.

40 Yoichi Dreazen, "Here's What War with North Korea Would Look Like," *Vox*, February 8, 2018, https://www.vox.com/world/2018/2/7/16974772 /north-korea-war-trump-kim-nuclear-weapon.

41 Franz-Stefan Gady, "Military Stalemate: How North Korea Could Win a War with the US," *The Diplomat*, October 10, 2017, https://thediplomat .com/2017/10/military-stalemate-how-north-korea-could-win-a-war -with-the-us.

42 Franz-Stefan Gady, "What Would the Second Korean War Look Like?," *The Diplomat*, April 19, 2017, https://thediplomat.com/2017/04/what -would-the-second-korean-war-look-like.

43 Central Intelligence Agency, "North Korea: Nuclear Reactor," July 9, 1982, https://nsarchive2.gwu.edu/NSAEBB/NSAEBB87/.

44 "NIE 4-82: Nuclear Proliferation Trends Through 1987," Director of the Central Intelligence Agency, July 27, 1982, 5, https://digitalarchive .wilsoncenter.org/document/116894.pdf?v=41ddf71781689548f17de72d e809cb51.

45 Ibid., 23.

46 "World Missiles: North Korea, Hwasong-15 (KN-22)," Missile Threat, Center for Strategic and International Studies, https://missilethreat.csis .org/country/dprk.

47 *Military Balance 2018* (London: International Institute for Strategic Studies, 2018), 275.

48 David E. Sanger and William J. Broad, "How U.S. Intelligence Agencies Underestimated North Korea," *New York Times*, January 6, 2018, https:// www.nytimes.com/2018/01/06/world/asia/north-korea-nuclear-missile -intelligence.html.

49 Choe Sang Hun, "'We No Longer Need' Nuclear or Missile Tests, North Korean Leader Says," *New York Times*, April 20, 2018, https://www.nytimes .com/2018/04/20/world/asia/kim-jong-un-hotline-korea.html.

50 Ibid.
51 "Press Statement of Policy Research Director of Institute for American Studies, Ministry of Foreign Affairs of the DPRK," KCNA Watch, December 16, 2018, https://kcnawatch.co/newstream/1544965814 -556007986/press-statement-of-policy-research-director-of-institute-for -american-studies-ministry-of-foreign-affairs-of-the-dprk.
52 "Removing the U.S. 'Nuclear Threat': What to Make of Thursday's KCNA Commentary," NK Pro, December 20, 2018, https://www.nknews.org /pro/removing-the-u-s-nuclear-threat-what-to-make-of-thursdays-kcna -commentary/.
53 "Joint Declaration of South and North Korea on the Denuclearization of the Korean Peninsula," February 19, 1992, Inventory of International Nonproliferation Organizations and Regimes, Center for Nonproliferation Studies, https://www.nti.org/media/documents/korea_denuclearization.pdf.
54 "N. Korea: No Denuclearization Until US Removes Nuclear Threat," Voice of America, December 20, 2018, https://www.voanews.com/a/n-korea-we -denuclearize-when-us-removes-its-threat/4708736.html.
55 "Address by President Moon Jae-in at a Joint Conference Co-hosted by the Council on Foreign Relations, the Korea Society and Asia Society," Cheongwadae, September 25, 2018, https://english1.president.go.kr /BriefingSpeeches/Speeches/74.
56 Ibid.

Seven: Regional Giants and the Korean Peninsula

1 "Is China Being Marginalized on Korean Peninsula?" *Global Times*, May 28, 2018, http://www.globaltimes.cn/content/1104531.shtml.
2 Fei Su, "China's Potential Role as Security Guarantor for North Korea," *38 North*, October 24, 2018, https://www.38north.org/2018/10/fsu102418/.
3 Ibid.
4 "Mao Zedong's Remarks at the Banquet for the North Korean Government Delegation," November 23, 1953, History and Public Policy Program Digital Archive, PRC FMA 203-00003-01, 1–3. Translated by Jeffrey Wang and Charles Kraus. https://digitalarchive.wilsoncenter.org /document/114167.
5 "180,000 Chinese Soldiers Killed in Korean War," *China Daily*, June 28, 2010, http://www.china.org.cn/china/2010-06/28/content_20365659 .htm.
6 "Mao Zedong's Remarks at the Banquet for the North Korean Government Delegation."
7 *2017 Bukhan daewaemuyeok donghyang* [2017 trends in North Korea's trade relations], 18-038, Korea Trade-Investment Promotion Agency, 2017, 1, https://news.kotra.or.kr/user/globalBbs/kotranews/787/globalBbsDataView .do?setIdx=249&dataIdx=168031&pageViewType=&column=&search =&searchAreaCd=&searchNationCd=&searchTradeCd=&searchStart

Date=&searchEndDate=&searchCategoryIdxs=&searchIndustryCateIdx
=&searchItemCode=&searchItemName=&page=1&row=10.

8   Ibid., 3.

9   "North Korea in the World: China-DPRK Merchandise Trade Volume
2000-2018," East-West Center and the National Committee on North
Korea, https://www.northkoreaintheworld.org/china-dprk/total-trade.

10 Ibid., 12.

11 Midterm Report by Panel of Experts Pursuant to Resolution 1874 (2009)
Addressed to the President of the Security Council, September 5, 2017, 4,
http://www.un.org/ga/search/view_doc.asp?symbol=S/2017/742.

12 Ibid.

13 Ibid.

14 Michael Schuman, "Pyongyang's China Connection," *U.S. News & World
Report*, September 19, 2017, https://www.usnews.com/news/best-countries
/articles/2017-09-19/how-china-keeps-north-koreas-economy-afloat.

15 Michael Swaine, "Chinese Views on South Korea's Deployment of
THAAD," *Chinese Leadership Monitor*, February 2, 2017, https://
carnegieendowment.org/2017/02/02/chinese-views-on-south-korea-s
-deployment-of-terminal-high-altitude-area-defense-thaad-pub-67891.

16 Quoted in "China Reacts with Anger, Threats After South Korean Missile
Defense Decision," Reuters, February 27, 2017, https://www.reuters.com
/article/us-southkorea-usa-thaad-china/china-reacts-with-anger-threats
-after-south-korean-missile-defense-decision-idUSKBN16709W.

17 David Josef Volodzko, "China Wins Its War Against South Korea's US
THAAD Missile Shield—Without Firing a Shot," *South China Morning
Post*, November 18, 2017, https://www.scmp.com/week-asia/geopolitics
/article/2120452/china-wins-its-war-against-south-koreas-us-thaad-missile.

18 "社评：中朝关系发展强劲给地区带来正能量" (Sheping: Zhonghan
guanxi fazhan qiangin gei diqu dai lai zhengnengliang) [Editorial: development of China–North Korea relations brings positive energy for the region],
Huanqiu Shibao, June 19, 2018, http://opinion.huanqiu.com/editorial/2018
-06/12295863.html.

19 Oriana Skylar Mastro, "Xi Jinping and Kim Jong Un Keep Meeting—
Here's Why," *National Interest*, June 26, 2018, https://nationalinterest.org
/feature/chinas-xi-north-koreas-kim-keep-meeting%E2%80%94heres
-why-26415.

20 Ibid.

21 "Power Rankings," *U.S. News & World Report*, https://www.usnews.com
/news/best-countries/power-full-list.

22 *The Military Balance 2018* (London: IISS, 2018), 233.

23 Ibid.

24 "Russia and the World: 2018 IMEMO Forecast," *New Perspectives* 26, no.
3 (2018): 16.

25 Quoted in Kathryn Weathersby, "Soviet Aims in Korea and the Origins of the Korean War, 1945–1950: New Evidence from Russian Archives," Working Paper No. 8, Wilson Center for International Scholars, November 1993, 11, https://www.wilsoncenter.org/sites/default/files/ACFB76 .pdf.

26 Ibid.

27 Kim Seong-Rae, "Putin jeongbueui daebukjeongchek: gwajaewa jeonmang" [The Putin government's North Korea policy: issues and prospects], *Hanbando Focus* 38 (Winter 2016): 63.

28 Ibid., 60.

29 Choe Sang-Hun, "Russia Hints North Korea Is Ready to Do Business," *New York Times*, August 21, 2011, https://www.nytimes.com/2011/08/22 /world/europe/22moscow.html.

30 Elizabeth C. Economy, "Russia's Role on North Korea: More Important than You Might Think," Council on Foreign Relations, June 7, 2018, https://www.cfr.org/blog/russias-role-north-korea-more-important-you -might-think.

31 "Russian, North Korean Diplomats Discuss Denuclearization Talks," TASS, December 24, 2018, http://tass.com/politics/1032121.

32 "Russia Insists on Guarantees During Denuclearization on Korean Peninsula—Diplomat," TASS, November 24, 2018, http://tass.com/world /1032333.

33 "North Korea Unlikely to Agree to Unilateral Denuclearization—Expert," TASS, November 23, 2018, http://tass.com/world/1032100.

34 Economy, "Russia's Role on North Korea: More Important than You Might Think."

35 "North Korea Nuclear Crisis: Putin Calls Sanctions Useless," BBC, September 5, 2017, https://www.bbc.com/news/world-asia-41158281.

36 Julian Ryall, "Activists Condemn Russia for Handing Over North Korean Defector," *Telegraph*, November 22, 2018, https://www.telegraph.co.uk/news /2018/11/22/activists-condemn-russia-handing-north-korean-defector.

37 Radina Gigova, "Putin Invites 'Comrade' Kim Jong Un to Visit Russia," CNN, June 14, 2018, https://edition.cnn.com/2018/06/14/world/putin -invites-comrade-kim-jong-un-to-visit-russia/index.html.

38 "Press Review: Putin-Kim Meeting Heavy on Symbolism and Europeans Refuse Russian Oil," TASS, April 26, 2019, http://tass.com/pressreview /1055881.

39 Amie Ferris-Rotman and Simon Denyer, "Putin: Kim Jong Un Needs International Security Guarantees to Give up Nuclear Arsenal," *Washington Post*, April 25, 2019, https://www.washingtonpost.com/world/putin -arrives-in-russian-far-east-ahead-of-first-ever-summit-with-kim-jong -un/2019/04/24/a2d941f8-65c6-11e9-a698-2a8f808c9cfb_story.html ?utm_term=.7ffbaf049f0a.

40   Minyoung Lee, "Key Takeaways from DPRK State Media Coverage of Kim-Putin Summit," NK Pro, April 26, 2019, https://www.nknews .org/pro/key-takeaways-from-dprk-state-media-coverage-of-kim-putin -summit/.

41   Economy, "Russia's Role on North Korea: More Important than You Might Think."

42   Brad Glosserman, "Japan-South Korea: So Close, Yet So Far," *The Diplomat*, February 28, 2018, https://thediplomat.com/2018/02/japan-south -korea-so-close-yet-so-far.

43   Ibid.

44   Rachel Blomquist and Daniel Wertz, "An Overview of North Korea–Japan Relations," NCNK, June 2015, https://www.ncnk.org/resources/briefing -papers/all-briefing-papers/overview-north-korea-japan-relations.

45   Nam Seung-mo, "I daetongryung, jeongyeok dokdo bangmun . . . yeokdae daetongryeong choecho" [President Lee visits Dokdo all of a sudden . . . first president to visit island], SBS News, August 20, 2012, https://news .sbs.co.kr/news/endPage.do?news_id=N1001321759.

46   Jason Strother, "Why Japan Is Angry over South Korea's Visit to an Island," *Christian Science Monitor*, August 10, 2012, https://www.csmonitor.com /World/Asia-Pacific/2012/0810/Why-Japan-is-angry-over-South-Korea -s-visit-to-an-island.

47   Bryan Harris and Robin Harding, "Japan–South Korea 'Comfort Women' Deal Under Threat," *Financial Times*, November 21, 2018, https://www.ft .com/content/2b50b1f2-ed3a-11e8-89c8-d36339d835c0.

48   Steve Miller, "South Korea Orders 2nd Japan Firm to Pay Forced Laborers," *Voice of America*, November 29, 2018, https://www.nytimes.com/2018 /11/21/world/asia/south-korea-japan-sex-slaves.html.

49   Julian Ryall, "South Korea Orders Japanese Firm to Compensate Forced Laborers as Relations Hit New Low," *Telegraph*, November 29, 2018, https://www.telegraph.co.uk/news/2018/11/29/south-korea-orders -japanese-firm-compensate-forced-laborers.

50   "Regarding the Decision by the Supreme Court of the Republic of Korea, Confirming the Existing Judgments on the Japanese Company (Statement by Foreign Minister Taro Kono)," Ministry of Foreign Affairs, November 29, 2018, https://www.mofa.go.jp/press/release/press4e_002242 .html.

51   "Government Statement on the Supreme Court's Decision on Forced Laborers," Ministry of Foreign Affairs, November 15, 2018, http://overseas .mofa.go.kr/us-newyork-ko/brd/m_4237/view.do?seq=1346034.

52   *Defense of Japan 2018* (Tokyo: Ministry of Defense, 2018), 292.

53   Niall McCarthy, "The World's Biggest Arms Importers Since 1950 [Infographic]," *Forbes*, March 12, 2018, https://www.forbes.com/sites /niallmccarthy/2018/03/12/the-worlds-biggest-post-war-arms-importers -infographic/#c1c2fba8e34c.

54 Martin Armstrong, "The USA's Biggest Arms Export Partners," *Statista*, October 12, 2018, https://www.statista.com/chart/12205/the-usas-biggest -arms-export-partners/.

55 Mike Yeo, "Japan Seeks Drones, Subs, F-35 Jets as Part of $243 Billion Defense-Spending Plan," *DefenseNews*, December 19, 2018, https://www .defensenews.com/global/asia-pacific/2018/12/19/japan-seeks-drones -subs-f-35-jets-as-part-of-243-billion-defense-spending-plan.

56 *Defense of Japan 2018*, 73.

57 Ibid.

58 Justin McCurry, "Japan Defence Ministry Sees Record Budget over North Korea Threat," *Guardian*, August 31, 2018, https://www.theguardian.com /world/2018/aug/31/japan-record-defence-budget-north-korea-china -threat.

59 Masayuki Yuda, "Rising Asia Tensions Push Japan's Defense Budget to Re-cord High," *Nikkei Asian Review*, December 22, 2017, https://asia.nikkei .com/Economy/Rising-Asia-tensions-push-Japan-s-defense-budget-to -record-high2.

60 Brad Lendon and Yoko Wakatsuki, "Japan to Have First Aircraft Carriers Since World War II," CNN, December 18, 2018, https://edition.cnn.com /2018/12/18/asia/japan-aircraft-carriers-intl/index.html.

61 "The North Korean Threat Remains," *Japan Times*, July 2, 2018, https:// www.japantimes.co.jp/opinion/2018/07/02/editorials/north-korean-threat -remains/#.XCQjE1z7RPY.

62 Ibid.

63 "North Korean Abductions of Japanese Citizens: A Timeline," Nippon .com, October 18, 2018, https://www.nippon.com/en/features/h00310/.

64 Ibid.

65 "North Korean Official in South Demands Japan Compensate for War Crimes," Channel News Asia, November 16, 2018, https://www .channelnewsasia.com/news/asia/north-korean-official-in-south-demands -japan-compensate-for-war-crimes-10938252.

66 Jesse Johnson, "North Korea Blasts Japan's Role in Pushing UN Human Rights Resolution amid Nuclear Talks," *Japan Times*, October 23, 2018, https://www.japantimes.co.jp/news/2018/10/23/national/north-korea -blasts-japans-role-pushing-u-n-human-rights-resolution-amid-nuclear -talks/#.XCQr2lz7RPY.

67 Quoted in Simon Denyer, "Japan's Abe Finds Himself on Sidelines amid Outreach with North Korea," *Washington Post*, September 23, 2018, https://www.washingtonpost.com/world/japans-abe-finds-himself-on -sidelines-amid-outreach-with-north-korea/2018/09/23/5dce8842-bdac -11e8-97f6-0cbdd4d9270e_story.html.

68 Kazuto Suzuki, "Japan's View of the North Korean Threat," *IAI Commen-taries* 22 (March 2018): 1, https://www.iai.it/sites/default/files/iaicom1822 .pdf.

69 "Peace in North Korea Could Cost $2 Trillion if History Is a Guide," *Fortune*, May 10, 2018, http://fortune.com/2018/05/10/cost-of-peace-in-north-korea; Brian Padden, "N. Korea Denuclearization Could Cost $20 Billion," *Voice of America*, June 6, 2018, https://www.voanews.com/a/north-korea-pricey-denuclearization/4426577.html.

70 "Explainer: What Will It Cost to Denuclearize North Korea?," Reuters, June 29, 2018, https://www.reuters.com/article/us-northkorea-nuclear-cost-explainer/explainer-what-will-it-cost-to-denuclearize-north-korea-idUSKBN1JP1LD.

71 "The Secretary of State to Mr. Min Yeung-Tchan, Special Envoy Without Credentials," Papers Relating to the Foreign Relations of the United States, with the Annual Message of the President Transmitted to Congress, December 5, 1905, Document 620, https://history.state.gov/historicaldocuments/frus1905/d620.

72 Ibid.

73 Dean Acheson, "Crisis in Asia: An Examination of U.S. Policy," speech delivered at the National Press Club, January 12, 1950, *Department of State Bulletin* 22, no. 551 (January 23, 1950): 111–118; "Secretary of State Dean G. Acheson's speech, Crisis in Asia—An Examination of U.S. Policy," The World and Japan: Database of Japanese Politics and International Relations, National Graduate Institute for Policy Studies (GRIPS), Institute for Advanced Studies on Asia (IASA), University of Tokyo, http://worldjpn.grips.ac.jp/documents/texts/docs/19500112.S1E.html.

74 "The Chief of the United States Military Advisory Group to the Republic of Korea (Roberts) to the Ambassador in Korea (Muccio)," January 7, 1950, *Foreign Relations of the United States*, 1959, Korea, vol. VII, https://history.state.gov/historicaldocuments/frus1950v07/comp1.

75 Ibid.

76 Ibid.

77 Weathersby, "Soviet Aims in Korea and the Origins of the Korean War, 1945–1950," 28.

78 "Joint Vision for the Alliance of the United States of America and the Republic of Korea," Office of the Press Secretary, White House, June 16, 2009, https://obamawhitehouse.archives.gov/the-press-office/joint-vision-alliance-united-states-america-and-republic-korea.

79 Nicholas J. Myers, "What Happened During Vostok 2018?," RealClear Defense, October 5, 2018, https://www.realcleardefense.com/articles/2018/10/05/what_happened_during_vostok_2018_113870.html.

80 Mathieu Boulegue, "What Russia's Vostok-2018 Exercises Mean for China and the West," *The Hill*, September 29, 2018, https://thehill.com/opinion/national-security/408505-what-russias-vostok-2018-exercises-mean-for-china-and-the-west.

Conclusion: Three Gateways

1 "Reviewing the Year: Kim Jong Un's 2019 New Year's Address, in Full," *NK News*, January 1, 2019, https://www.nknews.org/2018/12/reviewing-the -year-state-media-coverage-of-the-new-years-address/?c=1546318206514.

2 Quote in David E. Sanger, "Kim and Trump Back at Square One: If U.S. Keeps Sanctions, North Will Keep Nuclear Program," *New York Times*, January 1, 2019, https://www.nytimes.com/2019/01/01/world/asia/kim -trump-nuclear.html.

3 "Trump Shows Off Letter from Kim Jong Un, Says Relationship Is 'Strong,'" Global News, January 2, 2019, https://globalnews.ca/video/4808609/trump -shows-off-letter-from-kim-jong-un-says-relationship-is-strong.

4 Ibid.

5 Shin Seok-ho, "Shin Seok-ho gijaeui ooahan: 17nyeonjjae Buk yeonguhan jeonmungijaga bon 'Kim Jung Un shinnyeonsa' euimineun" [Elegant journalist Shin Seok-ho: the meaning of Kim Jong Un's New Year's speech after covering North for 17 years], *Donga Ilbo*, January 1, 2019, http://news.donga .com/home/3/all/20190101/93515446/1?utm_source=DongaApp&utm _medium=app&.

6 "Reviewing the Year: Kim Jong Un's 2019 New Year's address, in full."

7 *KDI gyeongjae jeonmang* [KDI Economic Outlook] 25, no. 2 (2018): 8.

8 "Korea's Economic Growth Forecast to Slow to 2.6% in 2019," *Korea Herald*, November 29, 2018, http://www.koreaherald.com/view.php?ud =20181129000671.

9 Patrick M. Cronin, Van Jackson, Elbridge Colby, et al., *Solving Long Division: The Geopolitical Implications of Korean Unification* (Washington, D.C.: Center for a New American Security, 2015), 10.

10 Tara O, *The Collapse of North Korea: Challenges, Planning and Geopoltics of Unification* (New York: Palgrave Macmillan, 2016), 2.

11 "Transcript of Telephone Conversation Between the President's Assistant for National Security Affairs (Kissinger) and the White House Chief of Staff (Haig), Washington, D.C., March 15, 1973," *Foreign Relations of the United States, 1969–1976*, vol. X, Vietnam, January 1973–July 1975, https:// history.state.gov/historicaldocuments/frus1969-76v10/d31.

12 Bruce W. Bennett, *Alternative Paths to Korean Unification* (Santa Monica, CA: RAND Corporation, 2018), ix.

13 Cronin, Jackson, Colby, et al., *Solving Long Division*, 10.

14 *South Koreans and Their Neighbors 2018, Asan Poll* (Seoul: Asan Institute for Policy Studies, 2018), 13.

15 Ibid., 13.

16 Ibid., 14.

17 Kim Jiyoon, Kildong Kim, and Kang Chungku, "South Korean Youths' Perceptions of North Korea and Unification," *Issue Brief* 3 (2018): 3.

18 Ibid., 7.
19 Ibid., 9.
20 "A Changing North Korea," Liberty in North Korea, https://www
    .libertyinnorthkorea.org/learn-a-changing-north-korea.

INDEX

Page numbers in italics refer to tables and figures.